THE SOURCEBOOK OF ARCHITECTURAL & INTERIOR ART 20

" Celebrating 20 years of connecting artists with their markets. "

THE SOURCEBOOK OF ARCHITECTURAL & INTERIOR ART 20

GUILD Sourcebooks
Madison, Wisconsin
USA

THE SOURCEBOOK OF ARCHITECTURAL & INTERIOR ART 20

GUILD Sourcebooks
An imprint of GUILD, LLC
931 East Main Street
Madison, Wisconsin 53703-2955
TEL 608-257-2590 • TEL 877-284-8453

ADMINISTRATION
Toni Sikes, CEO and Founder
Michael Baum, President
Carla Dillman, Director of Sourcebooks
Marcia Kraus, Director of Trade Relations
Kristina Buie, Administrative Assistant / Copy Editor

DESIGN, PRODUCTION, AND EDITORIAL
Jill Schaefer, Director of Editorial & Production, Writer
Barbara Hatley, Production Coordinator & Image Specialist
Laura Koeferl, Project Designer / Production Artist
Mary Jo Abell, Project Designer / Production Artist
Sue Englund, Production Artist
Jody Clowes, Writer & Editor
Susan Troller, Writer

ARTIST CONSULTANTS
Nicole Carroll • Amy Lambright • Annik Lott
Laura Marth • Paul Murphy

COVER ART: Linda Leviton, *Patterns of Nature/Wave* series, see page 277.
Photograph: Jerry Anthony Photography.
PAGE 3: Arthur Stern, *St. John Millenium Cross Window.*
Photograph: Blake Praytor.
FACING PAGE: Alice Van Leunen, *Ain Soph Aur: Limitless Light,* see page 320.

Special thanks to our 2005 Review Committee:
Paul Smith, Director Emeritus, American Craft Museum
Thomas Nisbet, Owner, Nisbet Architects
Randy Schmitgen, Director of ID, Fladd & Associates
Mare Tracy, Owner, ColorScapes

■

GUILD.com is the internet's leading retailer of original art and fine craft.
Visit www.guild.com.

A WONDROUS TWENTY YEARS

Anniversary celebrations are mostly self-indulgent. These milestones cause us to pause for a moment, to think back and remember, and to take stock of what we've accomplished.

It is difficult for me to believe that two decades have gone by since the idea that became THE GUILD began to take shape. At a time when the word "marketing" was still foreign to most artists, GUILD Sourcebooks were the first vehicle to present the work of artists to design professionals, and the first organized resource for those seeking commissioned art.

Today, THE GUILD is the leading marketer of artwork through its channels of sourcebooks, catalogs, and the GUILD.com website. Along the way, we have helped thousands of artists earn a living from their artwork.

This twentieth edition has a number of nostalgic features. There is an article on building careers, featuring artists who took a chance on THE GUILD in the beginning and have been with us ever since. Scattered throughout the book are stories about special commissions that came about through THE GUILD. We've even sprinkled in a few quotes from those most important people—the design professionals who put THE GUILD to its intended use, with marvelous results.

So please allow us a bit of self-indulgence as we celebrate these unforgettable, adventuresome, wondrous twenty years. As THE GUILD enters its third decade of playing matchmaker to artists and design professionals, we are delighted to continue this gratifying work, and to keep following the same passion that got us started so many years ago.

Toni Sikes
Publisher

Opposite: Warren Carther, *Sea of Time*, 1999, part two of *Chronos Trilogy*, Lincoln House office tower, Hong Kong. Photograph: Gerry Kopelow.

TABLE OF CONTENTS

8

Gerald Siciliano, *Nautilus*, see page 119. Photograph: Sandy Rosenberg.

TABLE OF CONTENTS

Pamela Joseph, *Water Nymph*, see page 66.

The Sourcebook of Architectural & Interior Art shows artwork of enduring value; we think you'll refer to it for years to come.
If at any time you're unable to reach an artist through contact information included in this book, call THE GUILD at 1-877-284-8453.
We keep track of updated phone numbers and the like, and are glad to share our most current information.

ARTISTS BY SECTION

ARTISTS BY SECTION

ARTISTS BY SECTION

ARTISTS BY SECTION

GREAT WAYS
TO USE *SOURCEBOOK 20*

1 QUALITY CONTROL. This book begins with an assurance that these artists are reliable and professional. Featured artists in THE GUILD have been juried in on the basis of experience, quality of work, and a solid reputation for working with architects and designers.

2 MOTIVATION. Taking your copy of THE GUILD to client meetings is highly recommended. Clients have been known to reach levels of extreme excitement upon viewing the artistic possibilities showcased here.

3 DEEPEN YOUR UNDERSTANDING. We believe a picture is worth a thousand words. But words provide the information you need to pursue your dreams. In the "Artist Statements" section (pages 327-366), our artists describe their inspiration, technique, training, and professional experience so that you can proceed with confidence.

4 GO AHEAD AND CALL. If something intrigues you while perusing *The Sourcebook of Architectural & Interior Art*—a shape, a form, or an exotic use of the commonplace—please, give the artist a call. Serendipity often leads to a wonderful creation.

5 DESKTOP DIRECTORY. *The Sourcebook of Architectural & Interior Art* is designed for quick reference, as well as leisurely browsing. Looking for an artist nearby? Check the "Location Index," which lists our artists by state. The "Index of Artists and Companies" will direct you to all the artists featured in the full-color pages, so finding a current phone number or checking product information is easily done. The information in your PDA may grow stale; *The Sourcebook of Architectural & Interior Art* is fresh each year.

6 BE INSPIRED. So many wonderful commissions have come about through THE GUILD over these twenty years, and behind every one is a story of creativity, teamwork, and dedicated effort. We've featured some of our favorites in these pages to inspire, intrigue, and encourage you.

7 FOLLOW OUR ARTISTS' WORK. We've published books for architects, designers, and art consultants for twenty years. Many of the artists whose work you see in this volume were also featured in earlier GUILD publications. These are listed at the end of each artist's statement for easy reference.

8 LEARN FROM THE PROS. For this anniversary edition, we asked twenty of our most successful artists to describe how THE GUILD has helped them build their careers. We're proud to have been a part of their journey from modest beginnings to ambitious, fully realized projects and national—even international—recognition.

9 EXPLORE EVEN MORE. This Sourcebook is just the beginning of what THE GUILD can offer. All of the artists included here-and many more-can be reached through our Custom Design Center at www.guild.com. Our design consultants will work with you to make the commission process both painless and satisfying.

10 OUR NEXT LANDMARK. THE GUILD will be 25 in the year 2010. We'd like to feature your project in that anniversary edition. Please take a minute and daydream about the artwork you'll commission in the next five years!

Building Careers:
20 Artists Reflect on 20 Years of THE GUILD

GUILD Sourcebooks are beautiful, inspiring volumes—but they're more than that. Their pages forge a critical link between artists and the architects, designers, and other professionals who shape our built environment.

Published every year since 1985, GUILD Sourcebooks are the leading guide to artists who work on commissions in North America. Since then, THE GUILD has published more than 400,000 Sourcebooks, which reach nearly 15,000 design professionals annually— from architects, art consultants, interior designers, and public arts administrators to liturgical specialists, developers, and landscape architects.

We're proud to say that thousands of art commissions have been generated through THE GUILD over the last twenty years, giving artists the opportunity to realize their grandest visions and creating spaces that take our breath away. GUILD Sourcebooks—and the many related services offered by THE GUILD—have developed and nurtured a broad national and international network that supports artists and enhances all of our lives.

Publishing the GUILD Sourcebooks has meant both hard work and great joy. Without a doubt, our most rewarding moments are when an artist signs up to be in our books again and again, telling us how our efforts are making a difference in his or her career and life. That's how we know that the idea we began with in the 1980s actually works in the real world.

So we hope you'll indulge us as some of our most devoted advertisers describe how THE GUILD has helped them build their careers.

John Pugh, *Light Walk* (left half), trompe l'oeil mural, 26' x 6'. Commissioned by Palo Alto Medical Foundation, CA. Photograph: Brian Brumley.

It can be challenging for artists to broaden their market, especially if their best work is tucked away in private residences and local companies. A beautiful page in THE GUILD is a tried-and-true way for artists to connect with potential clients nationwide.

Mark Eric Gulsrud
Architectural Glass – Tacoma, WA

Before I advertised with THE GUILD, my work was smaller in scale and created primarily for West Coast clients. Publication in the GUILD Sourcebooks was a means of promoting my work to a national and international audience.

In 2000, I won a commission at Hitchcock Presbyterian Church in Scarsdale, NY. The clients had seen my work in a previous GUILD Sourcebook and loved it. **The Scarsdale project was my first opportunity to complete a substantial body of work on the East Coast.** There was a good deal of competition for that job, but the clients made it clear that my advertisement in THE GUILD had won them over. I've found architects, designers, and art consultants who have tracked my work through GUILD Sourcebooks over the years. They remember it, and when the right commission comes along, they can confidently match the job with my work.

Jeff G. Smith
Architectural Glass – Fort Davis, TX

My first GUILD page appeared a couple of years after I graduated from college and was the first critical elective investment I made in my career. At that time I was paying the bills with modest residential projects and small commercial jobs. In recent years I have had the good fortune to execute major architectural commissions.

GUILD Sourcebooks have become a special thread running throughout my development as an artist. With a limited advertising budget, this cumulative sort of exposure has provided commission opportunities that otherwise would have been missed. Because GUILD Sourcebooks are beautifully printed, they tend to remain on shelves long after other dated materials have been culled; I am often contacted about a project from a GUILD Sourcebook that is five or more years old. GUILD contacts are from professionals who have both a need for your medium and a specific interest in unique work.

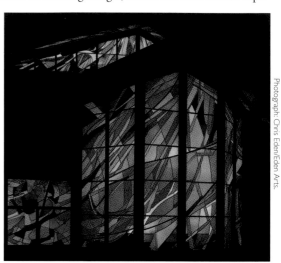

Photograph: Chris Eden/Eden Arts.

Reconciliation Chapel Windows, 2003, Seattle, WA, 15'H × 25.3'W. Commissioned by St. Bridget Catholic Church.

Arthur Stern
Architectural Glass – Benicia, CA

I've received some of my best commissions as a result of being in the GUILD Sourcebooks. When I first began advertising with THE GUILD, my work was primarily residential. **While I still really enjoy creating for homes, I am increasingly called upon for larger projects for public buildings, courthouses, banks, libraries, and churches all over the country.**

I had one art consultant, Kathy Hathorn at American Art Resources in Houston, tell me that she saw my work year after year in THE GUILD and knew where to find me

Photograph: Lawrence Barton.

if she ever had an opportunity to use my work. We ended up working together on a 24' atrium window, which was installed over the entrance to PeaceHealth Hospital in Longview, WA. This project earned a Millennium Design Award from the American Institute of Architects and has been widely published in books and magazines.

Connecting Internationally

As our world becomes smaller and smaller, opportunities for artists to work across borders are increasing dramatically. Art is a universal language, and architects, design professionals, and art consultants from around the globe read it in THE GUILD's pages.

Yoshi Hayashi
Paintings – San Francisco, CA

As the only artist working in Japanese lacquer in the GUILD Sourcebooks, I think my work really stands out and gets attention. Although it took several years before I began receiving commissions through THE GUILD, over time my advertisements have been quite worthwhile. **I have had a steady stream of commissions for public spaces and private residences in the U.S., Japan, and the Philippines,** and have

developed a very productive long-term relationship with a Los Angeles interior designer and art consultant through THE GUILD.

Photograph: Barbara Boissevain.

Spring Moon, San Francisco, CA, wall-hanging screen. Commissioned by DFS-West.

James T. Russell
Stainless Steel Sculpture – Lomita, CA

After twenty years of advertising with the GUILD Sourcebooks, my work has consistently been exposed to corporate art consultants. This exposure has increased the sales of my

Photograph: Sharon Shute.

artwork both nationally and internationally. I estimate that 75 percent of my sales originate through contacts made through the GUILD Sourcebooks. **As an emerging artist, I was creating three- to four-foot sculptures and selling my work through regional galleries. Now I'm an established international sculptor of monumental works.**

My artwork *Spirit Song* was installed in Beijing in 1998 as a result of a GUILD Sourcebook ad. I was commissioned by the Motorola Corporation to create a large sculpture for their headquarters. The project involved an extensive amount of coordination between my studio, the Chinese architects, consultants, and the two governments. The collaboration broke cultural and language barriers and came to symbolize the joining of Eastern and Western thought.

Spirit Song, 1997, Beijing, China, stainless steel, 6'H. Commissioned by Motorola Corporation Headquarters.

Warren Carther
Architectural Glass – Winnipeg, MB

Because my studio is not located in a major art center, I used to find it difficult to connect with architects, designers, and art consultants outside my area. **Through THE GUILD, I have been able to reach art professionals around the world and now have a large base of contacts with whom I work on a regular basis.** After fifteen years with THE GUILD, I still find that new people are exposed to my work with every edition. When I first started advertising, my projects were small and mostly local. The larger commissions I've received through THE GUILD have directly led to a reputation for crafting major projects.

My *Chronos Trilogy* (1999), three major works in one of Hong Kong's most prestigious office towers, was one of the largest art commissions in the world and virtually transformed the office towers into my own museum. Possibly thousands of people see the *Trilogy* daily, and it has been published worldwide. The *Trilogy* directly influenced the Alaska State Council on the Arts in choosing my work for the Anchorage International Airport, where another huge audience views my nine towers of glass each day.

17

Going Large in Scale

Creating art on a large scale is expensive, risky, and can offer unexpected challenges. Artists who dream big need clients and sites that will give them the opportunity to realize their ambitions. THE GUILD facilitates connections that allow artists to take their work to the next level.

Jonathan and Evelyn Clowes
Atrium Sculpture – Walpole, NH

Over the years, the GUILD Sourcebooks have become our main promotional effort. We have never experienced a flood of work, and at times have been discouraged by slower periods. However, at critical points in our careers, an interesting opportunity to create new work would come along. **THE GUILD has sustained us, challenged us, and given us access to extraordinary opportunities.**

In 1995, Mack Thames of Contract Art contacted us about a commission for Royal Caribbean Cruise Lines. He had seen our work in the GUILD Sourcebooks over the years and finally had a project for us. We completed *Diadem* in conjunction with the architect and an art consultant from London Contemporary Art. It was a very demanding project that included hiring engineers, contracting fabricators, and working with composites. We survived the project in good grace, prepared to take on other large projects.

Diadem, 1997, mixed media, 39' × 18' Dia. Commissioned by Royal Caribbean Cruise Lines.

Photograph: William Ingersoll.

Paul Housberg
Architectural Glass – Jamestown, RI

The GUILD Sourcebooks have enabled me to put my work in front of architects and designers who might not otherwise see it. Many of my larger commissions have come through THE GUILD, and **at least three of the projects I received through THE GUILD could be considered milestones in my career.**

The first was an 8' by 21' wall of cast glass blocks for The Dreyfus Corporation in New York. This was my first large-scale glass project, and resulted from a concept maquette published in *THE GUILD 5.*

The second—four 11' by 12' walls of cast, cut, and assembled glass elements for Pfizer Corporation—crystallized my interest in the texture and materiality of glass. More recently, the fused and cast glass piece for the lobby of Chicago's Peninsula Hotel was similar to the Pfizer commission, but less massive and more refined. I've received at least five commissions, three of significant size, directly from the publication of that piece in THE GUILD.

Untitled, fused and cast glass wall, 2001, 12' × 9'. Commissioned by The Peninsula Chicago Hotel, IL.

Photograph: Jon Miller/Hedrich-Blessing.

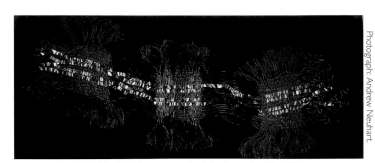

Liquid Fire Triptych, woven anodized aluminum wire, 24" × 48".

Photograph: Andrew Neuhart

Susan McGehee
Woven Metal – Manhattan Beach, CA

Advertising in THE GUILD has allowed me to reach art consultants and designers around the country who would otherwise be unaware of my work. Though my medium of woven wire and metal has not changed over the years, the scale of my work has certainly increased.

My first experience with large-scale work came when Jennifer Wood-Patrick of Art Advisory/Boston—who discovered me through GUILD Sourcebooks—commissioned me to create my first large piece: 5' wide by 25' long! This experience greatly expanded my knowledge of creating and installing really large pieces. THE GUILD is my only source of advertising, and the clients who find me through these sourcebooks keep my solo studio busy with a variety of interesting projects.

Karen Heyl
Stone Murals – Cincinnati, OH

Working with THE GUILD has exposed my work to many and varied art consultants throughout the U.S. Because of this exposure, I now get enough work to actually make a living carving stone murals. The books allow clients to find me instead of me having to find them! My career has changed in ways I never thought possible, and this could not have happened without my advertisements in the GUILD Sourcebooks. **My work now consists of very large-scale bas-relief carvings for lobbies in corporate settings—quite a change from the tabletop or pedestal pieces I was doing before advertising with THE GUILD.**

Photograph: Joy Coldough.

One of my favorite projects resulting from THE GUILD was for Vanderbilt University Research Center in Nashville, TN. That project allowed my work to take on a more abstract quality and design—something that was very different and fun for me to carve.

New Opportunities, New Directions

When artists are inspired to shift media or explore different territory, it may take time to find the right clients for their new work. A fresh new page in the GUILD Sourcebook is one of the most direct ways for artists to reinvent their public image.

Ellen Kochansky
Mixed Media – Pickens, SC

Before THE GUILD was born, Michael Monroe (GUILD's future artistic advisor) told me that what the fine art and crafts field needed was not only excellent work, but excellent images of excellent work. As the GUILD Sourcebooks have morphed to fit the changing and varied needs of artists, his prediction has come to pass.

When I made the move to three-dimensional work, I applied for a grant from the South Carolina Arts Commission to complete a town's fiftieth anniversary piece. The outcome of this project, along with my GUILD page showing the work, led to a huge wall sculpture for Bank of America and a commission from the Hub City Writers Project in Spartanburg County, SC—my favorite large work to date. **In the squishy mud of THE GUILD, I've left all my favorite footprints.**

Garden Party, 2000, mixed media, 24' x 6'. Commissioned by Bank of America, Charlotte, NC.

Ken vonRoenn
Architectural Glass – Louisville, KY

My work has certainly grown in scale and complexity since I first advertised with THE GUILD, and has moved from two to three-dimensional. THE GUILD helped introduce my work to clients who appreciated this direction, and this type of artwork has become a very important component of what I do today.

One specific project I received through THE GUILD that moved my work in a new direction was for a suspended glass sculpture, which I had never done before. Since then I have designed and constructed several such sculptures.

Bruce Wolfe
Bronze Sculpture – Piedmont, CA

Although I made my living as a painter for many years, I began my career with a love for bronze portraiture and was always looking for more time and opportunities to make sculpture. In 1993, I changed my GUILD ads to reflect my new focus on sculpting and have continued to advertise in this medium ever since. My GUILD ads helped to reinforce my credibility as a sculptor and worked in tandem with my own publicity efforts.

GUILD Sourcebooks have exposed my work to clients and commission managers I wouldn't have been able to reach on my own. The books also seem to be kept on the desks of landscape planners, architects, and art buyers. I am sure the GUILD Sourcebooks have helped prospective clients find my website and contact me for additional information about my work.

Rob Fisher
Metal Sculpture – Bellefonte, PA

I began a new artistic direction with GUILD Sourcebooks in 1999, when I showed a small helical stainless steel sculpture that I had completed for a company in Pittsburgh. This ad resulted in a commissions for a 10' by 15' version of the piece, as well as a variation of the same form for yet another client.

Since the publication of my suspended sculpture *Slice of Life*, I have created five new pieces that can be traced back to that ad alone. What is most gratifying is the scale of the commissions—both physically and monetarily—that have resulted from advertising with THE GUILD. By promoting my newest pieces in the Sourcebook, I'm sending the message that my work has been selected by many clients for their most important spaces.

A Slice of Life, 2002, Wilmington, DE, aluminum and stainless steel, 35' x 85' x 35'. Commissioned by AstraZeneca Pharmaceuticals.

Building Careers

Building Credibility

Being seen in print gives an instant boost to any artist's reputation. No resume, no matter how impressive, has the impact of great photographs on glossy paper in a beautifully produced book.

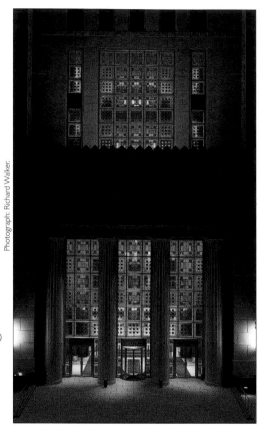

Photograph: Richard Walker.

Glass windows, 1998, Robert C. Byrd U.S. Courthouse, Charleston, WV.

David Wilson
Architectural Glass – South New Berlin, NY

Appearing in the GUILD Sourcebooks over time builds professional credibility, and my own participation has certainly helped me to secure projects. In addition, an accumulation of wonderful tear sheets has made for great portfolio packages, which I send out regularly to my own contacts. Looking at the books and tear sheets, it's very interesting to see how my work has changed over the years.

My earlier GUILD projects are quite small in scale compared to what I am doing now. **THE GUILD helped to build my reputation and gave me access to larger-scale secular projects.** Opportunities available through THE GUILD and have been the main factor in the change and development of my work over time.

Elle Terry Leonard
Architectural Ceramics – Sarasota, FL

Without a doubt, THE GUILD has been the springboard for my career. Designers and architects have confidence commissioning projects from professional artists: THE GUILD means that you and your work have already been juried. As I began to receive commission work through the GUILD Sourcebooks, I was able to enlarge my studio space and take on an apprentice and eventually some employees.

I have to laugh when I remember the way THE GUILD came into play with one designer. For ten years I rented the guesthouse of a designer, who had a very suc-

cessful business. During the first three years I tried repeatedly to interest her in my work, without success. One day I saw the GUILD Sourcebook on her coffee table and was able to say, "Oh, I'm in that book." That changed her whole perception of me! I wasn't just a local artist anymore; I had clout. We've since worked on many fabulous residential projects together.

G. Byron Peck
Painted Murals – Washington, DC

I use the GUILD Sourcebooks not only to spread the word of my studio's work year after year, but also as a great tool to send to favorite clients. Since our first advertisement with THE GUILD, we have always advertised our murals, but the projects we are doing today are much larger as we have expanded into mosaics and other forms of public art. Each of my RFQ packages contains GUILD materials,

and we regularly get calls from firms that have seen our work on GUILD's Custom Design Center or in the Sourcebook.

A turning point in these larger projects came when we got a call from a city office to create a nine-story trompe l'oeil façade, which was much bigger than anything we had done before. **The GUILD Sourcebook certainly helps an artist's credibility in terms of illustrating that he or she can deliver large projects successfully.**

Building Relationships

A long-term relationship with a professional who truly appreciates an artist's work can be as valuable as a long string of individual commissions. Developing projects together over time creates a partnership based on understanding and respect, and streamlining the commission process leaves more time for studio work.

Sandra Christine Q. Bergér
Glass – Burlingame, CA

I vividly recall receiving a phone call over twenty years ago from a glass artist on the other side of the country, telling me about this lady who saw a need for a book featuring artists of fine craft. That lady was, of course, Toni Sikes. I inquired and soon became one of the GUILD Sourcebook's charter artists.

An established resource for architects, designers, and art representatives, THE GUILD was the link that helped me obtain a marvelous commission for Thermo King's corporate headquarters. Not only was the commission fun and challenging, but it also pushed the three-dimensional work I had been developing to a much higher level. **What began twenty years ago as a marketing opportunity for my work has evolved into a long-term relationship not only with THE GUILD, but with a number of architects and design professionals as well.**

Elizabeth MacDonald
Ceramics – Bridgewater, CT

When Toni Sikes started THE GUILD, I was just beginning my work with a modular system in clay. Realizing that this method would be appropriate for commissions and architectural installations of all sizes, I began advertising in the GUILD Sourcebooks to give my work wider exposure than I could possibly give it on my own.

Not only have my pages in THE GUILD resulted in commissions, but they have also allowed me to build a portfolio of my work and build long-term relationships with design professionals. I have just finished working with two art consultants for whom I have created several commissions over the years. These most recent commissions have been installed in the Dartmouth-Hitchcock Medical Center in Lebanon, NH, and the Northern Lights Inn at Fort Wainwright in Fairbanks, AK.

Photograph: Bill Seitz

21

John Pugh
Trompe L'Oeil – Los Gatos, CA

THE GUILD has expanded my reputation and professional base. I have received many commissions through the GUILD Sourcebooks, but equally important are the number of architects, art consultants, and public art agents nationwide who are now familiar with my work. Since advertising with THE GUILD, I have added an array of national and international public art commissions to my resumé. In particular, a project with the City of Palm Desert, CA, which resulted from my ad in the GUILD Sourcebooks, was instrumental in giving momentum to a string of many city projects.

I've also developed a long-term working relationship with art consultant Suzanne Frazer, who found my work through THE GUILD. Since completing an initial trompe l'oeil mural commission for Silicon Graphics, we have worked on projects for Kaiser Permanente and the Palo Alto Medical Foundation. **That first project was definitely the beginning of a beautiful relationship.**

Building Careers

Building a Legacy

*Each of the artists listed below has published his or her work in GUILD Sourcebooks ten—
or more—times over the last twenty years. We think their success represents a remarkable legacy,
and look forward to supporting their careers for decades to come.*

Karen Adachi

Shawn Athari

Sandra C.Q. Bergér

Rita Blitt

Laura Militzer Bryant

Myra Burg

Susan Burnes

Barbara Cade

Warren Carther

Jill Casty

Mark Chatterley

Jonathan Clowes

Jeffrey Cooper

Alonzo Davis

Jerome R. Durr

Rob Fisher

Barbara Fletcher

Marilyn Forth

Douglas Freeman

Walter Gordinier

Carol Green

Mark Gulsrud

Yoshi Hayashi

Archie Held

Karen Heyl

Robert Holmes

Bill Hopen

Paul Housberg

Bruce Howdle

Margie Hughto

Marie-Laure Ilie

Pamela Joseph

BJ Katz

Guy Kemper

John Kinkade

Stephen Knapp

Ellen Kochansky

Silja Lahtinen

Tuck Langland

Duncan Laurie

Marlene Lenker

Elle Terry Leonard

Linda Leviton

Joyce P. Lopez

Elizabeth MacDonald

Ellen Mandelbaum

E. Joseph McCarthy

Susan McGehee

Trena McNabb

Pam Morris

James C. Myford

Tom Neugebauer

G. Byron Peck

Robert Pfitzenmeier

Michael F. Pilla

Bev Precious

John Pugh

Maya Radoczy

Kevin B. Robb

Koryn Rolstad

Timothy Rose

Brian Russell

James T. Russell

Alvin Sher

Gerald Siciliano

Susan Singleton

Jeff G. Smith

Arthur Stern

Martin Sturman

Marjorie Tomchuk

Angelika Traylor

Alice Van Leunen

Susan Venable

Kenneth vonRoenn

Doug Weigel

David Wilson

Bruce Wolfe

Nancy J. Young

Barbara Zinkel

Larry Zgoda

Elizabeth MacDonald, ceramic tile wall installation, New York, NY. Commissioned by Nobu Restaurant. Photograph: Paul Warchol.

Myra Burg and Liz Cummings, *Transitions*, mixed media, approx. 60"H x 120"W.
Photograph: Barry Blau Photography.

Architectural Glass

Career-building Projects:
Commissions Generated Through GUILD Sourcebooks

MARK ERIC GULSRUD
Wind Wall, 2002
Laminated stained glass and steel
9'H x 55'W
Sisters of St. Joseph of Orange, Orange, CA

Over the years THE GUILD has given me name recognition in the professional design field. I was referred to St. Joseph's by a design professional, and we worked together throughout the entire commission process—as well as on several subsequent projects. They chose me because of my unique approach to stained glass and its sympathetic integration into different environments.

I am constantly exploring new techniques and new directions in my work. This was my first monumental commission using the laminated glass process and was produced in collaboration with Derix Glasstudios of Germany and Fabricated Specialties, Ltd., in Seattle. Along with reinforcing my professionalism, THE GUILD has helped facilitate the development of my work. My relationship with Derix Glasstudio, for example, has developed largely through my appearance in GUILD Sourcebooks. I believe that THE GUILD— and the high quality of the work presented in its pages—offers the most effective format for me to reach a wider audience.

Photograph: Greg Epstein.

LESLIE RANKIN
Waterfall, 2004
Glass
35'H x 8'W
Private residence, Las Vegas, NV

Photograph: The Prephouse.

Before I started advertising in THE GUILD, my projects were much smaller in scale and it was difficult to prove myself. THE GUILD validates me.

This indoor waterfall flows from the second floor of the residence all the way down to the basement. The homeowner had asked their architect for something unique and artistic to fill the very large wall behind their stair. I got a call from the builder after the architect had shown him my page in THE GUILD. They saw that I was a local artist, and I bid the job. They loved my proposal, and the project turned out to be very challenging.

We had to fit scaffolding around the stair structures that were already imbedded in concrete. Each glass panel was eight feet wide and five feet tall, and weighed 450 pounds. Water flows over the front of the glass which I painted with metallics to reflect the light.

The client has already referred me to two friends who are building large custom homes, and I'm working with the builder on another residential project. I run into people all over Vegas who know about my thirty-five foot waterfall. I guess it was the talk of the town!

KATHY BRADFORD

NORTH STAR ART GLASS, INC. ■ 142 WICHITA ■ LYONS, CO 80540 ■ TEL 303-823-6511
FAX 303-823-5350 ■ E-MAIL KATHYBRADFORD@EARTHLINK.NET ■ WWW.KATHYBRADFORD.COM

Top left and center: (detail) *Rhythms of the City*. Top right: *Arcs and Arrows*, 2004, Quartararo Collection, Estes Park, CO, Etched and dichroic glass, 3' x 4'.
Bottom: *Rhythms of the City*, 2003, Aurora Firehouse #3, Aurora, CO, Etched and dichroic glass, 8' x 12'. Photographs: Kathy Bradford.

WARREN CARTHER

CARTHER STUDIO INC. ■ 80 GEORGE AVENUE ■ WINNIPEG, MB R3B 0K1 ■ CANADA ■ TEL 204-956-1615
FAX 204-942-1434 ■ E-MAIL WARREN@CARTHERSTUDIO.COM ■ WWW.CARTHERSTUDIO.COM

28

Top: *Euphony*, 2004, Anchorage International Airport, AK, nine towers of 3/4" curved and carved glass with applied color, dichroic glass, and laminations, steel and aluminum support structures, overall size135' × 27'. Bottom: *Euphony* (detail). Photographs: Dean Carman.

WARREN CARTHER

CARTHER STUDIO INC. ■ 80 GEORGE AVENUE ■ WINNIPEG, MB R3B 0K1 ■ CANADA ■ TEL 204-956-1615
FAX 204-942-1434 ■ E-MAIL WARREN@CARTHERSTUDIO.COM ■ WWW.CARTHERSTUDIO.COM

Bottom left and right: *Euphony* (detail). Photographs: Dean Carman.

J. GORSUCH COLLINS

J. GORSUCH COLLINS ARCHITECTURAL GLASS ■ 8283 WEST ILIFF LANE ■ LAKEWOOD, CO 80227
TEL 303-985-8081 ■ FAX 303-980-0692 ■ E-MAIL DALEWCOLLINS@JUNO.COM ■ WWW.GLOBALINC.COM/JGC

30

Top left: Cast glass and stainless steel screen, 2004, 7'W x 7.4'H. Top right and bottom: detail.

DAVID WILSON DESIGN

DAVID WILSON ■ 202 DARBY ROAD ■ SOUTH NEW BERLIN, NY 13843-2212 ■ TEL 607-334-3015 ■ FAX 607-334-7065
E-MAIL DAVIDWILSONDESIGN@FRONTIERNET.NET ■ WWW.DAVIDWILSONDESIGN.COM

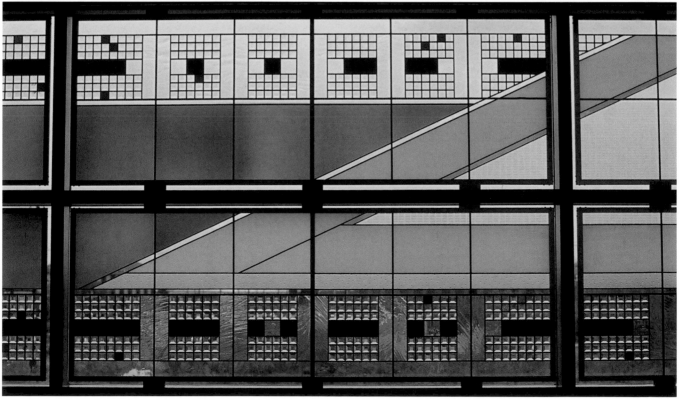

Top: Airtrain Monorail Station, 2002, Newark Liberty International Airport, NJ, glass, 6'H x 400'L.
Bottom: Airtrain Monorail Station (detail).

JEROME R. DURR

JEROME R. DURR STUDIO ■ 206 MARCELLUS STREET ■ SYRACUSE, NY 13204 ■ TEL 800-552-9836
FAX 315-478-1767 ■ E-MAIL JRDURR0ART@AOL.COM ■ WWW.JEROMEDURR.COM

Corporate entry, New York, NY, etched dichroic glass with silver leaf.

GLASSIC ART

LESLIE RANKIN ■ 5850 SOUTH POLARIS SUITE 700 ■ LAS VEGAS, NV 89118 ■ TEL 702-658-7588 ■ FAX 702-658-7342
E-MAIL GLASSICART@GLASSICART.COM ■ WWW.GLASSICART.COM

33

Top left: Carved and painted countertop with kiln-formed sink bowl. Top right: Waterfall, carved and painted glass with mirror, 35' × 8'.
Bottom left: Carved and painted glass with mirror, 3' × 8'. Photographs: The Prephouse, Boyd Pomarius.

MARK ERIC GULSRUD

ARCHITECTURAL GLASS/SCULPTURE ■ 3309 TAHOMA PLACE WEST ■ TACOMA, WA 98466 ■ TEL 253-566-1720 ■ FAX 253-565-5981
E-MAIL MARKGULSRUD@COMCAST.NET ■ WWW.MARKERICGULSRUD.COM

34

Becoming, 2005, meditation space at Good Samaritan Cancer Center, Puyallup, WA, leaded and laminated custom hand-blown glass with bevel prisms and engraved leaves.
Inset: *Becoming* (detail). Photograph: Eleanor Carpenter.

SARAH HALL

SARAH HALL STUDIO ■ 98 BOUSTEAD AVENUE ■ TORONTO, ON M6R 1Y9 ■ CANADA ■ TEL 416-532-6060
FAX 416-532-9361 ■ E-MAIL SARAH.HALL.STUDIO@SYMPATICO.CA ■ WWW.SARAHHALLSTUDIO.COM

Top: Main foyer window, 2003, Kuwait Embassy, Ottowa, CAN, 25'H x 20'W. Bottom left: Kuwait Embassy window (detail), screenprinted enamels with gold and copper leaf.
Bottom right: Kuwait Embassy window (detail), sandblasted enamels with gold and copper leaf. Created in collaboration with Peters Glass Studios, Paderborn, Germany.

LUTZ HAUFSCHILD

560 RAVEN WOODS DRIVE #101 ■ NORTH VANCOUVER, BC CANADA V7G 2T2 ■ TEL 604-929-4775
TEL 604-657-7258 (STUDIO/CELL) ■ FAX 604-929-4780 ■ E-MAIL LUTZ@GLASSFOCUS.COM ■ WWW.GLASSFOCUS.COM

36

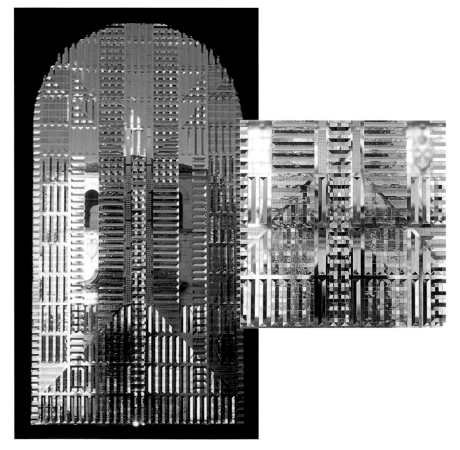

Top: *The Great Wave*, International Departure & Arrival Lounge, Vancouver International Airport, BC, 1" wide strips of tinted float glass, stacked and set between layers of safety glass, 131.17' × 28.17'. Photograph: John Moir. Bottom left: *Crucifixion*, Church of St. John the Divine, Victoria, BC, 3 layers of beveled, silkscreened, etched and laminated float glass, 108" × 61". Bottom right: *The Holy Spirit*, St. Ignatius Church, San Francisco, CA, 3 layers of textured, beveled and laminated float glass, 10' × 5'. Photographs: Lutz Haufschild.

LUTZ HAUFSCHILD

560 RAVEN WOODS DRIVE #101 ■ NORTH VANCOUVER, BC CANADA V7G 2T2 ■ TEL 604-929-4775
TEL 604-657-7258 (STUDIO/CELL) ■ FAX 604-929-4780 ■ E-MAIL LUTZ@GLASSFOCUS.COM ■ WWW.GLASSFOCUS.COM

37

Bottom: *Light in Equipoise*, Potter residence, Ottawa, ON, sliding panels of .5" tempered float glass, 8,500 bevels laminated to both sides, 16' x 10'. Photograph: William McElligott.

LAUREL HERTER

LAUREL HERTER DESIGN, INC. ■ 132 BRIDGE STREET ■ BLUFFTON, SC 29910 ■ TEL 843-757-6580 ■ FAX 843-757-6589
E-MAIL LAUREL@HERTERDESIGN.COM ■ WWW.HERTERDESIGN.COM

38

Top left: *Magnolia* window, 2003, Hilton Head Island, SC, carved, jeweled, and stained glass, 3' × 3'. Top right: *Love Scenes*, 2004, Hilton Head Island, SC, verre églomisé, 18"W × 44"H.
Bottom left: Detail of three-layered underwater scene with 1" spacers, 2001, Santa Cruz, CA, carved and painted 3/8" glass, 4'W × 18'H.
Bottom right: Ruby beveled entry, 2002, Hilton Head Island, SC, leaded, beveled, and brilliant-cut glass, 5'W × 9'H. Photographs: Eric Horan.

PAUL HOUSBERG

GLASS PROJECT, INC. ■ 875 NORTH MAIN ROAD ■ JAMESTOWN, RI 02835 ■ TEL 401-560-0880
FAX 401-560-0881 ■ E-MAIL INFO@GLASSPROJECT.COM ■ WWW.GLASSPROJECT.COM

39

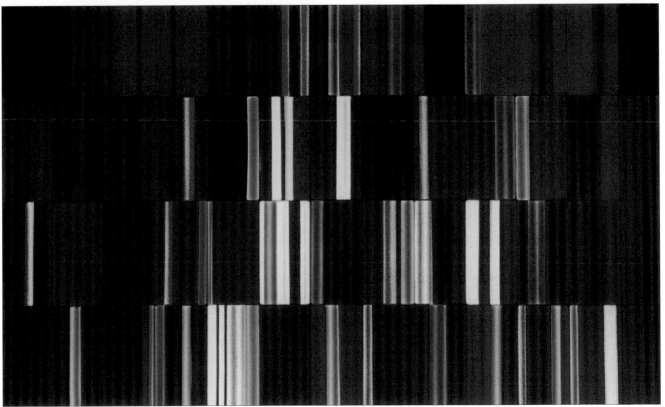

Kiln-formed glass lobby feature, 2003, 1818 Market Street, Philadelphia, PA, 6.5'W x 10'H. Photographs: Don Pearse Photographers, Inc.

INDIANA ART GLASS

GREGORY R. THOMPSON ■ 6400 BROOKVILLE ROAD ■ INDIANAPOLIS, IN 46219 ■ TEL 317-353-6369 ■ FAX 317-359-9630
E-MAIL GREG@INDIANAARTGLASS.COM ■ WWW.INDIANAARTGLASS.COM

Top left: *Coneflower Garden*, 2004, Margaret Mary Community Hospital, Batesville, IN. Top right: Water feature, 2004, Eli Lilly Corporate Campus, Indianapolis, IN. Bottom: Reeded glass stair railing, 2004, Clarian West Medical Center, Avon, IN.

JOHN LEWIS GLASS

JOHN LEWIS ■ 10229 PEARMAIN STREET ■ OAKLAND, CA 94603 ■ TEL 510-635-4607
FAX 510-569-5604 ■ E-MAIL JLEWISGLS@AOL.COM ■ WWW.JOHNLEWISGLASS.COM

Top left: Cast glass sculpture, 2003, Lookingglass Theatre Company, Chicago, IL, 8.25' × 3' × 15". Photograph: Robert Knowles.
Top right: Cast glass pedestal sink, 2001, private residence, San Francisco, CA, 3'H × 20"Dia. Photograph: Charles Frizzell.
Bottom: Cast glass columns, 2003, Mikimoto, Beverly Hills, CA, 8.33' × 5' × 12". Design: Shimoda Design Group. Photograph: Benny Chan/Fotoworks.

Favorite Images from the Past:
A GUILD Sourcebook Retrospective

Photograph: Walt Roycraft.

Guy Kemper
Altar window
Glass
Our Lady of the Woods Chapel
Bellarmine University, Louisville, KY
Published in *Sourcebook 17*

GUY KEMPER

KEMPER STUDIO ■ 1425 ELLISTON LANE ■ VERSAILLES, KY 40383 ■ TEL 859-873-3315
E-MAIL KEMPERSTUDIO@JUNO.COM ■ WWW.KEMPERSTUDIO.COM

43

Detail of 110' x 25' installation at Baltimore-Washington International Airport.

KESSLER STUDIOS, INC.

CINDY KESSLER ■ 273 EAST BROADWAY ■ LOVELAND, OH 45140 ■ TEL 513-683-7500
FAX 513-683-7512 ■ E-MAIL INFO@KESSLERSTUDIOS.COM ■ ■ WWW.KESSLERSTUDIOS.COM

44

Top: University Place Great Room, West Lafayette, IN, 2003.
Bottom left: Old St. Mary Catholic Church Day Chapel, Chicago, IL, 2002. Bottom right: Good Samaritan Hospital Waiting Room, Cincinnati, OH, 2004.

PETERS GLASS STUDIOS

WILHELM PETERS ■ AM HILLIGENBUSCH 25-27 ■ PADERBORN, GERMANY 33098 ■ TEL 011-49-5251-160-97-0
FAX 011-49-5251-160-97-99 ■ E-MAIL INFO@GLASS-ART-PETERS.COM ■ WWW.GLASS-ART-PETERS.COM

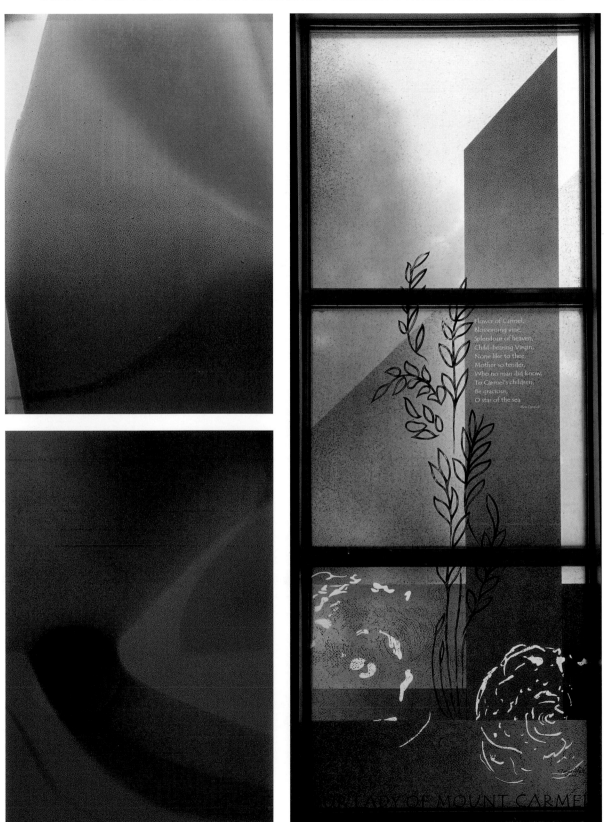

Top and bottom left: St. Marguerite d'Youville window (airbrushed details), 2003, Brampton, Ontario, 18" x 13". Right: *Flos Carmeli*, 2002, one of ten narthex windows for St. John of the Cross Catholic Community, Mississauga, Ontario, 8' x 3'. All works created in collaboration with artist Sarah Hall, Toronto, Ontario.

MONARCH STUDIOS, INC. ■ PO BOX 14104 ■ 2242 UNIVERSITY AVENUE #316 ■ ST. PAUL, MN 55114
TEL 612-810-4754 ■ FAX 651-436-6614 ■ E-MAIL MONART7@MR.NET ■ WWW.MFPILLA.COM

46

Chapel Gathering Space, 2002, Sisters of the Presentation of the Blessed Virgin Mary, Dubuque, IA.

JEFF G. SMITH

ARCHITECTURAL STAINED GLASS, INC. ■ PO BOX 1126 ■ FORT DAVIS, TX 79734-1126 ■ TEL 432-426-3311 ■ FAX 432-426-3366
E-MAIL JGS@ARCHSTGLASSINC.COM ■ WWW.ARCHSTGLASSINC.COM

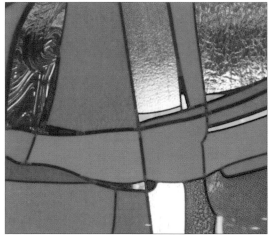

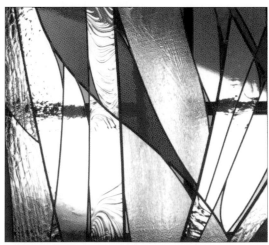

47

Altar Window, Immaculate Conception Catholic Church, Denton, TX, 24'H x 12'W.

ARTHUR STERN

ARTHUR STERN STUDIOS ■ 1075 JACKSON STREET ■ BENICIA, CA 94510
TEL/FAX 707-745-8480 ■ E-MAIL ARTHUR@ARTHURSTERN.COM ■ WWW.ARTHURSTERN.COM

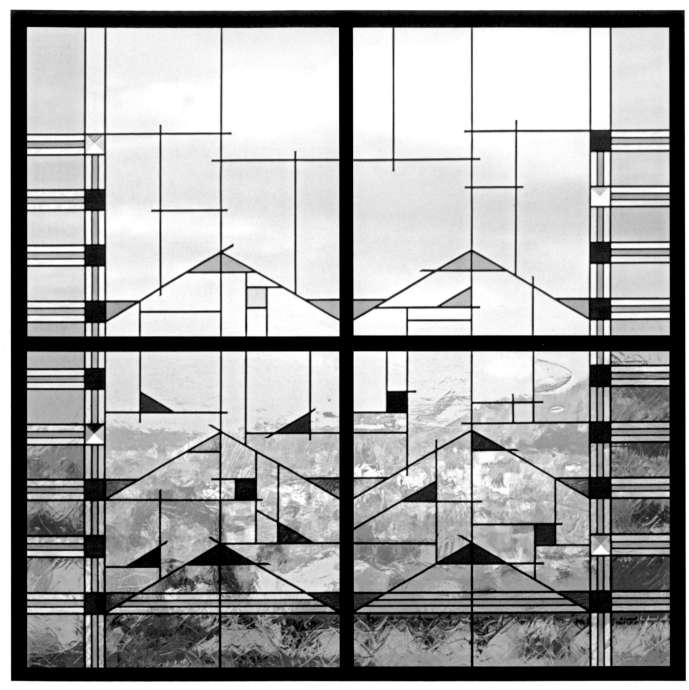

Frozen Music, Berger residence, San Francisco, CA, leaded hand-blown and plate glass with beveled glass prisms, 6' x 6'.

ARTHUR STERN

ARTHUR STERN STUDIOS ■ 1075 JACKSON STREET ■ BENICIA, CA 94510
TEL/FAX 707-745-8480 ■ E-MAIL ARTHUR@ARTHURSTERN.COM ■ WWW.ARTHURSTERN.COM

Frozen Music, Berger residence, San Francisco, CA, leaded hand-blown and plate glass with beveled glass prisms, 6' x 6'.

SERANDA VESPERMANN

VESPERMANN GLASS GALLERY ■ 309 EAST PACES FERRY ROAD ■ ATLANTA, GA 30305 ■ TEL 404-266-0102 OR 770-936-0633
FAX 404-266-0190 OR 770-986-9101 ■ E-MAIL SERANDA@VESPERMANN.COM ■ WWW.VESPERMANN.COM

50

Cable, Enlightening the Universe, The Cable Center, Denver, CO, 6'Dia.

KENNETH F. vonROENN, JR.

ARCHITECTURAL GLASS ART, INC. ■ 815 WEST MARKET STREET ■ LOUISVILLE, KY 40202 ■ TEL 800-795-9429
FAX 502-585-2808 ■ E-MAIL INFO@AGAINC.COM ■ WWW.AGAINC.COM

Top: Orlando International Airport, FL, antique, sandblasted, and dichroic glass with laminated glass jewels, 100' × 15'. Inset: Orlando International Airport (detail).
Bottom: Private residence, Cape Cod, laminated beveled glass, each door 36" × 80". Glass design: Polhemus Savery DaSilva Architects-Builders.
Photograph: Randall Perry Photography.

Career-building Projects:
Commissions Generated Through GUILD Sourcebooks

LINDA LEVITON
Heart of Nature, 2004
Copper
5' x 5' x 8"
Richard M. Ross Heart Hospital, Ohio State
University Medical Center, Columbus

Shortly after I purchased my first GUILD Sourcebook page, Brenda Kroos, a consultant from Cleveland, called me about a job she was working on. Although that project didn't come through, Brenda kept monitoring my work through THE GUILD. Eventually she visited my studio, where she saw a dress I'd made from copper leaves. When Brenda began working with the Ross Heart Hospital, she suggested I design a piece for it using the leaf technique. I initially proposed a form reminiscent of the Red Dress logo associated with a women's heart health campaign.

The hospital committee liked my work, but not the reference to the campaign. They asked me to create a large heart, so I modified the leaves and used a vibrant red lacquer. Since this installation I have done several more large projects with Brenda and have developed relationships with other consultants. The scale of my work has increased, and I've been challenged to grow as an artist. Each time I do a large or unique commission, I show it in THE GUILD so readers can see my work grow and change.

52

LARRY ZGODA
Main window, 2000
Stained glass
18'H x 10'W
Our Lady of the Angels Chapel
Marian Village, Lockport, IL

The Marian Village project came about via Liturgical Consultant Father Thomas Paul, who found my work in the GUILD Sourcebooks. Because of my ads with THE GUILD, the artwork selection committee was already familiar with my work and knew they wanted a design much like the ones I had done before—abstractions of the circle, triangle, and square. The windows were more saturated in color than anything I had ever done. There was a lot of light and not a lot of foliage outside, so the colors had to be rich.

I found my work with Father Paul and the design committee to be very helpful. I'm comfortable working in the kind of situation where the client is as involved with the design as the artist.

I am currently at work on a series of nine windows for the University of Denver, including a beacon window that will become a new campus landmark. I learned about the project through THE GUILD Commission Opportunities e-mail. I've been with THE GUILD almost every year for twenty years. My ads have kept my name in front of people who are interested in the kind of work I do, and my work has become known across the country.

LARRY ZGODA

3932 NORTH OAKLEY ■ CHICAGO, IL 60618 ■ TEL 773-463-3970
E-MAIL LZ@LARRYZGODASTUDIO.COM ■ WWW.LARRYZGODASTUDIO.COM

53

Residential entry, 2004, Arlington Heights, IL, stained and leaded glass with forged steel armatures. Photograph: Richard Bruck.

Architectural Ceramics, Mosaics & Wall Reliefs

SUSAN AHREND

COTTONWOOD DESIGN ■ 321 SAINT JOSEPH AVENUE ■ LONG BEACH, CA 90814
TEL/FAX 562-438-5230 ■ WWW.COTTONWOODTILE.COM

56

Top: *Guatemalan Flowers*, 2003, private collection, ceramic tile, 3'H x 4'W. Bottom: *Tropical Reef* (left) and *Island Dolphins*, 2004, Vista Grande Elementary School, Palos Verdes, CA, ceramic tile, 40"H x 22"W each. Photographs: Jay Ahrend.

MARY LOU ALBERETTI

ALBERETTI STUDIOS ■ 16 POSSUM DRIVE ■ NEW FAIRFIELD, CT 06812 ■ TEL 203-746-1321
E-MAIL MLALB@AOL.COM ■ WWW.SOUTHERNCT.EDU/~ALBERETT/

Top left: *Sweet Firebird*, 2004, ceramic relief, 12" × 13" × 2". Top center: *Triana*, 2004, ceramic relief, 13.5" × 13.5" × 2".
Top right: *Grifo*, 2004, ceramic relief, 12" × 14" × 2.5". Bottom: *Granada Mystery*, 2004, ceramic relief, 11.5" × 19" × 2". Photographs: Bill Quinnell.

CARL & SANDRA BRYANT

FORBEY'S ART & TILE COMPANY ■ PO BOX 756 ■ LYNDEN, WA 98264 ■ TEL/FAX 360-318-1936
E-MAIL FORBEYSALES@FORBEYART.COM ■ WWW.FORBEYART.COM

58

Top left: *Restaurant* (detail), 2003, glass mosaic, 48" x 48". Top right: *Northwest Undersea*, 2003, glass mosaic, 60" x 45". Photograph: Kevin Clarke (photoworksstudio.com).
Bottom left: *Floral II*, 2003, glass mosaic, 30" x 24". Photograph: Kevin Clarke (photoworksstudio.com).
Bottom right: *Cello Player*, 2004, glass mosaic, 32" x 24". Photograph: Kevin Clarke (photoworksstudio.com).

DORA De LARIOS

8560 VENICE BOULEVARD ■ LOS ANGELES, CA 90034 ■ TEL 310-839-8305
E-MAIL DELARIOS@COMCAST.NET ■ WWW.DORADELARIOS.COM

Top: *Life Force*, 2003, Montage Resort & Spa, Laguna Beach, CA, porcelain sculptural mural, 7.5'H x 40'W x 4.5"D. Photograph: Tommy LaFleur.
Bottom: *Life Force* (detail). Photograph: Neal Carlos.

JANE B. GRIMM

1895 PACIFIC AVENUE #305 ■ SAN FRANCISCO, CA 94109 ■ TEL 415-922-2823 ■ FAX 415-563-6926
E-MAIL JBGRIMM@NETSCAPE.NET ■ WWW.JANEBGRIMM.COM

60

Top: *Anemone I*, 2003, ceramic on wood, 5" x 5" x 1". Bottom: *Vortex X*, 2004, ceramic on wood, 6" x 6" x 2". Photographs: Donald J. Felton.

CHRISTOPHER GRYDER

METAMORPHEUS ▪ 2718 CUMBERLAND STREET NW ▪ ROANOKE, VA 24012 ▪ TEL 540-366-9839
E-MAIL CHRIS@CHRISGRYDER.COM ▪ WWW.CHRISGRYDER.COM

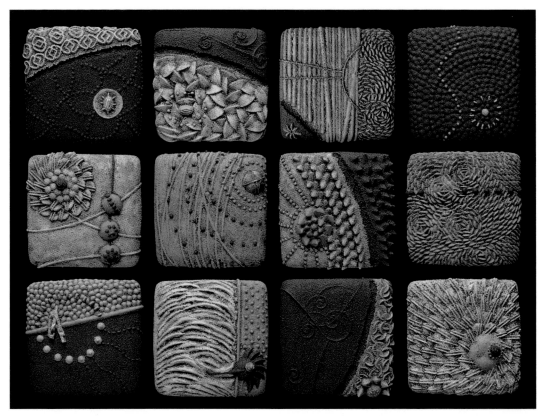

Top: *Ecliptic*, 2004, ceramic relief, 12 12" x 12" tiles. Photograph: Ben Coleman.
Bottom: *Gyrus Meridian*, 2003, private corporation, Ann Arbor, MI, ceramic relief, 60 12" x 12" tiles.

JOAN ROTHCHILD HARDIN

JOAN ROTHCHILD HARDIN CERAMICS ■ 393 WEST BROADWAY #4 ■ NEW YORK, NY 10012 ■ TEL 212-966-9433
FAX 212-431-9196 ■ E-MAIL JOAN@HARDINTILES.COM ■ WWW.HARDINTILES.COM

62

Top: Tiled panel with silk-screened logo tiles installed on the reception desk at Yoga Mandali, New York, NY, 2004, 105 4.25" tiles, 30"H x 66"W.
Bottom: Tiled panel (detail). Photograph: Kevin Noble.

KAREN HEYL

1310 PENDLETON STREET ■ CINCINNATI, OH 45202 ■ 907 SONIA PLACE ■ ESCONDIDO, CA 92026
TEL 513-421-9791 ■ TEL 760-489-7106 ■ E-MAIL KLHEYL@AOL.COM ■ WWW.KARENHEYL.COM

63

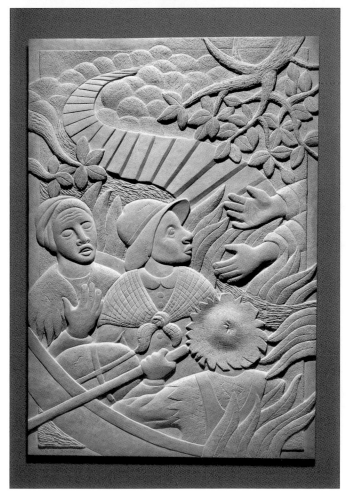

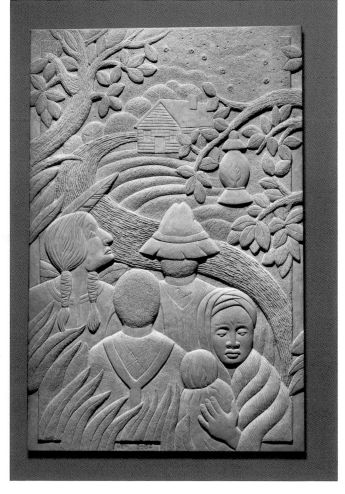

Top: *Flight to Freedom*, 2004, National Underground Railroad Freedom Center, Cincinnati, OH, Indiana limestone, six panels, 43' long.
Bottom left: *Flight to Freedom*, one of six panels. Bottom right: *Flight to Freedom*, one of six panels, each 4' × 6' × 3". Photographs: Charles Behlow.

CLAUDIA HOLLISTER

333 SOUTH STATE STREET, PMB 158 #V ■ LAKE OSWEGO, OR 97034
TEL 503-636-6684 ■ FAX 503-636-0436 ■ E-MAIL CHD@EUROPA.COM

Top left: *Circus Cloud* (detail). Top right: *Nutcracker Cloud* (detail).
Bottom: *Castle Cloud*, 2004, Comer Children's Hospital, Chicago, IL, porcelain, 36"W × 16"H × 4"D. Photographs: Grace Weston.

HOWDLE STUDIO INC.

BRUCE HOWDLE ■ 225 COMMERCE STREET ■ MINERAL POINT, WI 53565 ■ TEL 608-987-3590
E-MAIL BRUCE@BRUCEHOWDLE.COM ■ WWW.BRUCEHOWDLE.COM

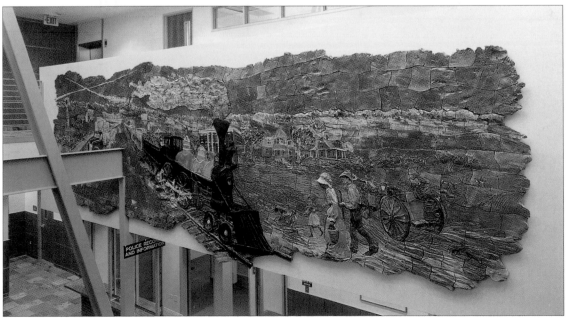

Top: *Reaching for New Heights,* 2003, TDS Metrocom Building, Madison, WI, 6' x 15'H. Photograph: Skot Weidemann, Middleton, WI.
Bottom: Brighton police municipal court facility, 2002, Brighton, CO, 9' x 27'. Photograph: Frank Ooms.

PAMELA JOSEPH

MANOSE STUDIOS, INC. ■ 407 ASPEN OAK DRIVE ■ ASPEN, CO 81611 ■ TEL 970-920-4098 ■ FAX 970-920-2242
E-MAIL MANOSE@ROF.NET ■ WWW.PAMELAJOSEPH.COM

66

Water Nymph, tile mural, 2004, Aspen, CO, ceramic, 8' x 4.5'.

ELLE TERRY LEONARD

ARCHITECTURAL CERAMICS ■ 1840 HYDE PARK STREET ■ SARASOTA, FL 34239 ■ TEL 941-362-9527
E-MAIL ETERRYLEONARD@AOL.COM

Top left: *Loggia* (detail). Top right: *Loggia* (detail).
Bottom: *Loggia*, private residence, Tampa, FL, handmade tile with terra cotta trim and baseboard. Photographs: Christopher Bunn.

ELIZABETH MACDONALD

PO BOX 186 ■ BRIDGEWATER, CT 06752 ■ TEL 860-354-0594 ■ FAX 860-350-4052
E-MAIL EPMACD@EARTHLINK.NET ■ WWW.ELIZABETHMACDONALD.COM

68

Evening Sky (triptych), 2002, powdered ceramic stains and clay on wood, 6' x 5'. Photograph: Bob Rush.

MOTAWI TILEWORKS

NAWAL MOTAWI ■ 170 ENTERPRISE DRIVE ■ ANN ARBOR, MI 48103 ■ TEL 734-213-0017 ■ FAX 734-213-2569
E-MAIL MOTAWI@MOTAWI.COM ■ WWW.MOTAWI.COM

Handmade ceramic tile backsplash and wainscoting in custom glaze with custom base molding, chair rail, and decorative relief tiles, 2004, private residence.
Photographs: Justin Maconochie.

Career-building Projects:
Commissions Generated Through GUILD Sourcebooks

BRUCE HOWDLE
Sportsman's Park, 1995
Ceramic sculpture
7.5'H x 23'W - 90 degree corner
Sportsman's Park, Cicero, IL
Commissioned through: Sonoc/Hutter/Lee LTD, Chicago, IL

Making a living as an artist is difficult in a world that does not particularly understand or value visual literacy, but I have managed to support myself with public and private commission work since 1976. THE GUILD provides a place at the table for artists, and has allowed us to reach design professionals in a way that just wasn't available before.

Artists who wish to take on large projects must be adept at communicating verbally and expressing very specifically how a project will look. The Sportsman's Park project is a perfect example of how THE GUILD can generate a commission when you're open to communications—even at the last minute!

An architect who was working on behalf of the racetrack and had seen my work in the GUILD Sourcebooks presented my images to the selection committee. A representative called me to tell me they liked my work and asked to see a sketch for the project – for a review in forty-five minutes! I quickly worked on the design and faxed him my proposal from the bank where my wife worked. It was one of the simplest and quickest designs I'd ever done, but I got the commission.

70

KAREN HEYL
Health, Healing, and Wellness, 2001
Indiana limestone
48"H x 18"W each
Scripps Memorial Hospital, Chula Vista, CA

Photograph: Charles Behlow Photography.

A consultant that knew about my work through THE GUILD contacted me for this project. It was the third time she had called me, but the first time we actually ended up working on a project together. This was a competition for five commissions throughout the hospital, and I was selected to create a piece for the lobby.

Scripps Memorial's clientele is mostly Latino, and the committee asked me to work with diversity as my theme. I like working with natural imagery because it is so timeless and symbolic. I used corn to represent, cactus for perseverance, and flowers for growth. In Mexican folklore hummingbirds are the spirits of dead soldiers—I wouldn't have known that without some research. I educate myself through these kinds of projects!

Although my first big commission was my largest job to date—it was fifty feet tall—I could not afford to work on such a large scale if it weren't for my corporate commissions. And so far I have never had one job lead to another. It's really THE GUILD. Over the years I have advertised in eight GUILD publications, and I believe this is one of the main reasons I can make a living from my art. THE GUILD works for me!

Photograph: Christopher Kean.

LIBBY WARE

LIBBY WARE STUDIOS ■ 2005 POTTERY LANE ■ DAYTONA BEACH, FL 32128-6559
TEL 386-304-6102 ■ FAX 386-788-1641 ■ E-MAIL LIBBY@LIBBYWARE.COM ■ WWW.LIBBYWARE.COM

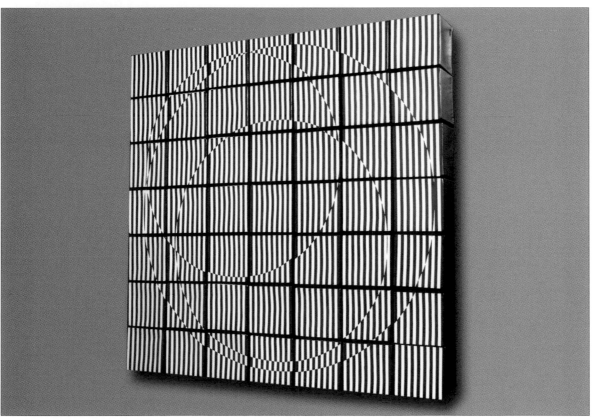

Top: *Music of the Spheres*, 2004, 49 porcelain cubes, 4' × 4'. Bottom: *Celestial Spheres*, 2004, 49 porcelain cubes, 4' × 4'. Photographs: Jack McCarty.

Architectural Elements

" It is important for me to see the new and innovative designs from around the country. The GUILD Sourcebook is my first stop every time. I know that these are serious artists who also are savvy in the ways of the art business. Thank you, GUILD, for bringing such artists into my life and making my searches easy. "

Nancy Noyes
Artist Showcase
Denver, CO

74

Ocean Lavatory, in *Utopia* color, 6"H x 17.5"Dia. Photograph: Lee Puckett.

NICHOLAS BRUMDER

BRUMDER ORNAMENTAL IRON, INC. ■ 40128 INDUSTRIAL PARK ■ GEORGETOWN, TX 78626
TEL 512-869-2830 ■ FAX 512-869-0140 ■ E-MAIL NICHOLAS@TEXAS.NET

Left and bottom right: Gate for the columbarium and chapel at St. Paul's Methodist Cathedral, Houston, TX, forged steel and tube. Architect: David C. Baer FAIA.

Top right: Window grille for private residence, forged steel tube and repoussé sheet steel. Photographs: Swain Edens.

Center right: Railing for private residence in forged and polished bronze; newel in polished steel and bronze.

STEVE FONTANINI

STEVE FONTANINI ARCHITECTURAL & ORNAMENTAL BLACKSMITHING ■ PO BOX 2298 ■ JACKSON, WY 83001 ■ TEL 307-733-7668
FAX 307-734-8816 ■ E-MAIL SFONTANINI@WYOMING.COM ■ WWW.STEVEFONTANINIBLACKSMITH.COM

76

Top: Gate, a private ranch, Teton County, WY, traditionally joined, forged aluminum powder coated with copper vein finish, 16'L x 6'H.
Photograph: David Angello. Bottom left: Entry/Garden Gate, forged mild steel and bronze, 65" x 37". Bottom right: Railing, private residence,
Teton County, WY, traditionally joined, forged mild steel clear wax finish, 111'L. Photograph: Florence McCall.

CHRISTIAN HECKSCHER

LIFT DESIGN INC. ARCHITECTURAL DETAILS ■ PO BOX 1380 ■ VINEYARD HAVEN, MA 02568 ■ TEL/FAX 508-696-6284
E-MAIL LIFTDESIGNHDA@EARTHLINK.NET ■ WWW.LIFTDESIGNETCHING.COM

Seven custom etched nickel murals, 2003, Ana Hotel, Tokyo, Japan. Inset: Etched mural (detail).

HUCK FISHER METALWORKERS

CHRISTOPHER HUCK ■ LAURA FISHER ■ (WINTER) CALLE 5 DE MAYO #205-B, BARRIO JALATLACO ■ OAXACA, MX 68080
(SUMMER) 146 BLUENOSE DRIVE ■ PO BOX 538 ■ LUNENBURG, NS B0J 2C0 ■ CANADA
TEL 011-52-951-118-0847 (MX) 902-634-7125 (CAN) ■ E-MAIL INFO@HUCKFISHER.COM ■ WWW.HUCKFISHER.COM

Friesian Gate and Weathervane, Chester, Nova Scotia, solid aluminum, stainless steel, and bronze, gate: 8'H × 16'W; weathervane: 5.5'H × 8.5'W.
Photograph: Julian Beveridge Photography.

FAITH SCHEXNAYDER

FLATFORK STUDIO ■ 709 WEST GIBSON STREET ■ AUSTIN, TX 78704 ■ TEL 512-448-2256
E-MAIL SCHEX@AUSTIN.RR.COM ■ WWW.FLATFORKSTUDIO.COM

Top: *Corinthian Column Quadrant*, 2001, Pieces of the Past Antiques, Austin, TX, foam sculpture, 8' × 7' × 3'.
Bottom: Carved frieze, 2002, private residence, commissioned by Telaque Paque Builders foam, 3' × 13'. Photographs: Bill Bastas Photographer.

DON SCHMIDT

CUSTOM METALS, INC. ■ 4544 DONS ROAD ■ MADISON, WI 53711 ■ TEL 608-222-4699 ■ FAX 608-222-7026
E-MAIL CUSTMTL@AOL.COM ■ WWW.CUSTOMMETALS.COM

80

Staircase, 2003, private residence, stainless steel, iron, bronze, copper, and glass, 30' x 11' x 15'. Photographs: Steven J. Ash.

TYLER STUDIOS, LTD.

SETH TYLER ■ 6200 WEST MEQUON ROAD ■ MEQUON, WI 53092
TEL 262-391-5153 ■ E-MAIL WWW.SETHTYLER.NET

Top: *Herringbone* range hood, 2004, private collection, heavily rusted steel, 30"H x 50"W x 26"D. Bottom left: Mask Andirons, 2001, private collection, forged stainless and mid-steel, 24"H x 24"W x 18"D. Bottom right: Table, 2004, private collection, copper top on forged and fabricated steel base, sanded gun-blue and clear-coat finish, 30.5"H x 66"W x 45"D. Photographs: George Lottermoser.

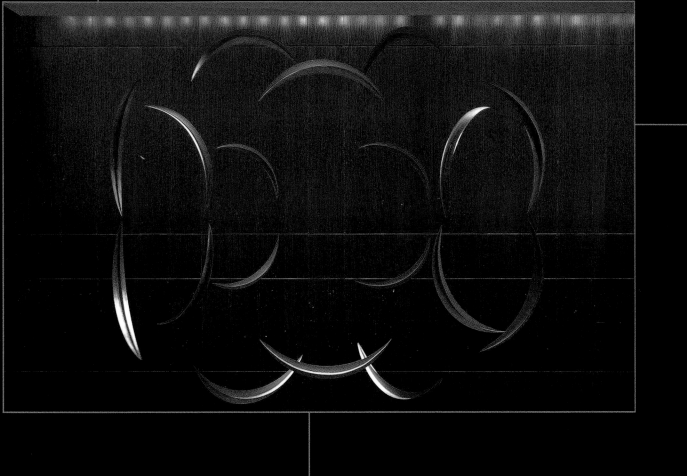

CLOWES SCULPTURE

JONATHAN CLOWES ■ EVELYN CLOWES ■ 98 MARCH HILL ROAD ■ WALPOLE, NH 03608 ■ TEL/FAX 603-756-9505
E-MAIL STACEY@CLOWESSCULPTURE.COM ■ WWW.CLOWESSCULPTURE.COM

85

Soaring Spirits, 2004, White County Medical Center, Searcy, AR, stainless steel rod and painted aluminum, 25'W × 20'D × 50'H.

Career-building Projects:
Commissions Generated Through GUILD Sourcebooks

JONATHAN AND EVELYN CLOWES
Soaring Spirits Atrium Sculpture, 2004
Stainless steel rod and painted aluminum
25'W x 20'D x 50'H
White County Medical Center
Searcy, AR

The vision and guidance of Susan Gammon, an interior designer in Fayetteville, Arkansas, were invaluable in creating this successful installation. She approached us after seeing our work in *Sourcebook 17*, and this project became a fantastic collaboration.

Originally, this atrium was to have a large chandelier. Susan and architect Bill Gray of Little Rock thought a sculptural piece might be more interesting. They came to us with a concept that included clouds and birds. During our first visit, we discussed some bird concepts we had already played with, and those eventually developed into *Soaring Spirits*. Our problem-solving skills and ability to install a large-scale projects under budget secured the project for us.

Addressing site-specific concerns often yields a new direction and powerful results. This project is quite different from the work we advertised in **THE GUILD** years ago. Even compared to our recent pieces, it is a radical departure. *Soaring Spirits*, for which all the birds were pressed in the same die, represents the first time we have used many repeated elements to achieve a gesture.

86

Photograph: White County Medical Center.

JUDY DIOSZEGI
Summer Days, 2001
Nylon and aluminum
Corridor: 60'H x 16'W x 160'L
Kites: 6'W x 8'L; tails: 30"W x 44'-90'L
Streamer banners: 30"W x 75'-100'L
Donald W. Reynolds Center on Aging,
University of Arkansas Medical Sciences,
Little Rock

Photograph: John C. Dioszegi.

Art consultant Greg Thompson called us about this project after seeing our pages in *Sourcebooks 10, 12*, and *14*. The client wanted the three-story space filled with color and the feeling of Arkansas summer days. We began with banners for the reception area and then created kites and banners depicting clouds, mountains, and waterways for the atrium. They soar forty to sixty feet high, in a carefree placement designed not to obstruct the view.

The installation was quite challenging, beginning with two hours of maneuvering the lift through the door. Keeping the huge kites taut required refinements to our suspension system. And although our detailed maquette was invaluable, we made many adjustments once the banners were in place and could be viewed from every floor.

It was a great thrill to complete this project, which received an Outstanding Achievement Award from the Industrial Fabrics Association. *Summer Days* is larger than most of our previous work, and its success, which we can demonstrate to clients through the award and our GUILD tearsheets, has allowed us to pursue other large commissions.

JUDY DIOSZEGI

JUDY DIOSZEGI, DESIGNER ■ 1295 MARGATE LANE ■ GREEN OAKS, IL 60048 ■ TEL 847-367-8395 ■ FAX 847-367-8395*51
E-MAIL JDIOX2@AOL.COM ■ WWW.JDIOSZEGI.COM

87

Top left and right: *Five Faces of Art*, 2003, Highland Park High School, IL, 100% nylon flagcloth, vertical panels: 9'H × 3'W, swags: 15'L to 18'L × 22"W.
Bottom: *Ever Upward!*, 2004, Sacred Heart Hospital, Tomahawk, WI, 100% nylon flagcloth, triangles: 5', tails: 13'L to 25'L × 30" tapering to 2"W.

ROB FISHER

ROB FISHER SCULPTURE LLC ■ 228 NORTH ALLEGHENY STREET ■ BELLEFONTE, PA 16823 ■ TEL 814-355-1458
FAX 814-353-9060 ■ E-MAIL ROB@ROBFISHERSCULPTURE.COM ■ WWW.ROBFISHERSCULPTURE.COM

Blue Skies (top) and *Silver Lining* (bottom),, 2004, Penn Stater Conference Center Hotel, State College, PA, suspended sculptures, aluminum and stainless steel.

88

ROB FISHER

ROB FISHER SCULPTURE LLC ■ 228 NORTH ALLEGHENY STREET ■ BELLEFONTE, PA 16823 ■ TEL 814-355-1458
FAX 814-353-9060 ■ E-MAIL ROB@ROBFISHERSCULPTURE.COM ■ WWW.ROBFISHERSCULPTURE.COM

Top: *Birds of Paradise*, 2004, Two West Liberty Building, Malvern, PA, suspended sculpture, aluminum and stainless steel.
Bottom: *Walk in the Woods*, 2004, Christ Hospital, Cincinnati, OH, suspended sculpture, aluminum and stainless steel.

GOLDSTEIN & KAPELLAS STUDIO

DANIEL GOLDSTEIN ■ JOHN KAPELLAS ■ 224 GUERRERO STREET ■ SAN FRANCISCO, CA 94103 ■ TEL 415-621-5761
FAX 415-431-4844 ■ E-MAIL DANIELJGOLDSTEIN@YAHOO.COM ■ WWW.GOLDSTEINANDKAPELLAS.COM

90

Top: *Concentric,* 2004, Sallie Mae Corporation, Reston, VA, anodized aluminum, 13' x 13' x 10'. Photograph: Maxwell MacKenzie.
Bottom: *Transport,* 2001, Norcal Waste Systems, Inc., San Francisco, CA, glass and steel, 54" x 96" x 12".

TIMOTHY ROSE

COALSHED STUDIO ■ PO BOX 2052 ■ BUILDING 153, FOURTH AND WATERFRONT STREETS ■ MARE ISLAND, CA 94592
TEL 707-562-3158 ■ FAX 415-331-5041 ■ E-MAIL TROSEART@AOL.COM ■ WWW.MOBILESCULPTURE.COM

Top: *Blue Zig-Zag* mobile, 2005, painted sheet metal and wire, 4' x 10' x 4'. Bottom: *Double Suns* mobile, 2005, painted sheet metal and wire, 3' x 12' x 3'.

Favorite Images from the Past:
A GUILD Sourcebook Retrospective

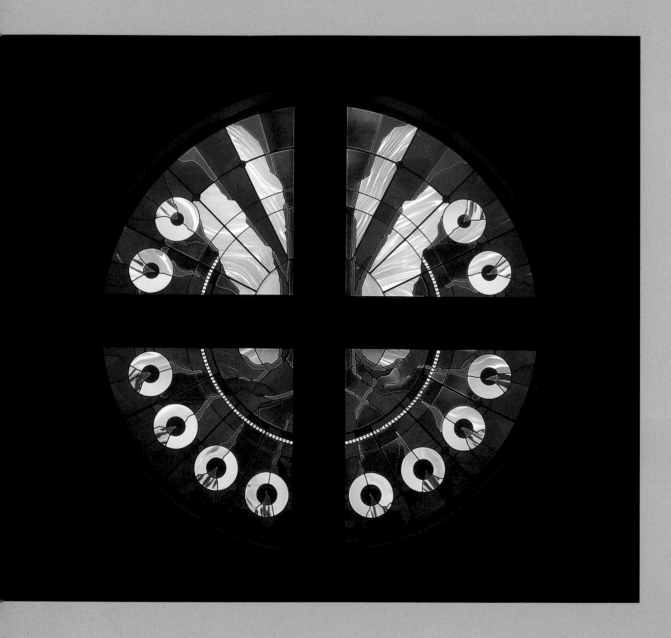

Michael F. Pilla
Pentecost
Glass
Saint Ambrose Catholic Church
Published in *Sourcebook 16*

SABLE STUDIOS

PAUL SABLE ■ 2737 ROSEDALE AVENUE ■ SOQUEL, CA 95073 ■ TEL 800-233-7309
E-MAIL PAUL@SABLESTUDIOS.COM ■ WWW.SABLESTUDIOS.COM

93

Left: *Dawn of Spring's Bouquet*, 2000, Boy's Town Children's Hospital, Omaha, NE, acrylic, 15' × 15' × 18'. Top right: *A Mist of Fragrant Time*, 2000, private residence, acrylic, 10' × 12'.
Center right: *Sky Ballet*, Metro Plaza, San Jose, CA, acrylic, 4' × 6' × 17'. Bottom right: *Spectral Arc*, 1998, Lucent Technologies, Altamonte Springs, FL, acrylic, 4' × 5' × 11'.

Public Art

" Viewing art in the pages of the GUILD Sourcebook is like discovering a treasure chest. It provides us with a unique vision to expand our horizons and remind us that creativity is endless. "

Jillian Glowienke

A. E. TED AUB

STUDIO: GENEVA, NY ■ REPRESENTED BY SUSAN ALBERT ATHAS ■ 110 SHAWMUT ROAD ■ CANTON, MA 02021
TEL 781-828-8011 ■ FAX 781-575-0653 ■ E-MAIL FTBF@VERIZON.NET

Top left: *When Anthony Met Stanton*, Seneca Falls, NY. Inset: *When Anthony Met Stanton* (detail). Photographs: Linda Solan.
Bottom: *Paraiso Invierno*, Village of Merrick Park, Coral Gables, FL.

CHRIS BENNETT

BENNETT STUDIO ■ 26983 ROUTE J40 ■ KEOSAUQUA, IA 52565-8348 ■ TEL 319-592-3228 ■ FAX 319-592-3463
E-MAIL CBENNETT@NETINS.NET ■ WWW.BENNETTSTUDIO.COM

97

Top: *Dwight Vredenburg Memorial*, 2003-2004, Hy-Vee Foods Corporate Headquarters, West Des Moines, IA, bronze, life-size figure, overall size 40' × 6' × 6'.
Bottom left: *Dwight Vredenburg Memorial* (detail). Bottom right: *Pool of Bethesda*, 2004, Bethesda Lutheran Home Services, Watertown, WI,
bronze with water element, life-size figures, overall size 30'Dia.

CHARLES STRAIN SCULPTURE

CHARLES STRAIN ■ 7600 WEST CARR LANE ■ HARRISBURG, MO 65256 ■ TEL/FAX 573-874-3174
E-MAIL CSTRAIN@SOCKETS.NET ■ WWW.CHARLESSTRAIN.COM

98

Top: *Horse & Rider*, 2002, bronze, 87" × 80" × 78". Bottom left: *Lovers*, 2003, bronze, 24" × 9" × 36".
Photograph: Scott Smith. Bottom right: *Moondance*, 2002, bronze, 45" × 22" × 74".

DAVID B. DAHLQUIST

RDG DAHLQUIST ART STUDIO ■ 316 SW FIFTH STREET ■ DES MOINES, IA 50309 ■ TEL 515-284-1675
FAX 515-246-0459 ■ E-MAIL DDAHLQUIST@RDGUSA.COM ■ WWW.RDGUSA.COM

99

Top and bottom: *Intercollegiate Athletics: Founded on Education*, 2004, Art-in-State-Buildings commission for Jacobson Plaza, Iowa State University, Ames, Iowa, mixed media with plasma-cut steel, Plexiglas, metal-halide fixtures, cast stone, and terra cotta, 13.5'H x 3.5'W. Connected by colored concrete paving spanning over 150 feet. Inset: Detail . Photographs: Kun Zhang.

ALLEN DAVID

LIANE MCALLISTER MARKETING ■ 181 EAST 73RD STREET, SUITE 16E ■ NEW YORK, NY 10021 ■ TEL/FAX 212-535-0716
E-MAIL SALTINE38@AOL.COM ■ WWW.ALLENDAVIDDESIGN.COM

100

Top: Glass screen, La Trobe University, Melbourne, AUS, relief with fused wired glass and colored glass, 12'H x 36'L.
Bottom: Glass fountain, Dizengoff Circle, Tel Aviv, ISR, glass laminated with Lucite structure with surface of slumped glass, 12'H.

LYNN GOODPASTURE

10753 WEYBURN AVENUE ■ LOS ANGELES, CA 90024
TEL 310-470-2455 ■ FAX 310-470-4257 ■ E-MAIL LGOODPAST@AOL.COM

Top: *The Children's Clock*, 2003, La Cienega Blvd. & Melrose Avenue, West Hollywood, CA, opalescent glass and metal, 12.5'Dia. Photograph: Josh Barash.
Bottom: *The Children's Clock* (detail).

SARAH HAVILAND

906 SOUTH STREET ■ PEEKSKILL, NY 10566 ■ TEL 914-734-4979
E-MAIL SARAHHAVILAND@EARTHLINK.NET ■ WWW.SARAHHAVILAND.COM

Top left: *Trio*, 2001, Grounds for Sculpture, Hamilton, NJ, bronze, 9' x 8' x 6'.
Top right: *Pier Glass*, 1995, Hudson River Museum, Yonkers, NY, fiberglas cement with Plexiglas mirrors, 72" x 40" x 24". Photograph: Howard Goodman.
Bottom: *Copper Beech: People's Trust*, 2003, The Arts Exchange, White Plains, NY, copper mesh, steel, wood, and mirror, 15' x 12' x 12'. Photograph: Howard Goodman.

ERIC HIGGS

HIGGS SCULPTURE STUDIO, INC. ■ 2245 FOURTH AVE. SOUTH ■ ST. PETERSBURG, FL 33712
TEL 727-641-5161 ■ FAX 727-321-5640 ■ E-MAIL ERIC@ERICHIGGS.COM ■ WWW.ERICHIGGS.COM

103

Top: *Crossroads*, 2001, Charles Schwab Corporate Park, City of Pleasanton, CA, steel, 30' × 16' × 10'. Photograph: William Porter. Bottom left: *Horizon*, 2004, Whole Foods Market, Sarasota, FL, basalt, 12' × 14' × 6'. Photograph: Alex McKnight. Bottom right: *Waterworks VI*, 2004, private estate, Kentfield, CA, basalt, 8' × 8' × 8'.

ELIZABETH MacQUEEN

ELIZABETH MACQUEEN SCULPTURE & FINE ART ■ 19791 HUNTER'S LOOP ■ FAIRHOPE, AL 36532
TEL 251-928-9735 / 251-610-9022 ■ E-MAIL MACQUEENSCULPTOR@AOL.COM ■ WWW.MACQUEENFINEART.COM

104

Chinese Pioneers, Railroad Square, San Luis Obispo, CA, 9'H with a 5' concrete base. Photograph: Forrest L. Doud.

MAX-CAST

STEVE MAXON ■ DORIS PARK ■ PO BOX 662 ■ 611 B AVENUE ■ KALONA, IA 52247
TEL 319-656-5365 ■ FAX 319-656-3187 ■ E-MAIL MAX-CAST@KCTC.NET ■ WWW.MAX-CAST.COM

105

Irving B. Weber, Portrait of a Gentleman, 2003, Iowa City, IA, bronze. Photograph: Mark Tade.

BRUCE A. NIEMI
Torch, 2000
Silicon bronze
15' x 4' x 4'
Cary Academy, Cary, NC

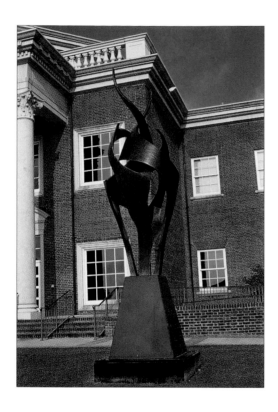

Torch represents the energy that knowledge produces and the interaction between teachers and students, our future leaders. This commission came through Holly Jones, an art consultant for Cary's SAS Institute, who was also artist-in-residence at Cary Academy at the time. Holly showed my work to a founding member of the Academy, who was inspired by my *Eternal Flame Memorial* published in *GUILD 10*. Eventually, Cary Academy commissioned me to create a piece with a similar feeling for the school.

It was exciting to get a commission for a large-scale bronze, since at the time I'd only been working in bronze for a few years. It pushed me to do some engineering to make the piece stronger. I also believe *Torch* has led to other opportunities: It was featured in *Sourcebook 18*, and I've shared it with many clients via tearsheets and my website. I later placed a stainless steel sculpture, *Interim VIII*, through Cary Percent for the Arts. And who knows . . . the students at Cary are young now, but they could be future art buyers!

RIIS BURWELL
Spirit Form Emerging, 2004
Bronze
17' x 4' x 6'
The District at Green Valley Ranch,
Henderson, NV

I've made several versions of *Spirit Form Emerging*, and this one was directly inspired by the sculpture advertised on my page in *Sourcebook 18*. That was the original version, made in 2002 as a tribute to victims of the 9/11 tragedy. Mark Zachman, the art consultant for American Nevada Company, and its president, John Kilduff, were both impressed with the sculpture and began thinking about commissioning it in a larger size for their Green Valley Ranch.

I believe they were sold after I sent a 32-inch bronze version for their consideration. In the end John Kilduff purchased that small piece for the complex's library and a large one for placement at the ranch. It was one of the largest sculptures I have ever built, and I found it very satisfying.

I first joined THE GUILD in 1998, and it remains the primary vehicle for advertising my work. The promotion of my sculpture through THE GUILD's sourcebooks and tearsheets has greatly benefited my career.

ROSLYN MAZZILLI

ROSLYN MAZZILLI SCULPTURE, NY
E-MAIL ROSLYN@ROSLYNMAZZILLI.COM ■ WWW.ROSLYNMAZZILLI.COM

There, Oakland City Center, Oakland, CA, polychrome aluminum, 20' x 19' x 18'.

NATIONAL SCULPTORS' GUILD

2683 NORTH TAFT AVENUE ■ LOVELAND, CO 80538 ■ TEL 800-606-2015 ■ FAX 970-667-2068
E-MAIL NSG@FRII.COM ■ WWW.NATIONALSCULPTORSGUILD.COM

Top left: *River Market Pig* by Sandy Scott, Little Rock River Market, bronze, 4.5'H × 4'W × 5'D.
Top right: *Anglers* by Jane DeDecker, Clinton Presidential Center Entry, bronze, 8.5'H × 4.5'W × 3.5'D.
Bottom: *Eagle of the Rock* by Sandy Scott, Clinton Presidential Center Entry, bronze, 8.5'H × 10'W × 6.5'D. Photographs: Jafe T. Parsons Photography.

NATIONAL SCULPTORS' GUILD

2683 NORTH TAFT AVENUE ■ LOVELAND, CO 80538 ■ TEL 800-606-2015 ■ FAX 970-667-2068
E-MAIL NSG@FRII.COM ■ WWW.NATIONALSCULPTORSGUILD.COM

109

Top left: *Fiesta* by Carol Gold, Clinton Presidential Center Entry, bronze, 6'H x 9'W x 2'D.
Top right: *Harriet Tubman* by Jane DeDecker, Clinton Presidential Center Entry, bronze, 5.5'H x 6'W x 4'D.
Bottom: *Encircling the Future* by Mark Leichliter, Little Rock National Airport Signature Sculpture, powder-coated steel, 16'H x 12'W x 3'D. Photographs: Jafe T. Parsons Photography.

DANIEL OBERTI

DANIEL OBERTI CERAMIC DESIGN ■ 3796 TWIG AVENUE ■ SEBASTOPOL, CA 95472 ■ TEL 707-829-0584
FAX 707-829-2136 ■ E-MAIL DANIEL@DANIELOBERTI.COM ■ WWW.DANIELOBERTI.COM

110

Top: *Sphere.* Bottom left: *Venus,* ceramic and steel. Bottom right: *Shadow Catcher.*

SHELLEY PARRIOTT

3437 ROUTE 212 ■ BEARSVILLE, NY 12409 ■ TEL 845-679-6390
E-MAIL THEARTSTUDIOWDST@AOL.COM ■ WWW.SHELLEYPARRIOTT.COM

111

Color Field Sculpture, transparent steel mesh, 10' × 10' × 5'. Inset: *Color Field Sculpture* (detail).

ROBERT PERLESS

ROBERT PERLESS STUDIO ■ 37 LANGHORNE LANE ■ GREENWICH, CT 06831
TEL 203-869-0710 ■ FAX 203-869-0718 ■ E-MAIL ROBERT@PERLESS.COM ■ WWW.PERLESS.COM

112

Top: *Sun Dagger*, 2004. Utah Valley State College, Wasatch Campus, Heber City, UT. Silicon bronze and polymer prisms. Gnomon 13.75' H, 22.5' L. Dial 35.8' by 51'W.
Bottom left: *Sun Dagger*, close-up of rainbow crossing sunline at noon transit on autumnal equinox. Bottom right: *Sun Dagger*, gnomon at noon transit.

DAVID LAWRENCE PHELPS

PHELPS SCULPTURE STUDIO ■ 11621 NORTH SANTA FE AVENUE B-12 ■ OKLAHOMA CITY, OK 73114
TEL 405-752-9512 ■ E-MAIL DAVIDLPHELPS@GMAIL.COM ■ WWW.PHELPSSCULPTURE.COM

113

Top: *Pastoral Dreamer*, 2003, University of Oklahoma, Norman, OK, bronze, 5' x 16' x 9', edition of 6.
Bottom: *Grace*, 2001, JRB Art, Oklahoma City, OK, bronze, 2' x 6' x 4', edition of 20.

Favorite Images from the Past:
A GUILD Sourcebook Retrospective

Photograph: Greg Murphey.

Bev Precious
University Continuum, 2002
Stainless steel, dichroic glass, bronze, and limestone
16' x 8' x 12'
University of Indianapolis, IN
Published in *Sourcebook 18*

BEV PRECIOUS

PRECIOUS DESIGN STUDIOS, INC. ■ 950 NORTH ALABAMA STREET ■ INDIANAPOLIS, IN 46202
TEL/FAX 317-631-6560 ■ E-MAIL BBPREC@AOL.COM

Top: *Catalyst*, 2004, Minnetrista Cultural Center, Inc., Muncie, IN, stainless steel, limestone, and dichroic glass, 28' × 24' × 26'. Bottom left and right: *Catalyst* (detail).

HENRY RICHARDSON

PO BOX 408 ■ 101 GOOSE POND ROAD ■ TYRINGHAM, MA 01264 ■ TEL 917-670-5794
E-MAIL HENRY@HENRYRICHARDSON.COM ■ WWW.HENRYRICHARDSON.COM

116

Top left: *Chiseled Orb* and *Mortal Coil*, 2004, DeCordova Museum and Sculpture Park, Lincoln, MA, chiseled glass.
Right: *City of Danbury 9/11 Memorial* for Connecticut Victims, 2004, chiseled glass, 12' and 5,500 lbs. Photograph: Gabriel Stranahan.
Bottom left: *Coming of Age*, 1999, private collection, chiseled glass, 5'Dia and 8,000 lbs. Photograph: Andrew Swaine.

MAUREEN A. SEAMONDS

THE PRODUCE STATION STUDIOS ■ 723 SENECA STREET ■ WEBSTER CITY, IA 50595 ■ TEL 515-832-5120
FAX 515-832-4851 ■ E-MAIL SEAMONDS@WMTEL.NET ■ HTTP://MYSPACE.WMTEL.NET/SEAMONDS_FTP/

Prairie Sentinel, Myrtle Beach, SC, clay and encaustic, Timberlane, 72" × 36" × 32".
Inset: *Prairie Sentinel* (detail).

GERALD SICILIANO

GERALD SICILIANO STUDIO DESIGN ASSOCIATES ■ 9 GARFIELD PLACE ■ BROOKLYN, NY 11215-1903
TEL/FAX 718-636-4561 ■ E-MAIL GERALD.SICILIANO@VERIZON.NET ■ WWW.GERALDSICILIANOSTUDIO.COM

118

Top: *Due Skiene (Pamela)*, Botticino marble, 23" x 35" x 7".
Bottom left: *Gert*, private collection, New York and South America, Botticino marble, 33" x 22" x 6". Photographs: Frank Siciliano.
Bottom right: *Icarus Descended*, Kyungnam Provincial Government, Changwon, South Korea, Korean marble, 10.5' x 6' x 3.6'.

GERALD SICILIANO

GERALD SICILIANO STUDIO DESIGN ASSOCIATES ■ 9 GARFIELD PLACE ■ BROOKLYN, NY 11215-1903
TEL/FAX 718-636-4561 ■ E-MAIL GERALD.SICILIANO@VERIZON.NET ■ WWW.GERALDSICILIANOSTUDIO.COM

119

Left: *Balena*, Mountain View, CA, Zimbabwe black granite, 10' × 3' × 3', available in bronze or granite and scaled to specifications.
Top right: *Nautilus*, commissioned by John Templeton Foundation, Radnor, PA, stainless steel, 25' × 15' × 2', available in bronze and stainless steel. Photograph: Sandy Rosenberg.
Bottom right: *Pugilista*, collection of Dong Baek Art Center, Pusan, South Korea, black Belgian marble, 27.5' × 12' × 10', available in bronze and stainless steel. Photograph: Frank Siciliano.

Favorite Images from the Past:
A GUILD Sourcebook Retrospective

Photograph: Robert Ruschak.

James C. Myford
Dependence, 1990
Aluminum
86" x 26" x 13"
Published in *Sourcebook 19*

TERRY THOMMES

THOMMES STUDIO INC. ■ 6185 SW GAINES AVENUE ■ STUART, FL 34997 ■ TEL 772-286-2386 ■ FAX 772-220-4797
E-MAIL TERRY@THOMMESART.COM ■ WWW.THOMMESART.COM

121

Navigator, 2004, Key West Customs House, Key West, FL, welded steel, 11.5' × 3.5' × 5'. Photograph: Thommes Studio.

LUIS TORRUELLA

TENERIFE BUILDING ■ 1507 ASHFORD AVENUE, APT. 1201 ■ SAN JUAN, PR 00911 ■ TEL/FAX 787-722-8728
TEL (CELL) 787-384-0026 ■ E-MAIL LUISTORRUELLA@AOL.COM ■ WWW.LUISTORRUELLA.COM

122

Top: *La Red,* 2004, Parque de las Ciencias, Bayamón, PR, painted and brushed aluminum, 20' x 110' x 1'. Photograph: Alberto Gratacos.
Bottom: *Mare, Solaris, Terra,* 2004, Fundación Angel Ramos, Hato Rey, PR, 13' x 4' x 4' each.

JAMES TYLER

67 JEFFERSON STREET ■ NYACK, NY 10960 ■ TEL 845-548-8918
E-MAIL TYLERSCULPTURE@EARTHLINK.NET ■ WWW.TYLERSCULPTURE.COM

123

Brickhead 3, 2004, Davlan Park, Indianapolis, IN, ceramic brick sculpture with interactive sound elements, 85" x 54" x 60".

Non-Representational Sculpture

" We encourage clients to use original art both on a monumental scale and in more modest ways. When art is woven throughout a space, it adds tremendously to the environment. "

John Mudgett
Industrial Designer/Interior Space Designer
Lawrenceville, NJ

MICHAEL BAUERMEISTER

6560 AUGUSTA BOTTOM ROAD ■ AUGUSTA, MO 63332 ■ TEL/FAX 636-228-4663
E-MAIL MICHAEL@BAUERMEISTER.COM ■ WWW.MICHAELBAUERMEISTER.COM

126

Left: *Tall Vessels* (left to right), stained birch, 65" x 19"; linden, 40" x 11"; birch, 73" x 20". Top right: *Tall Vessels* (left to right), walnut, 38" x 12"; oak, 50" x 14"; painted oak, 26" x 11".
Center right: *Sprout Vessels*, various woods, 17"-40" tall. Bottom right: *Two Painted Vessels* (left to right), linden with paint, 34" x 14"; right, birch with paint, 56" x 15".

SANDRA CHRISTINE Q. BERGÉR

QUINTALSTUDIO ■ 100 EL CAMINO REAL SUITE #202 ■ BURLINGAME, CA 94010
TEL 650-348-0310 ■ FAX 650-348-8733 ■ E-MAIL QUINTAL@QUINTALSTUDIO.COM

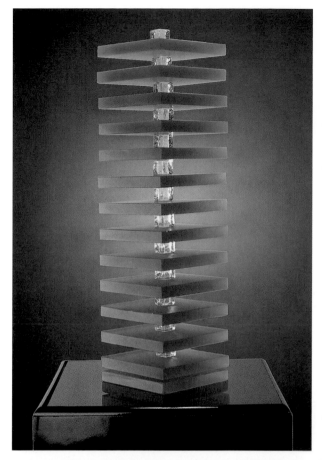

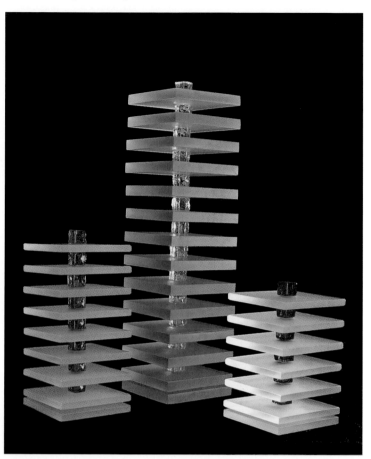

Towers of Light series, all finely etched plate and cast glass sculpture. Top left: *Sky Tower*, 6"W x 6"D x 24"H.
Top right: *Sea Towers*, each 5.5" W x 5.5"D x 13.5"H and 8.5"H with *Sky Tower* (center). Bottom: *Sky Tower* in garden. Photographs: William A. Porter.

128

Inspiration, 1988, steel, 26'. Photograph: Michael Zagalik.

129

Mystery and Grandeur, 2004, stainless steel, 61" x 45" x 10", wall sculpture. Photograph: Jim Maidhof.

BRIAN RUSSELL STUDIO

BRIAN RUSSELL STUDIO ■ 10385 LONG ROAD ■ ARLINGTON, TN 38002 ■ TEL 901-867-7300 ■ FAX 901-867-7843
E-MAIL INFO@BRIANRUSSELLSTUDIO.COM ■ WWW.BRIANRUSSELLSTUDIO.COM

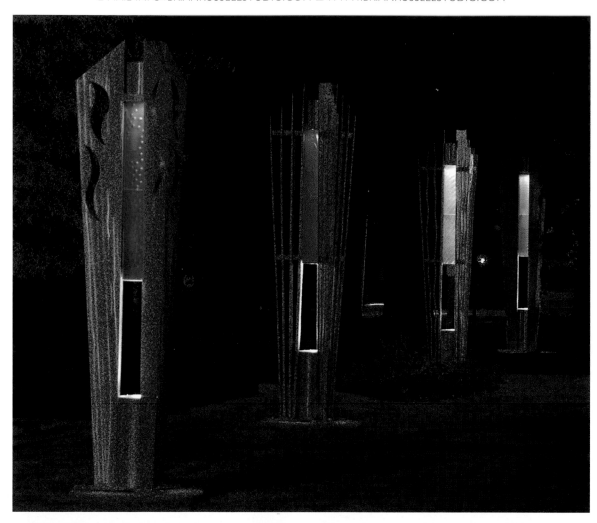

130

Top: *The Virtues*, 2004, Church Health Center, Memphis, TN, forged aluminum and cast glass, 120"H.
Bottom left: *The Virtues*, (daylight view). Bottom right: *The Virtues: Patience* (detail).

RIIS BURWELL

RIIS BURWELL STUDIO ■ 3815 CALISTOGA ROAD ■ SANTA ROSA, CA 95404 ■ TEL/FAX 707-538-2676
E-MAIL RIIS@RIISBURWELL.COM ■ WWW.RIISBURWELL.COM

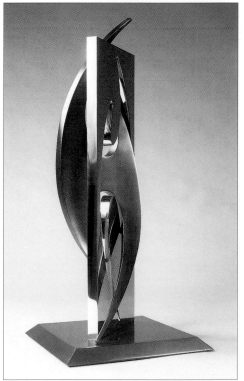

131

Top left: *Spirit Form Emerging*, 2004, Green Valley Ranch Resort, Henderson, NV, bronze, 17' × 4' × 6'.
Right: *Cloud Form*, 2004, Paradise Ridge Winery Sculpture Grove, Santa Rosa, CA, bronze and stainless steel, 116" × 63" × 63".
Bottom left: *Bird*, 2004, bronze, 24" × 10" × 10".

JOSEPH L. CASTLE, III

CASTLE SCULPTURE, LLC ■ 331 BAY HORSE ROAD ■ BELLEVUE, ID 83313 ■ TEL 208-788-1305 ■ FAX 208-788-2519
E-MAIL JOSCASTLE@AOL.COM ■ WWW.CASTLESCULPTURE.COM

132

Top left: *Relationship Series VI*, Bellingham, WA, bronze. Right: *The Ascending Lark*, bronze. Photograph: Susan Bulkin. Bottom left: *Relationship Series VIII*, Bellingham, WA, bronze.

L.T. CHEROKEE

L.T. STUDIOS ■ 40 PROSPECT AVENUE ■ NORTHPORT, NY 11768
TEL 631-261-3342 ■ E-MAIL LTSCULPT@MSN.COM

Top left: *Tributary — Water/Fog*, 2002, Courtyard 9/11, NY, bronze, 6'H. Top right: *Madame Lena*, 2004, Touro Health & Sciences lobby, NY, bronze, 9'H. Bottom left: *Sacrifice — Water/Mist*, 2003, Bald Hill Cultural Center, NY, bonded stone, 9'H. Bottom right: *The Passage — Water/Mist*, 2004, Mather Hospital, NY, fiberglass and stone, 8'H.

JEREMY CLINE

INCLINE GLASS ■ 768 DELANO AVENUE ■ SAN FRANCISCO, CA 94112 ■ TEL 415-469-8312
FAX 415-469-8463 ■ E-MAIL JC@JEREMYCLINE.COM ■ WWW.JEREMYCLINE.COM

Red Birds of Paradise, 6' 8"H x 25"W. Photograph: Latchezar Boyadjiev.

BRENT COLLINS

90 NORTH HIGHWAY 169 ■ GOWER, MO 64454 ■ TEL/FAX 816-424-3436
E-MAIL BRENT_SCULPTOR@YAHOO.COM ■ WWW.SCKANS.EDU/~BRIDGES/BCOLLINS/BCOLLINS.HTML

135

Top left: *Gordian Knot*, 2004, wood maquette for bronze to be installed at Nodaway Valley Bank, St. Joseph, MO, 39" x 39" x 29". Photograph: Phillip Geller.
Top right: *Hyperbolic Hexagon 2*, 1999, mahogany, 30" x 30" x 11". Photograph: Phillip Geller. Bottom left: *Vox Solis (Voice of the Sun)*, 2002, Hyatt Regency Convention Center,
Shanghai, China, bronze, 20'L. Photograph: Robert Nelson. Bottom right: *Atomic Flower 2*, 2003, mahogany maquette for bronze edition, 29" x 29" x 20". Photograph: Phillip Geller.

JONATHAN COX

768 PRIVATE DRIVE 3952 ■ WILLOW WOOD, OH 45696 ■ TEL 740-867-0658 ■ FAX 304-696-6505
E-MAIL COXJ@MARSHALL.EDU ■ WWW.JONATHANCOXSCULPTURE.COM

136

Top: *Growth from Within*, 2005, Avampato Discovery Museum, Charleston, WV, birch, mahogany, and ebony, 5.42' × 11.33' × 9". Photograph: Mike Keller.
Inset: *Growth from Within* (detail). Bottom left: *Changing Course*, 2004, marble, 5.33' × 3.08' × 7".
Bottom right: *Brancusi's Chisel*, 2004, marble, bronze, and mahogany, 10.33" × 16" × 8.5".

DALE ROGERS STUDIO

DALE ROGERS ■ PO BOX 8274 ■ WARD HILL, MA 01835 ■ TEL 978-556-1607 ■ FAX 978-556-1683
E-MAIL DALE@DALEROGERSSTUDIO.COM ■ WWW.DALEROGERSSTUDIO.COM

137

Top: *Dog*, 2004, rusted steel, 60" × 74" × 12". Bottom left: *Ball Tower*, 2005, stainless steel with rusted steel ball, 72" × 27" × 23".
Bottom right: *Trapped Ball*, 2005, stainless steel with rusted steel ball, 72" × 27" × 23". Photographs: Angie Beaulieu.

PHILIP S. DRILL

80 MAIN STREET ■ WEST ORANGE, NJ 07052 ■ TEL 973-736-9350 ■ FAX 973-736-3776
E-MAIL PSDRILL@DRILLCONSTRUCTION.COM ■ WWW.PSDRILL.COM

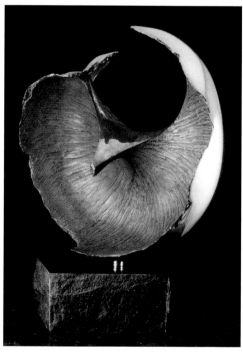

138

Left: *Rebecca*, 1981, stainless steel, 28" x 17" x 17". Top right: *Aruba III*, 1993, bronze, 38" x 14" x 16". Bottom right: *Wuxi*, 1989, bronze, 27" x 24" x 15".

CAROL FLEMING

STUDIO TERRA NOVA ■ 4 WHITFIELD LANE ■ ST. LOUIS, MO 63124 ■ TEL 314-692-7800
E-MAIL LADUECLAY@CAROLFLEMING.COM ■ WWW.CAROLFLEMING.COM

139

Top: Seven ceramic columns, 2003, Magellan Healthcare at River Port Commons, Earth City, MO, 8'H.
Bottom: Two of nine ceramic eggs, Magellan Healthcare at River Port Commons, Earth City, MO.

JARRETT HAWKINS

HAWKINS & HAWKINS CUSTOM ■ 7234 OHIO AVENUE ■ DEER PARK, OH 45236 ■ TEL 513-891-7509
E-MAIL HAWKINS@ONE.NET ■ WWW.HAWKINSANDHAWKINS.BIZ

140

Top left: *Untitled*, available in bronze or cast iron, 42"H x 14" x 14". Top right: *Untitled*, available in cast iron or bronze, 53"H x 17" x 13".
Bottom left: *Untitled*, cast iron, 39"H x 14" x 12". Bottom right: *Untitled*, bronze, 39"H x 14" x 12". Photographs: Jarrett Hawkins.

ARCHIE HELD

ARCHIE HELD STUDIO ■ NO. 5 18TH STREET ■ RICHMOND, CA 94801 ■ TEL 510-235-8700 ■ FAX 510-234-4828
E-MAIL ARCHIEHELDSTUDIO@COMCAST.NET ■ WWW.ARCHIEHELD.COM

141

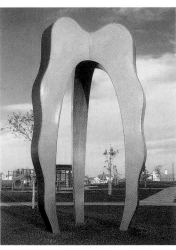

Left: *Crossing,* 2004, San Bruno, CA, bronze, stainless steel, and water, 25'H x 9'Dia. Top right: *Glass Water Wall,* 2002, Tahoe, CA, glass, bronze, stones, and water, 8'H x 4' x 20".
Center right: *High Spirits,* 1994, SAP Labs, LLC, Palo Alto, CA, bronze, 10'H x 2.5'Dia. Photograph: John South.
Bottom right: *Huddle,* 2004, City of Stockton, CA, stainless steel and bronze, 8'H x 4.42'Dia.

STEVE JENSEN

1424 TENTH AVENUE ■ SEATTLE, WA 90122 ■ TEL 206-323-8020
FAX 206-322-1400 ■ E-MAIL SJWWALLPAPER@AOL.COM

142

Top: *Everett Swirls*, Everett Cultural Commission, WA, carved cedar, 12' × 18'. Photograph: Linda Young.
Bottom left: *Flight*, aluminum, 102" × 62". Bottom right: *Fishin' Poles*, carved cedar, 10'H, 11'H, and 12'H.

PATTIE AND MARK JOHNSON

GLASS ILLUSIONS STUDIO ■ 12511 EAST SPEEDWAY ■ TUCSON, AZ 85748 ■ TEL 520-722-8947
E-MAIL GLASSART4U@AOL.COM ■ WWW.GLASSILLUSIONSSTUDIO.COM

143

Ancient Warrior. Photograph: Arvid Danielson.

TALIAFERRO JONES

442 DUFFERIN STREET, UNIT N ■ TORONTO, ON M6K 2A3 ■ CANADA ■ TEL 416-538-3304 ■ FAX 416-538-8272
E-MAIL TALIAFERRO@TALIAFERROJONES.COM ■ WWW.TALIAFERROJONES.COM

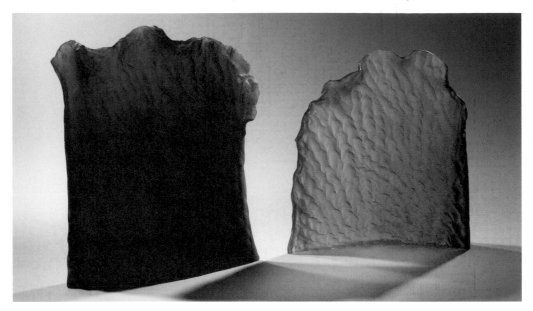

144

Top: *Splish Splash*, kiln-cast crystal, 16" × 27" × 1.5". Bottom: *Embrace*, kiln-cast crystal, 26" × 28" × 17".

145

Top: *Dea*, bronze, 24" × 41" × 31". Bottom left: *Maya*, marble and brushed stainless steel, 40" × 60" × 41".
Bottom right: *Star Dance* (model), brushed stainless steel, 13" × 10" × 10". Photographs: Erin Kiernan.

ANTHONY KRAUSS

41 LOWER BYRDCLIFFE ROAD ■ WOODSTOCK, NY 12498 ■ TEL 845-679-6360 ■ FAX 845-679-2271
E-MAIL ANTHONYKRAUSS@AOL.COM ■ WWW.FLETCHERGALLERY.COM

146

Folded Pyramid, Ulster County Office Building, Kingston, NY, mirrored stainless steel, 10' x 6' x 2'. Photograph: Jason Zhang.

LUKE DAVID SCULPTURE

LUKE DAVID ■ 1230 QUAIL RIDGE ■ SOLVANG, CA 93463 ■ TEL 805-252-8864
FAX 253-399-7647 ■ E-MAIL LUKEDAVID@EARTHLINK.NET ■ WWW.LUKEDAVIDSCULPTURE.COM

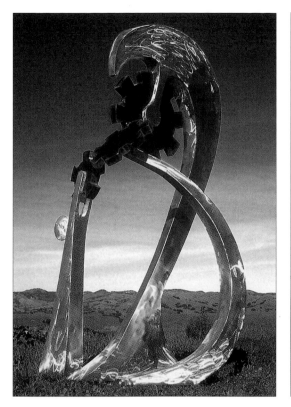

Top left: *Set in Motion*, 2005, private collection, bronze, 8' × 4' × 3'. Top right: *A Forest*, 2003, private collection, bronze, 28" × 18" × 16". Bottom left: *Offering*, 2000, West of Eden Sculpture Garden, Santa Ynez, CA, bronze and concrete, 7' × 5' × 2'. Bottom right: *Gift*, 2002, Michael Johnson Fine Art, San Diego, CA, bronze, 36" × 18" × 10".

MAW STUDIO

MARK A. WALLIS ■ 2608 EAST STATE ROAD 46 ■ SPENCER, IN 47460 ■ TEL 812-829-1747
E-MAIL MAWSTUDIO46@SBCGLOBAL.NET ■ WWW.MAWSTUDIO.COM

148

Top left: *Standing in Concert,* 1999, Indianapolis, IN, steel, 7' × 8' × 18'. Top center: *Dancing Spirit,* 2004, Des Moines, IA, powder-coated steel, 22" × 24" × 102".
Top right: *Samurai,* 2004, St. Louis, MO, steel kinetic sculpture, 36" × 40" × 89". Bottom: *Homage to Damar,* 2004, Camby, IN, painted steel, 21' × 21' × 13'.

JAMES C. MYFORD

320 CRANBERRY ROAD ■ GROVE CITY, PA 16127 ■ TEL/FAX 724-458-9672
E-MAIL JCMYF@ZOOMINTERNET.NET ■ WWW.MYFORDSCULPTURE.COM

 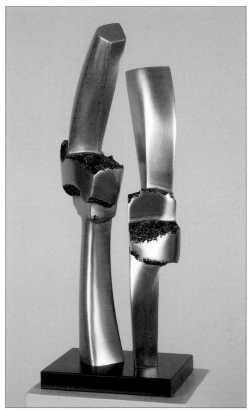

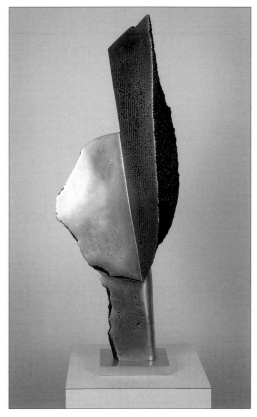 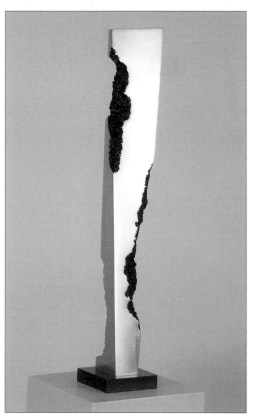

Top left: *Monolithic Forms*, 2001, aluminum, 38" × 12" × 7". Top right: *Emergence*, 2003, aluminum, 24" × 8" × 6".
Bottom left: *Southwest/46*, 2003, aluminum, 46" × 16" × 12". Bottom right: *Monolithic Form*, 2003, aluminum, 33" × 6" × 5". Photographs: Robert Ruschak.

W. R. NAGER - SCULPTOR, INC.

426 NW NINTH AVENUE ■ HOMESTEAD, FL 33030 ■ TEL 786-243-8810
FAX 786-243-1520 ■ WWW.BLACKSMITHDESIGNS.COM

150

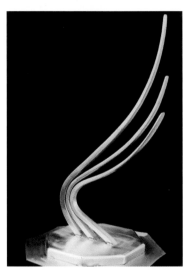

Left: *The Cave*, 1990, stainless steel. Top right: *The Creation*, 2004, polished stainless steel and bronze. Photograph: Mineko Mendenhall.
Center right: *The Resurrection*, 2004, stainless steel. Photograph: Mineko Mendenhall. Bottom right: *Paired for Life*, 1988, mirror-polished stainless steel.

BRUCE A. NIEMI

NIEMI SCULPTURE GALLERY & GARDEN ■ 13300 116TH STREET ■ KENOSHA, WI 53142 ■ TEL 262-857-3456 ■ FAX 262-857-4567
E-MAIL SCULPTURE@BRUCENIEMI.COM ■ WWW.BRUCENIEMI.COM

151

Top: *Imagination Takes Flight,* 2000, Lake Villa District Library, IL, steel, 10'H × 15'W. Bottom left: *Interim XII,* 2000, stainless steel, 10.5' × 13.5' × 10'.
Bottom right: *Celestial Trio,* 2001, Milwaukee River Walk, WI, stainless steel, 17' × 8' × 6'.

Career-building Projects:
Commissions Generated Through GUILD Sourcebooks

JAMES T. RUSSELL
Stellare, 2000
Stainless steel
6' x 4.5' x 4' on a 5' pedestal
Oceana Cruise Ship
Commissioned by: Princess Cruises

My sculpture *Stellare* is a central attraction on the cruise ship Oceana, which travels most of the world. It is seen twenty-four hours a day, and people constantly tell me they saw my sculpture on the ship.

The art consultant for Princess Cruises originally saw my pages in THE GUILD Sourcebook and had followed my career over several years through my advertisements in THE GUILD. The commission for *Stellare* was the beginning of a wonderfully prosperous relationship with this consultant.

This project required extensive travel, and it was challenging to work with architects and technicians who spoke limited English, as well as to coordinate with the American designers. Because the wall current on the ship is a not standard voltage, my tools had to be battery-powered! But it was wonderful and challenging to work together on an aesthetic solution—one that I feel turned out extremely well.

SANDRA CHRISTINE Q. BERGÉR
Arctic Ice, 1999
Glass
23" x 11" x 11"
Thermo King Corporation World
Headquarters, Minneapolis, MN

My sculpture *Prismatic Ice* appeared in *Sourcebook 15*, where it caught the attention of art consultant Leslie Palmer-Ross. Leslie wanted a piece that was "icy," unusual, and appropriate for Thermo King's president's newly remodeled office suite. They requested a full-scale model, and after making seven variations, I submitted what my studio team and I felt was our best effort.

To our surprise, the client was less than enthusiastic. They thought it was "too glacial," and instead wanted the "tip of the iceberg." We developed another model, presented a sample of the glass, and received approval to begin fabrication.

Because they asked us to extend the commission beyond the limits of our experience, we were challenged to develop new techniques. *Arctic Ice* took five-and-a-half months to create, from casting to completion. Carefully assembled from eighteen solid blocks, it suggests both molten glass and super-cooled liquid.

KEVIN ROBB

KEVIN ROBB STUDIOS ■ 7001 WEST 35TH AVENUE ■ WHEAT RIDGE, CO 80033 ■ TEL 303-431-4758
FAX 303-425-8802 ■ EMAIL 3D@KEVINROBB.COM ■ WWW.KEVINROBB.COM

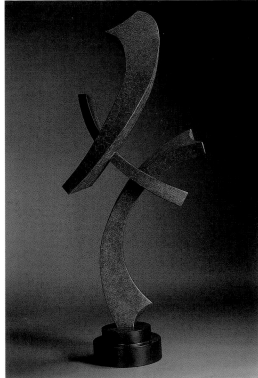

153

Top left: *Swan Dance IV,* 2004, fabricated bronze, 48" × 22" × 10" on 5" base. Photograph: John Bonath.
Right: *Quilt Flower,* 2003, Premier Bank, Roseville, MN, stainless steel, 69" × 50" × 34" on 32" base.
Bottom left: *Shooting Stars,* 2005, fabricated bronze, 53" × 44" × 35". Photograph: John Bonath.

BERNARD J. ROBERTS

W1952 ROOSEVELT RD. ■ OCONOMOWOC, WI 53066
EMAIL LOIS01@NETWURX.NET ■ WWW.BERNARDJROBERTS.COM

154

Top left: *Embrace* (front view), 3' × 3'. Top right: *Embrace* (side view), 3' × 5'.
Bottom left: *Wave Form*, 3' × 4'. Bottom right: *Embrace*, 3' × 5'. Photographs: Rick Schmidt.

BERNARD J. ROBERTS

W1952 ROOSEVELT RD. ■ OCONOMOWOC, WI 53066
EMAIL LOIS01@NETWURX.NET ■ WWW.BERNARDJROBERTS.COM

Top and bottom left: *Ripples* (detail). Right: *Ripples* (partial view), overall size up to 9'H x 4-8"W. Photographs: Rick Schmidt.

JAMES THOMAS RUSSELL

JAMES T. RUSSELL SCULPTURE ■ 1930 LOMITA BOULEVARD ■ LOMITA, CA 90717 ■ TEL 310-326-0785 ■ FAX 310-326-1470
E-MAIL JAMES@RUSSELLSCULPTURE.COM ■ WWW.RUSSELLSCULPTURE.COM

156

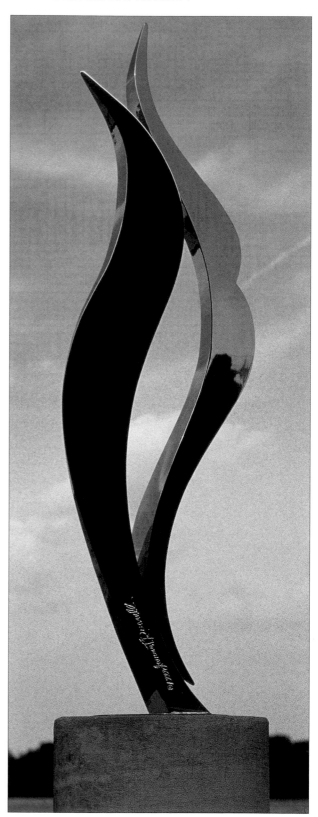

Top left: *Spirit Song*, 1998, Motorola Headquarters, Beijing, China, polished stainless steel, 6'H. Photograph: Sharon Shute.
Right: *Tribute*, 2000, Charles Walsh Sr. Memorial, Burlington, IA, polished stainless steel, 7'H. Photograph: David Holtz.
Bottom left: *Sojourn*, 1991, Utah State University, Logan, UT, polished stainless steel, 13'H. Photograph: Sharon Shute.

JEFFREY J. RUTLEDGE, M.F.A.

RUTLEDGE STUDIO ■ 1964 NORTH MAIN STREET ■ DAYTON, OH 45405 ■ TEL 937-278-4900
E-MAIL JEFF@RUTLEDGE-ART.COM ■ WWW.RUTLEDGE-ART.COM

157

Spirole, 2004, stainless steel, 6' × 6' × 6'.

BARBARA SORENSEN

455 LAKEWOOD DRIVE ■ WINTER PARK, FL 32789 ■ TEL 407-644-8850 ■ FAX 407-628-0340
E-MAIL ARTIST@BARBARASORENSEN.COM ■ WWW.BARBARASORENSEN.COM

158

Top left: *Muse Installation*, private residence, Winter Park, FL, bronze, 10'H; 12'H; 8'H each. Photograph: Randall Smith. Top right: *Siren I*, private residence, Snowmass Village, CO, bronze, 10'H. Photograph: Allen Becker. Bottom: *Siren Installation*, private residence, Aspen, CO, bronze, 10'H each. Photograph: Pat Sudmeir.

MARK STASZ

STASZ STUDIO ■ PO BOX 424 ■ BELLEVUE, ID 83313 ■ TEL/FAX 208-788-0865
E-MAIL MARK@STASZSCULPTURE.COM ■ WWW.STASZSCULPTURE.COM

159

Top left: *Eternal Flow*, 1999, steel, 96" × 72" × 36". Top right: Squier commission, 2003, bronze and granite, 144" × 72" × 72".
Bottom left: *Circular Compression*; 2001; steel, stainless steel, and travertine; 168." × 72" × 36". Bottom right: *Trio*, 2003, steel and travertine, 132" × 84" × 42". Photographs: Stasz Studio.

DAVID STROMEYER

TEL NOV–MAY (TX) 512-442-5982 ■ TEL JUNE–OCT (VT) 802-933-2518
E-MAIL DAVID@DAVIDSTROMEYER.COM ■ WWW.DAVIDSTROMEYER.COM

Top: *3-3-3*, 2002, painted steel, 24' x 14' x 20'. Bottom left: *Faceted Rock*, 2004, painted steel, 8' x 11' x 9'. Bottom right: *Song for My Father*, 1989, painted steel, 12' x 13' x 15'.

RICHARD SWANSON

SWANSON STUDIOS ■ 585 SOUTH RODNEY STREET ■ HELENA, MT 59601 ■ TEL 406-442-8106
E-MAIL RICHARD@SWANSON.COM ■ WWW.RICHARD.SWANSON.COM

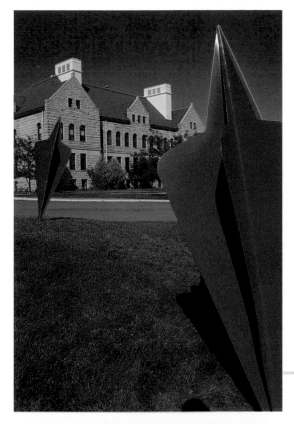

161

Top left: *Dervishes*, 2001, painted aluminum, 3 units, 7'H. Right: *Scintillion*, 1995, galvanized metal, 16' × 5.5' × 4.5'. Bottom left: *Papillon*, 2002, powder-coated aluminum, 7.17'H × 8'.

Favorite Images from the Past:
A GUILD Sourcebook Retrospective

Brian Russell
Hemisphere 18 Twist, 2002
Cast glass and forged steel
20" x 9" x 9"
Published in *Sourcebook 18*

RICHARD TAYLOR

RICHARD TAYLOR LLC ■ 3007 NORTH NEWHALL STREET ■ MILWAUKEE, WI 53211
TEL 414-967-1449 ■ FAX 414-961-7002 ■ E-MAIL RRTAYLOR@WI.RR.COM

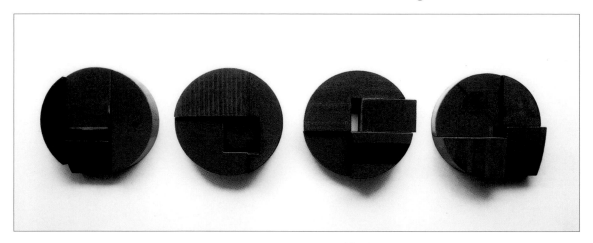

Top: *Anza Borrego,* 2004, steel and mixed media, 24" × 108" × 6". Bottom left: *Above and Beyond,* 2003, aluminum and Imron®, 15' × 6' × 6'.
Bottom right: *A Beam of Sun to Shake the Sky,* 2004, Milwaukee Public Library, aluminum and Imron®, 15' × 7' × 4' (two pieces). Photograph: Kevin Miyazaki.

WAYNE TRAPP

WAYNE TRAPP STUDIOS ■ 427 RUSSELL BEACH ROAD ■ VILAS, NC 28692 ■ TEL 828-297-4722
E-MAIL WAYNETRAPP@HOTMAIL.COM ■ WWW.WAYNETRAPP.COM

164

Top left: *Big Blue,* powder cast steel, 3' x 4' x 10'. Top center: *Kyoto and Beyond,* weathering steel, 10' x 5' x 5'. Top right: *Sun Search,* Broyhill Center,
Appalachian State University, Boone, NC, powder cast steel, 16' x 4' x 4'. Bottom: *Golden Garden,* private residence, Charlotte, NC, weathering steel and gold leaf.

WAYNE TRAPP

WAYNE TRAPP STUDIOS ■ 427 RUSSELL BEACH ROAD ■ VILAS, NC 28692 ■ TEL 828-297-4722
E-MAIL WAYNETRAPP@HOTMAIL.COM ■ WWW.WAYNETRAPP.COM

Top left: *Keeping the Moment*, Fairmont State University, WV, stainless steel, 26' × 12' × 10'. Top center: *Tangible Tango*, Research Triangle Park, NC, stainless steel, 22.33'H.
Top right: *Sun Shrine*, weathering and stainless steel, 9' × 5' × 5'. Bottom: *Spirit of Travel*, Main Street Meridian, Lindburg City Center, Atlanta, GA, stainless steel.

Career-building Projects:
Commissions Generated Through GUILD Sourcebooks

ARCHIE HELD
Entry, 1999
Bronze and water
162" x 61" x 23"
Private residence, Oakland, CA

The clients for this particular commission were very passionate about my work when we met. They had seen my work in person and on numerous websites before finding THE GUILD, where they found what they were looking for: my direct contact information. They felt I could create a contemporary, bold statement to complement their dream house, and expected the finest craftsmanship.

This was a very special project for them, and they didn't want to work through an intermediary. They were willing to pay a good sum for the right work and they wanted all the money to go directly to me. (They would later introduce me to a gallery that has since commissioned several large public pieces.)

When I first started advertising in THE GUILD, I was making tabletop pieces. Since then everything has changed. To do what I do now takes a small village. THE GUILD has paid off for me many times over, directly and indirectly. My advice to new artists is to create work that makes you proud, get good photos, and put them in THE GUILD!

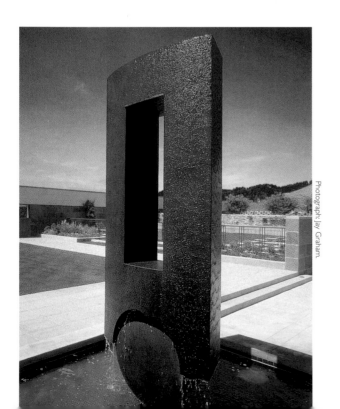

Photograph: Jay Graham.

JONATHAN COX
The Discovery II, 2005
Marble and poplar
9'2" x 4'1" x 17"
Western Asset Management (1st floor lobby)
Pasadena, CA
Commissioned by: Art Source LA, Inc.

Photograph: Francine Ellman.

This is a smaller version of a piece I featured in *Sourcebook 19* and installed at the Huntington Museum of Art in West Virginia. Although it was only my first GUILD page, within a few months I received a call from Francine Ellman, the head of Art Source L.A. She's really sharp and has worked with many GUILD artists over the years.

Francine felt my work might be appropriate for a major project encompassing five huge corporate interiors in London, Singapore, Tokyo, and Sydney, in addition to Los Angeles, where *The Discovery* was eventually installed. The L.A. location is drop-dead gorgeous and highly visible, in a lobby right outside the corporate offices. And it was so very simple! I sent additional materials, Art Source L.A. made a presentation, and the CEO really responded to my work. I received an advance, created and shipped the piece, and ArtSource L.A. handled the installation and had it professionally photographed. It's been a very good experience.

EDWIN C. WHITE

EDWIN WHITE DESIGNS ■ 90 KIRKMAN FORD ROAD ■ SILER CITY, NC 27344 ■ TEL/FAX 919-742-6154
E-MAIL EWDESIGNS@CENTERNET.NET ■ WWW.EDWINWHITEDESIGNS.COM

Mengembang, 2004, Hilton Hotel, Kuala Lumpur, Malaysia, titanium, 17' x 9.5' x 10'. Rotation by water turbine. Photograph: Dennis Kok.

Representational Sculpture

" As mentioned, I have been a fan of the GUILD Sourcebook
for many, many years and rely on it for my projects in Asia
and the U.K. "

Nancy Hogstrom
International Art Source
San Diego, CA

170

Westerville Firemen's Memorial (maquette), 2004, Westerville, OH, wax, final dimensions 10' x 8' x 10' in bronze. Photograph: Roger Rowitz

LAURIE BRECHEEN BALLARD

ESSENTIALIST SCULPTOR ■ 1531 PASADENA AVENUE ■ BARDSDALE, CA 93015 ■ TEL 805-570-1145 ■ FAX 805-524-3133
E-MAIL LAURIEB@LBBSCULPTURE.COM ■ WWW.LBBSCULPTURE.COM

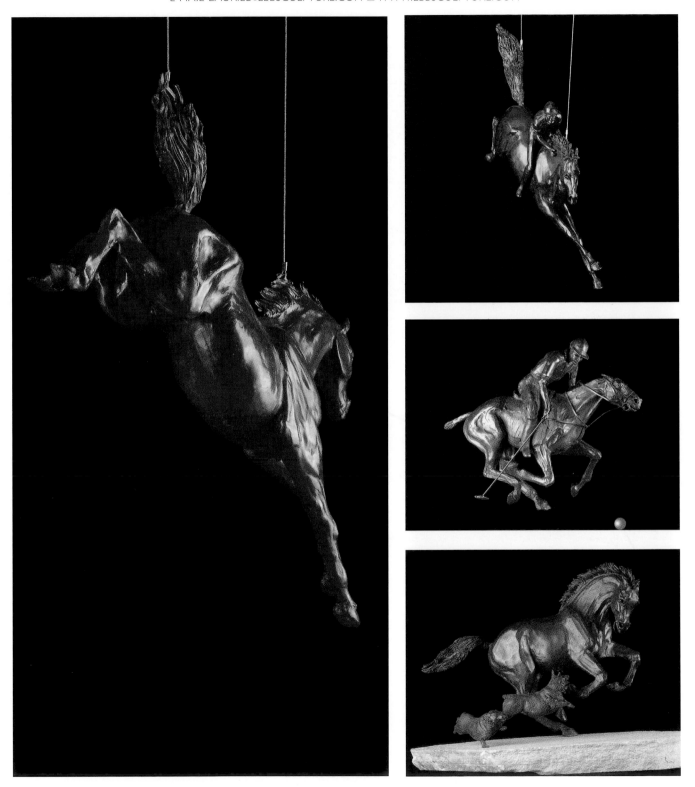

171

Left: *Flight without Wings (Flying Horses Series)*, bronze, 23" x 25", edition of 15. Top right: *Duet in Flight (Flying Horses Series)*, bronze, 27" x 25", edition of 5.
Middle right: *Dead Eye (Flying Horses Series)*, bronze, 15" x 20", edition of 15. Bottom right: *Pursuit of Excellence*, bronze, 15" x 17", edition of 15.

GILBERT BEALL

2801 B HANCOCK DRIVE ■ AUSTIN, TX 78731 ■ TEL 512-784-3494 ■ FAX 512-732-2518
E-MAIL GILBERT@GILBERTBEALLART.COM ■ WWW.GILBERTBEALLART.COM

172

Top: *The Family*, 2001, Remembrance Gardens, Austin, TX, bronze, 8'H. Bottom left: *The Caddie*, 2001, Village Bank and Trust, Lakeway, TX, bronze, 7'H.
Bottom right: *The Golfer*, 2001, Village Bank and Trust, Lakeway, TX, bronze, 9'H.

RUTH BURINK

BURINK SCULPTURE STUDIO ■ 1550 WOODMOOR DRIVE ■ MONUMENT, CO 80132 ■ TEL 719-481-0513
E-MAIL RUTH@BURINKSCULPTURE.COM ■ WWW.BURINKSCULPTURE.COM

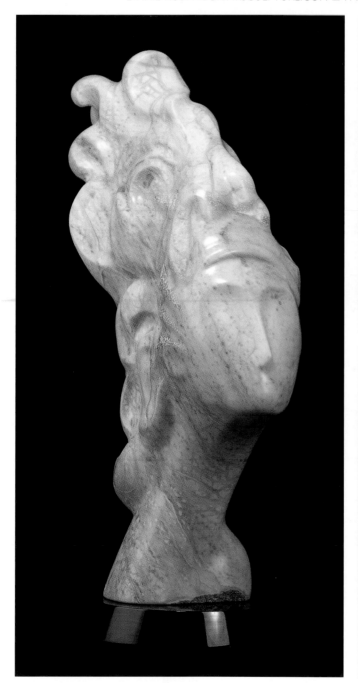

Left: *Elisabeth B., Air Force Pilot,* 2004, alabaster, 29" × 17" × 10". Top right: *Ann Richards, Governor of Texas,* 2004, marble, 21" × 13" × 13".
Bottom right: *Jennifer J., Breast Cancer Survivor,* 2004, travertine, 22" × 13" × 9". Photographs: Sky Hall.

Favorite Images from the Past:
A GUILD Sourcebook Retrospective

Tuck Langland
Resting Dancer
Bronze
Life-size on a 4'-long bench
Published in *Architect's 14*

BOBBIE K. CARLYLE

1233 NORTH COUNTY ROAD 29 ■ LOVELAND, CO 80537 ■ TEL 970-622-0213 ■ FAX 970-622-9904
E-MAIL BOBBIECARLYLE@ATT.NET ■ WWW.BOBBIECARLYLESCULPTURE.COM

175

Top left: *Benediction*, bronze, 30"H. Right: *Self Made Man*, bronze, sizes vary from 10.5" to 14', poster also available.
Bottom left: *Upper Limits*, bronze, 22"H, also available life-size, edition of 350.

GESSO COCTEAU

45-565 WILLIAMS ROAD ■ INDIAN WELLS, CA 92210 ■ TEL 760-341-3988 ■ FAX 760-347-2495
E-MAIL CSILKENSEN1@DC.RR.COM

176

Left: *Flamenco Nouveau*, 2001, cast bronze, 72" × 56" × 21", edition of 12. Top right: *The Runner*, 1995, cast bronze, 12" × 15" × 8", edition of 25 and cast bronze, 72" × 57" × 24", edition of 6. Bottom right: *Swept Away*, 1995, cast bronze, 16" × 16" × 8", edition of 25.

GESSO COCTEAU

45-565 WILLIAMS ROAD ■ INDIAN WELLS, CA 92210 ■ TEL 760-341-3988 ■ FAX 760-347-2495
E-MAIL CSILKENSEN1@DC.RR.COM

177

Ti Amo, 2004, cast bronze, 135" x 139" x 60", edition of 12. Also available 26" x 27" x 10", edition of 25.

DARRELL DAVIS

136 SOUTH COLLINS STREET ■ ARLINGTON, TX 76010 ■ TEL 800-600-3140 ■ E-MAIL DAVISBRONZE@AOL.COM

178

Heron and the Sun, bronze, 7'H.

ANN DeLUTY

12 RANDOLPH STREET ■ BELMONT, MA 02478
TEL/FAX 617-484-0069 ■ E-MAIL A.DELUTY@COMCAST.NET ■ WWW.ANN-DELUTY.WS

179

Top left: *Red Shell*, 1998, tiger-eye alabaster on marble base, 18" x 8" x 7". Top right: *Orange Delight*, 1999, translucent alabaster on marble base, 18" x 11" x 9".
Bottom: *Whales*, 1999, cockscomb alabaster on marble base, 10.5" x 17.5" x 10.5".

180

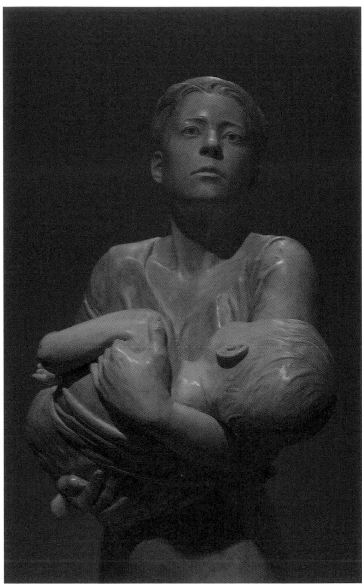

Left: *Healing*, 2004, life size. Right: *Healing*, (detail). Photographs: Megan Van Valer.

DWIGHT WILLIAM DUKE

DUKE STUDIOS ■ 134 LIVESEY LANE ■ PO BOX 271 ■ EASTSOUND, WA 98245 ■ TEL 360-376-6544 ■ FAX 360-376-7544
E-MAIL INFO@DUKESTUDIO.COM ■ WWW.DUKESTUDIO.COM

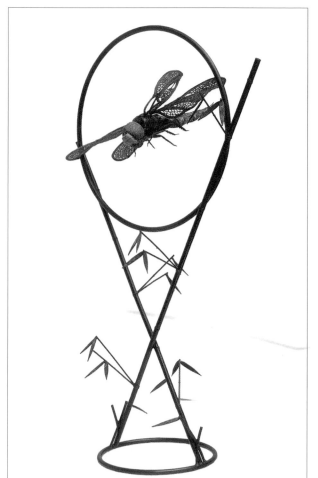

181

Top left: *In Pursuit*, 2000, bronze, 84" × 48" × 24". Top right: *In Pursuit* (detail).
Middle right: *Fly on the Wall*, 2001, bronze, 29" × 39" × 3". Bottom: *Transformation*, 2004, bronze, 10" × 30" × 16". Photographs: Dwight William Duke.

JOAN OF ART GALLERY

KIMBER FIEBIGER ■ 3020 EAST FRANKLIN AVENUE ■ MINNEAPOLIS, MN 55406 ■ TEL/FAX 612-338-2511
E-MAIL KIMBER@JOANOFART.COM ■ WWW.JOANOFART.COM

182

Top left: *C'est la Vie*. Top right: *Deviled Egg*. Bottom left: *H.D.* Bottom right: *My Green Egg Named Ham*. Photographs: Cindy Thompson.

BARRY WOODS JOHNSTON

SCULPTURE WORKS, INC. ■ 2423 PICKWICK ROAD ■ BALTIMORE, MD 21207 ■ TEL 410-448-1945 ■ FAX 410-448-2663
E-MAIL BARRY@SCULPTORJOHNSTON.COM ■ WWW.SCULPTORJOHNSTON.COM

183

Saint Francis of Assisi, 2000, bronze, 38"H, edition of 20.

JUSTIN LAWYER FINE ART

3198 RAMONA STREET ■ PALO ALTO, CA 94306 ■ TEL 415-860-1531 ■ E-MAIL INFO@JUSTINLAWYERFINEART.COM
WWW.JUSTINLAWYERFINEART.COM

184

Top left: Dan Chen, *Born Free*, bronze, 36" × 35" × 13".
Right: Bobbie Carlyle, *Sunriser III*, bronze, 106"H.
Bottom left: Joshua Tobey, *Denali*, bronze, 32" × 41" × 18" with optional 36"H base.

TUCK LANGLAND

12632 ANDERSON ■ GRANGER, IN 46530
TEL/FAX 574-272-2708 ■ E-MAIL TUCKANDJAN@AOL.COM

Top left: *Serengeti Wind,* bronze, 15"H. Top right: *Dance of Dormancy,* Bronson Hospital, Kalamazoo, MI, bronze, 5'H.
Bottom: *Dr. Will & Dr. Charlie Mayo,* Mayo Clinic, Rochester, MN, bronze, life size.

CAMMIE LUNDEEN

LUNDEEN SCULPTURE ■ 338 EAST FOURTH STREET ■ LOVELAND, CO 80537 ■ TEL 970-669-7176 ■ FAX 970-669-9493
E-MAIL GEORGE@LUNDEENSCULPTURE.COM ■ WWW.LUNDEENSCULPTURE.COM

186

Top: *Babysitter*, 6.83' × 9' × 4.5', edition of 21. Bottom left: *Frolic*, 5' × 5' × 29", edition of 50. Bottom right: *Battle of the Market*, 10" × 18" × 16", edition of 100.

GEORGE LUNDEEN

LUNDEEN SCULPTURE ■ 338 EAST FOURTH STREET ■ LOVELAND, CO 80537 ■ TEL 970-669-7176 ■ FAX 970-669-9493
E-MAIL GEORGE@LUNDEENSCULPTURE.COM ■ WWW.LUNDEENSCULPTURE.COM

187

Top left: *Turning the Pages*, 18" x 19" x 14", edition of 100. Right: *Field of Blue*, 24" x 10" x 7", edition of 100. Bottom left: *Peacekeeper*, 14" x 17" x 8", edition of 100.

PETER W. MICHEL

PETER W. MICHEL, SCULPTOR ■ 36 KELLOGG STREET ■ CLINTON, NY 13323 ■ TEL 315-853-8146 ■ FAX 315-859-1480
E-MAIL PETER@PETERMICHEL.COM ■ WWW.PETERMICHEL.COM

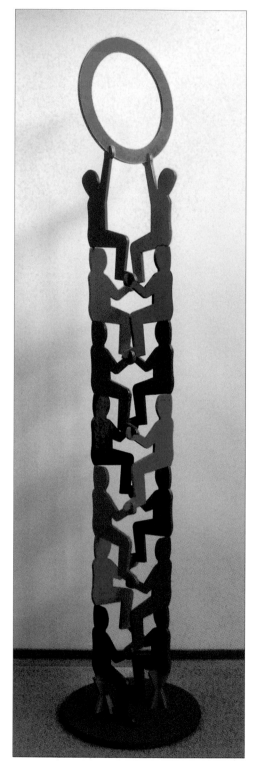

188

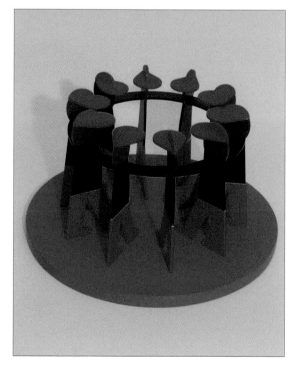

Left: *Sitting Folk Totem 1*, 2002, painted wood, 86" x 20"Dia. Top right: *Folk Circle Mandala*, 2002, painted wood, 89" x 84" x 10".
Bottom center: *Sitting Folk Totem 2*, 2002, painted wood, 43" x 12"Dia. Bottom right: *The Players*, 2004, painted wood, 6.5" x 12"Dia.

CLARK FLEMING MITCHEL

7451 HUNTLEY STREET ■ SEBASTOPOL, CA 95472 ■ TEL 707-829-3941
E-MAIL MITCHEL@MONITOR.NET ■ WWW.ALMASTONE.COM

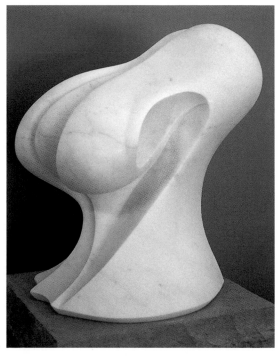

189

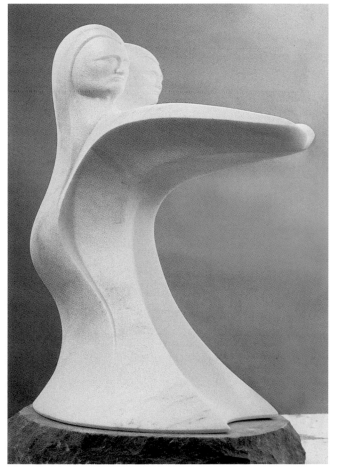

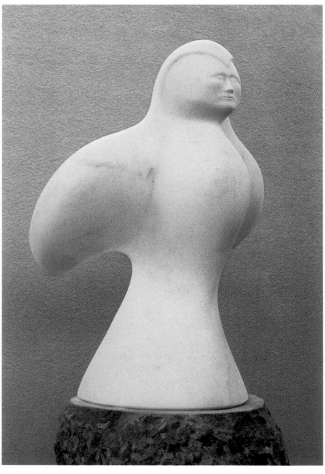

Top left: *Expanding Sphere*, 1981, bronze, 38" × 30" × 27". Top right: *Bowing Figure*, 2001, marble, 31" × 21" × 18".
Bottom left: *Pointing Figures*, 2003, marble, 36" × 16" × 25". Bottom right: *Angel*, 2004, marble, 32" × 16" × 25".

JANE RANKIN

19335 GREENWOOD DRIVE ■ MONUMENT, CO 80132 ■ TEL 719-488-9223 ■ FAX 719-488-1650
E-MAIL JRANKIN@MAGPIEHILL.COM ■ WWW.JANERANKIN.COM

190

Top: *Join the Parade* (partial view), 2003, bronze, life-size.
Bottom left: *Wheels,* 2003, bronze, 39" x 38" x 19".   Bottom right: *Joy,* 2002, bronze, 44" x 24" x 24".

ROSETTA

405 EIGHTH STREET SE #15 ■ LOVELAND, CO 80537 ■ TEL 970-667-6265
E-MAIL ROSETTASCULPTURE@EARTHLINK.NET ■ WWW.ROSETTASCULPTURE.COM

191

Heron Fountain, 2004, bronze, 48" x 65" x 65". Photograph: Mel Schockner.

CYNTHIA SPARRENBERGER

SPARRENBERGER STUDIO ■ 5975 EAST OTERO DRIVE ■ ENGLEWOOD, CO 80112
TEL 303-741-3031 (STUDIO) ■ TEL 303-618-8974 (CELL) ■ E-MAIL CYNTHIA6@MAC.COM ■ WWW.SPARRENBERGERSTUDIO.COM

192

Top: *Late for School,* 2002, bronze, 11.5' × 5' × 4.5'.
Bottom left: *A Wing and a Prayer* (back), 2000, bronze, 63"H. Bottom right: *A Wing and a Prayer* (front). Photographs: Marcia Ward/The Imagemaker.

ELLEN TYKESON

ELLEN TYKESON SCULPTURE ■ 1033 SHARON WAY ■ EUGENE, OR 97401
TEL 541-687-5731 ■ E-MAIL ETYKESON@YAHOO.COM

193

Left: *Gertrude Bass Warner Memorial*, 2004, Jordan Schnitzer Museum of Art, University of Oregon, bronze and redwood, 72" × 47" × 18".
Top right: *Journey* (detail). Bottom right: *Journey*, 2004, PeaceHealth Cottage Grove Hospital, Cottage Grove, OR, bronze, 84" × 38" × 38". Photographs: David Simone.

Career-building Projects:
Commissions Generated Through GUILD Sourcebooks

DANIEL OBERTI
Circumagi Uno, 2004
Corten steel and Ferro cement
44' x 48"
Private residence, La Jolla, CA
Commissioned by: CEO of Biogen Idec

One year after investing in my first GUILD Sourcebook page, I was beginning to lament my decision. Then I received a call from Leah Goodwin of Aesthetics, Inc., a multi-discipline design firm located in San Diego. To my delight they had chosen my work to present to Biogen Idec, a pharmaceutical company that was creating a landscape of waterfalls and gardens for their new facility. Leah was looking for human-scale sculpture that would create a sense of wonder and felt my sculpture would fit well with the stone architecture and circular elements in the landscape.

Soon after I sent them more images, they commissioned three pieces for the new Biogen Idec Campus. Then to my delight, the CEO called and said he wanted two of my sculptures for his own home, one of which is shown here. I flew down to supervise the installation and was acknowledged at the grand opening of their new facility.

I would never have reached this client without Aesthetics, Inc. using THE GUILD Sourcebook as a regular resource. As Ms. Goodwin says, "It's all about knowing clients' needs and learning what new works artists are producing, and then finding ways to connect them." My one page in the Sourcebook led to a more than tenfold return on my investment. Thank you, Guild Sourcebooks.

CHRISTOPHER BENNETT
George Soumas Memorial, 2002
Bronze
Life-size
Hotel Pattee, Soumas Court, Perry, IA

Photograph: John Jamison.

Perry's historic Hotel Pattee received a new lease on life in the mid-1990s, when it underwent a major restoration. The surrounding blocks were also redeveloped, and Project Hometown Perry was formed to recognize the contributions of local citizens. My sculpture of former mayor George Soumas was commissioned for Soumas Court, under the window of his old law office. Architect John Leusinck wanted to hire a sculptor from Iowa, and found me by thumbing through a copy of *GUILD 13* that had been on his shelf for years.

The son of Greek immigrants and Iowa's most decorated WWII veteran, George Soumas spent his life in service to others. He was known simply as "George" among the business community's several coffee klatches. I have commemorated him sitting at a table with his plastic (now bronze) cup in hand, smiling for anyone who might wish to join him.

By the time we were installing this piece, Hy-Vee Foods had already contacted me to design a memorial to one of their founders (featured on page [97]). They knew about the Soumas composition, and were anxious to see it unveiled.

WANNER SCULPTURE STUDIO

DAVID WANNER ■ JORDAN WANNER ■ 5828 NORTH 97TH STREET ■ MILWAUKEE, WI 53225 ■ TEL/FAX 414-462-3569
E-MAIL INFO@WANNERSCULPTURESTUDIO.COM ■ WWW.WANNERSCULPTURESTUDIO.COM

195

Left: *Pope John XXIII*, bronze, life size. Top right: Ivan Meštrović, bronze, life size. Middle right: *Saint Raphael*, bronze, life size. Bottom right: *Archer*, bronze, under life size.

BRUCE WOLFE

BRUCE WOLFE LTD. ■ 206 EL CERRITO AVENUE ■ PIEDMONT, CA 94611
TEL 510-655-7871 ■ FAX 510-601-7200 ■ WWW.BRUCEWOLFE.COM

196

Top left: *Ilus Davis*, Illus Davis Civic Center Park, Kansas City, MO, bronze, 9.25'. Right: *John Hannah*, Michigan State University, Lansing, bronze, 7.33'.
Bottom left: *Barbara Jordan*, Austin-Bergstrom International Airport, TX, bronze, 7'.

BRUCE WOLFE

BRUCE WOLFE LTD. ■ 206 EL CERRITO AVENUE ■ PIEDMONT, CA 94611
TEL 510-655-7871 ■ FAX 510-601-7200 ■ WWW.BRUCEWOLFE.COM

197

Top left: *T. Jack Foster*, Foster City Hall, CA, bronze, 8'. Right: *Ilus Davis*, Ilus Davis Civic Center Park, Kansas City, MO, bronze, 9.25'.
Bottom left: *St. Francis*, private collection, Carmel, CA, bronze, 7'.

Liturgical Art

KATHY CARTER

BURNING BUSH STUDIOS ■ 2055 WILSON LANE ■ GOODLETTSVILLE, TN 37072 ■ TEL 615-643-7212
E-MAIL KATHY@YATSAR.COM ■ WWW.YATSAR.COM

200

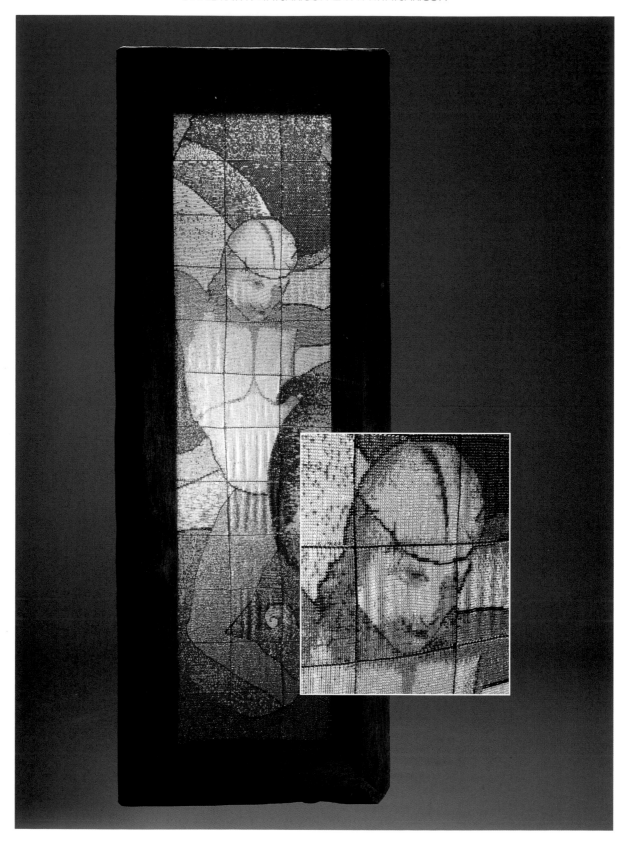

Yeshua Present, 2004, beadwork, 4.5' × 1.5'. Photograph: Curtis Southerland Inset: *Yeshua Present* (detail). Photograph: Tamara Reynolds.

ERLING HOPE

HOPE LITURGICAL WORKS ■ 1455 SAG/BRIDGE TURNPIKE ■ SAG HARBOR, NY 11963 ■ TEL/FAX 631-725-4294
E-MAIL ERLING@HOPELITURGICALWORKS.COM ■ WWW.HOPELITURGICALWORKS.COM

Top: *From Chaos*, 2001, UCC Insurance Board, MD, wood, gold leaf, oil paint, 4' x 4' x 4'. Bottom left: *Font 2*, stone, wood, 18" x 16" x 32".
Bottom right: *Station XII*, Immaculate Heart of Mary Catholic Church, bronze, stone. Photograph: Chad Mahlua

MAUREEN McGUIRE

MAUREEN MCGUIRE DESIGN ASSOCIATES, INC. ■ 924 EAST BETHANY HOME ROAD ■ PHOENIX, AZ 85014
TEL 602-277-0167 ■ FAX 602-277-0203 ■ E-MAIL MMCGUIRE@FASTQ.COM ■ WWW.MAUREENMCGUIREDESIGNS.COM

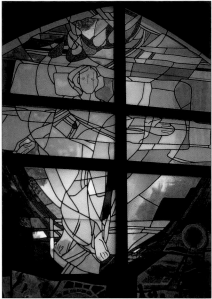

Top left: *Creator* window, Our Lady of Most Holy Souls Church, Little Rock, AR.
Top right: *Resurrection* window, chapel at Old North United Methodist Church, Indianapolis, IN. Bottom: *Music* window, private residence, Tucson, AZ.

LEONE McNEIL

LEAD & LIGHT WORKS ■ PO BOX 552 ■ MENDOCINO, CA 95460
TEL 707-937-5227 ■ FAX 707-937-5099 ■ E-MAIL LEONE@MCN.ORG

203

Left: *Let the Children Come Unto Me*, 16' × 7'. Inset: *Yellow #1*, 30" × 32".

Favorite Images from the Past:
A GUILD Sourcebook Retrospective

Laura Militzer Bryant
System/Shift, 2003
Weaving on copper
8' x 5'
Northrup Grumman IT Headquarters
McLean, VA
Published in *Sourcebook 19*

PEARL RIVER GLASS STUDIO

ANDREW CARY YOUNG ■ 142 MILLSAPS AVENUE ■ JACKSON, MS 39202 ■ TEL 601-353-2497 ■ TEL 800-771-3639
FAX 601-969-9315 ■ E-MAIL PEARLSTUDIO@BELLSOUTH.NET ■ WWW.PRGS.COM

Top left: *Rose Window,* 2004, Christ United Methodist Church, Jackson, MS, stained glass. Bottom left: *Rose Window* (exterior), etched and laminated plate glass.
Right: *Cross Bearer,* Christ United Methodist Church, Jackson, MS, stained glass. Photographs: Andrew Cary Young.

CLAUDE RIEDEL

5133 BRYANT AVENUE SOUTH ■ MINNEAPOLIS, MN 55419
TEL 612-824-5308 ■ FAX 651-645-2439 ■ E-MAIL RIEDE006@UMN.EDU

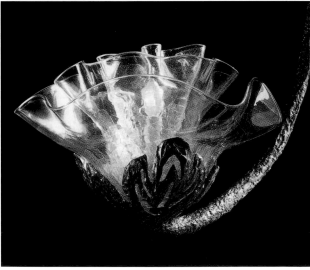

Top left: Ner Tamid, 2003, Congregation Anshai Torah, Dallas, TX, blown and fused glass, copper foil, and electric light.
Right: Ner Tamid, 2000, Bet Shalom Synagogue, Minnetonka, MN, fused glass, copper foil leading, and gas flame.
Bottom left: Ner Tamid, 1999, Shir Tikva Synagogue, Minneapolis, MN, blown glass, lead solder, wire, and electric light. Inset: Ner Tamid flame (detail). Photographs: Ted Wentink.

JUANITA YODER

148 MONMOUTH STREET ■ HIGHTSTOWN, NJ 08550 ■ TEL 609-448-5335
E-MAIL JUANITA@JYKART.COM ■ WWW.JYKART.COM

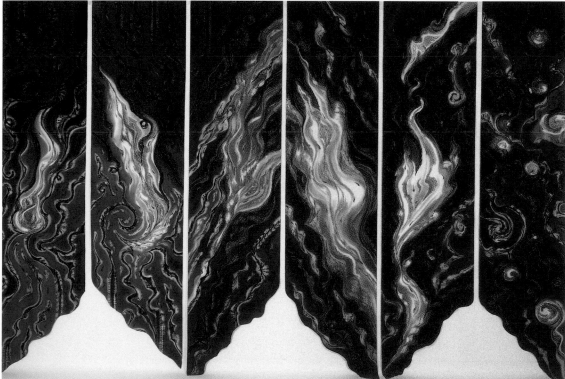

Infusion, 2001, Princeton University Chapel, six paintings on silk, 13' x 3' each. Photographs: Taylor Photo.com.

Furniture & Lighting

" Your resource books have been a part of my business R&D as a consultant/broker since the 80's, and I continue to look forward to utilizing them in the future. Thank you for your strict professionalism and regard for high caliber art. "

Bruce Olson
L'idée, Corporate Art Concepts, Inc.
Cincinnati, OH

DWAYNE S. CRANFORD

STONE 2 FURNITURE ■ 150 MOUNT FISHER COURT ■ LIVERMORE, CO 80536 ■ TEL 970-407-8991 ■ FAX 970-407-1800
E-MAIL STONE2FURNITURE@MSN.COM ■ WWW.STONE2FURNITURE.COM

210

Top: Red flagstone set, 2004, Aspen, CO, stone and welded steel chairs, 38" x 20" x 20". Bottom left: Sculpted swivel chair, 2004, Sedona, AZ, stone and welded steel, 36" x 20" x 20. Bottom right: Flagstone bench, 2004, Fountain Hills, AZ, stone and welded steel, 30" x 40" x 22". Photographs: Digi Graphics.

BILL & SANDY FIFIELD

FIFIELDS, THE STUDIO ■ PO BOX 366 ■ CONIFER, CO 80433 ■ TEL 303-838-5072
E-MAIL MACFIFIELD@ATT.NET ■ WWW.MACFIFIELD.COM

211

Left: *Spur Cabinet*, 2004, mahogany and glass, 14"D × 20"W × 72"H.
Top right: *Spur Cabinet* (top detail). Bottom right: *Spur Cabinet* (side detail).

HUBBARDTON FORGE

154 ROUTE 30 SOUTH ■ CASTLETON, VT 05735 ■ TEL 800-826-4766 ■ FAX 802-468-3284
E-MAIL INFO@VTFORGE.COM ■ WWW.VTFORGE.COM

212

Top left: *Fullered Notch Direct Wall Sconce* with opal glass. Top center: *Lunae Table Lamp* with amber art glass.
Top right: *Prairie Semi-Flush* with white art glass. Bottom: *Mackintosh Oval Adjustable Pendant* with oval opal glass bowl.

K DAHL GLASS STUDIOS

RICK STECKEL, KATHY DAHLBERG STECKEL ■ PO BOX 9 ■ 202 FIR AVENUE ■ CRAWFORD, CO 81415 ■ TEL 970-921-6160
FAX 970-921-6162 ■ E-MAIL KATHY@KDAHLGLASS.COM ■ WWW.KDAHLGLASS.COM

213

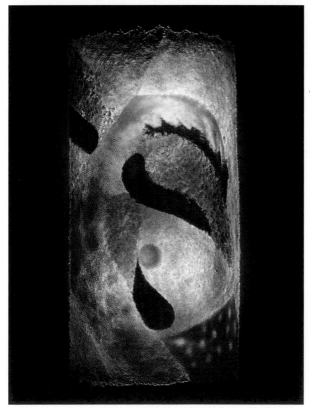
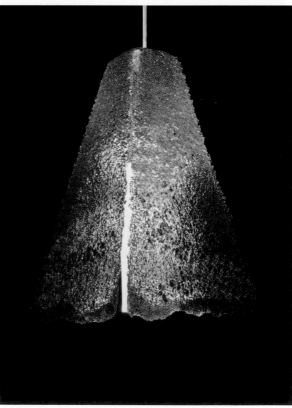

Top: Chandelier, 2005, private residence, kiln-formed glass, 24"Dia. Bottom left: Sconce, 2005, private residence, kiln-formed glass, 22"H.
Bottom right: Pendant, 2005, private residence, kiln-formed glass with blown glass liner, 9"H.

VARA KAMIN

VARA KAMIN IMPRESSIONS OF LIGHT®, INC. ■ 2205 CALIFORNIA STREET NE, SUITE 300 ■ MINNEAPOLIS, MN 55418
TEL 612-920-0105 ■ FAX 612-920-4776 ■ E-MAIL INFO@VARAKAMIN.COM ■ WWW.VARAKAMIN.COM

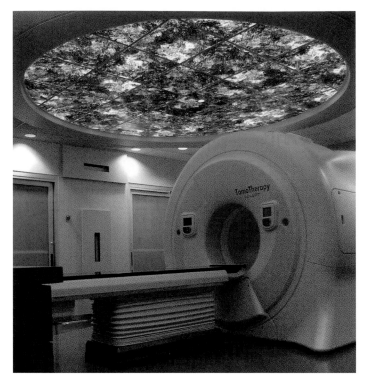

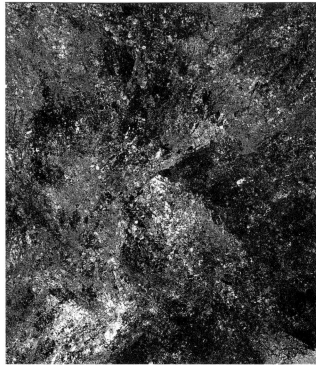

214

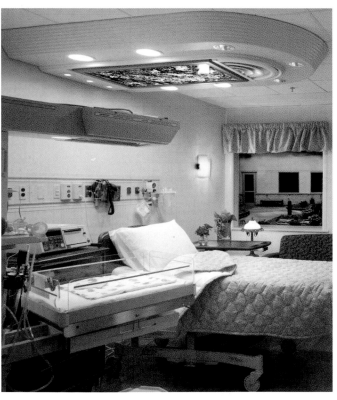

Top left: *Moon Drops*, 2004, Department of Radiation Oncology and Molecular Radiation Sciences, Johns Hopkins Hospital, Baltimore, MD, replicated image on acrylic panel, 12' × 12'. Photograph: Courtesy of Johns Hopkins Hospital. Top right: *Moon Drops*, 1998, original painting, acrylic on board, 4' × 3'. Photograph: Jon Liebendorfer. Bottom left: *Sea Garden*, 1997, original painting, acrylic on board, 5' × 4'. Photograph: Dan Dennehy. Bottom right: *Sea Garden*, 2004, Labor and Delivery Suite, St. Peter Community Hospital, MN, replicated image on acrylic panel, 2' × 4'. Photograph: Courtesy of Wellness Environments.

ERIC DAVID LAXMAN

478 MOUNTAINVIEW AVENUE ■ VALLEY COTTAGE, NY 10989 ■ TEL 845-304-7615 ■ FAX 845-348-3687
E-MAIL ERIC@ERICLAXMAN.COM ■ WWW.ERICLAXMAN.COM

215

Top left: *Pedestal Table*, steel and glass, 30"H × 20" × 20". Top right: *Sogoni Side Table*, patinated steel and glass,
22"H × 20"W × 20"D. Bottom: *Vortex Table*, silicon bronze and glass, 30"H × 66" × 66". Photographs: Sal Cordaro.

PAM MORRIS

EXCITING LIGHTING INC. ■ 475 GATE 5 ROAD STUDIO 100 ■ SAUSALITO, CA 94965 ■ TEL 415-332-0168 ■ FAX 415-332-0169
E-MAIL PAM@PAM-MORRIS-DESIGNS.COM ■ WWW.PAM-MORRIS-DESIGNS.COM

216

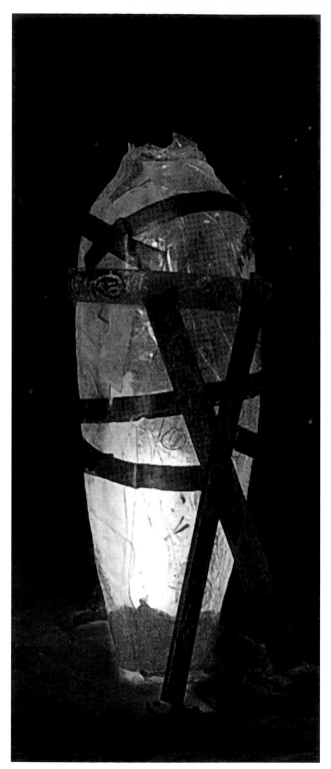
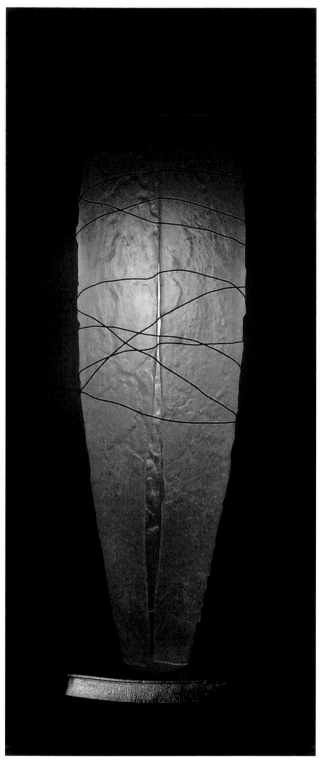

Left: *Lost Languages*, kiln-formed glass, forged iron, incandescent light, 36"H. Right: *Spirit Free*, kiln-formed glass, cast bronze nickel-plated halogen light, 24"H x 7"W.

KERRY VESPER

VESPER SCULPTURE AND DESIGN ■ 3030 NORTH CIVIC CENTER #4 ■ SCOTTSDALE, AZ 85251
TEL/FAX 480-429-0954 ■ E-MAIL KERRY@KERRYVESPER.COM ■ WWW.KERRYVESPER.COM

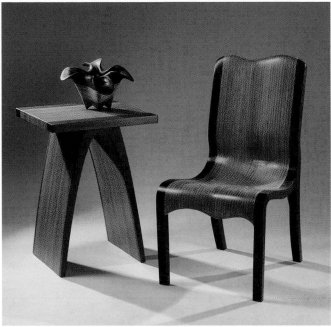

217

Top left: *Kaa Chini*, Baltic birch and wenge, 40" × 39" × 35". Top right: Chair, end table, and sculptural bowl.
Bottom: Altar table, sapele, wenge, and Baltic birch, 36" × 60" × 26". Photographs: Ron Deriemacker.

Murals & Trompe L'Oeil

" Thank you for opening up our eyes to all that is possible in a world of creative talent! "

Fred Ott
Inner-Visions, Inc.
Oak Hill, VA

220

Artist: Paul Cox, The Royal College of Surgeons, London.

ART ON A GRAND SCALE™

RICHARD SOLOMON, ARTISTS' REPRESENTATIVE ■ 305 EAST 50TH STREET ■ NEW YORK, NY 10022 ■ TEL 212-223-9545
FAX 212-223-9633 ■ E-MAIL SOLOMONART@AOL.COM ■ WWW.RICHARDSOLOMON.COM

221

Artist: Gary Kelley, Barnes and Noble Booksellers.

ART ON A GRAND SCALE™

RICHARD SOLOMON, ARTISTS' REPRESENTATIVE ■ 305 EAST 50TH STREET ■ NEW YORK, NY 10022 ■ TEL 212-223-9545
FAX 212-223-9633 ■ E-MAIL SOLOMONART@AOL.COM ■ WWW.RICHARDSOLOMON.COM

Artist: Gregory Manchess, Andersen Windows and Doors Corporation lobby, Bayport, MN.

ART ON A GRAND SCALE™

RICHARD SOLOMON, ARTISTS' REPRESENTATIVE ■ 305 EAST 50TH STREET ■ NEW YORK, NY 10022 ■ TEL 212-223-9545
FAX 212-223-9633 ■ E-MAIL SOLOMONART@AOL.COM ■ WWW.RICHARDSOLOMON.COM

223

Artist: Stephen Johnson, New York Metropolitan Transportation Authority, DeKalb Avenue Station, Brooklyn.

Career-building Projects:
Commissions Generated Through GUILD Sourcebooks

DIANNA THORNHILL MILLER
Countryside, 1995
LeatherMosaic™ wall installation
Private residence, Aboite, IN

Countryside was designed for a client whose home is like a museum, with a collection purchased almost exclusively through GUILD's *Artful Home* series. They knew my work by reputation—it's been very visible in town since 1976, when my late husband and I pioneered our LeatherMosaics™ medium. When her designer suggested my work, the client responded warmly to its strong colors and imagery, then exclaimed, "Oh, and she's been published!" They say the prophet hath no honor in his own country, and it's true; real credibility always comes from the outside.

At that point my GUILD advertisements featured sculpture and mobiles, but she chose two leather works—the one shown here, which was specially designed for the space, and a large octagonal piece. *Countryside* is a narrative, and tells a story about the place where they live. I actually went out and sketched nearby. For me art is like literature: nonobjective art is like poetry, while representational work is like prose. I love the visual weight and color intensity of the leathers, and design my compositions so that their values and hues choreograph the eye.

224

Photograph: Neal Bruns.

JANE STERRETT
Ideas, Technology, and Solutions, 2002
Digital print from an original
mixed-media collage
33"W x 40"H
Center for Advanced Medicine
OSF St. Joseph's Medical Center
Bloomington, IL

I trained as a painter, but now I also work as an illustrator. I've developed a unique collage style using photographs, fabric, and other materials, which I print digitally and color with acrylic, pastel, and crayon. I like putting images together to tell a story. I didn't think this style would have an application outside illustration and have been surprised to find it works on a larger scale. I hope to continue in this direction.

I worked on this commission with Diana Spellman of Spellman, Brady & Co., who saw my page in *Sourcebook 17*. An interior designer who specializes in healthcare facilities, Diana felt my work's color and complexity suited the center. I wanted to express the center's use of medical technology and the society in which we live, working in isolated communities while communicating through technology.

Shortly after this piece was installed, OSF Healthcare System commissioned two different prints for their newest office building. As Diana says, "Jane's work speaks to the patients and their families."

SKIP DYRDA

NEW WORLD PRODUCTIONS ■ 253 SOUTH LINKS AVENUE ■ SARASOTA, FL 34236 ■ TEL 941-366-5520
E-MAIL INFO@EMURALS.COM ■ WWW.EMURALS.COM

225

Top left: *Main Street, West*, private residence, Rosemary Beach, FL. Top right: *Main Street, East*, private residence, Rosemary Beach, FL.
Bottom: *A Taste of Italy*, Luigino's Restaurant, Lake Mary, FL.

STEPHANIE GASSMAN

4219 MIRIANA WAY ■ SARASOTA, FL 34233 ■ TEL 941-341-0721 ■ FAX 941-342-9541
E-MAIL SLGASSMAN@AOL.COM

226

Mural/wall relief with votive candles, 2004, private residence, 10'H x 30'W x 3.5"D. Photographs: Herb Booth.

BARNEY JUDGE

4099 NORTH TERRITORIAL EAST ■ ANN ARBOR, MI 48105 ■ TEL 734-827-2155 ■ FAX 734-827-2156
E-MAIL BJUDGE@BARNEYJUDGE.COM ■ WWW.BARNEYJUDGE.COM

Top: Portion of lobby mural, Uptown Palladium Theater, Birmingham, MI, 30' x 60'. Bottom left: Dining room mural, Shiraz restaurant, Southfield, MI, 7' x 13'.
Bottom right: Portion of nursery mural, Trinity Church, Livonia, MI, 8' x 92'. Photographs: Gene Meadows.

BRYAN KING

ARTIFICE, INC. ■ 1829 NORTH QUESADA STREET ■ ARLINGTON, VA 22205 ■ TEL 703-626-7900
FAX 703-533-8790 ■ E-MAIL BDK31959@YAHOO.COM ■ WWW.ARTIFICEINC.COM

Top: *Architectural mural*, 1998, American Society for Industrial Security, Alexandria, VA, 23' x 40'.
Bottom: *Cambridge*, 2004, private residence, Washington, DC, 5' x 54'. Photographs: Brandon Webster.

DIANNA THORNHILL MILLER

OMNI ART DESIGN ■ 1716 WEST MAIN STREET ■ FORT WAYNE, IN 46808
TEL 260-422-3677 ■ E-MAIL OMNIART@MYEXCEL.COM

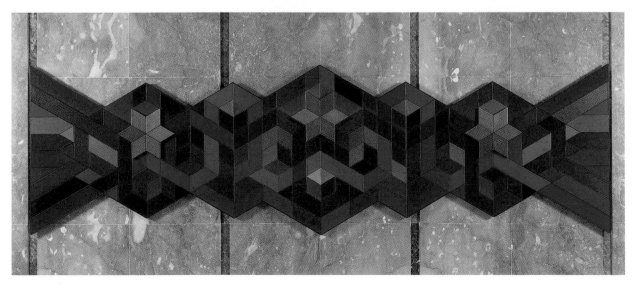

Top: *Home Town*, National City Bank, Leather Mosaic™ mural, 3'H x 8'W. Center: *Fox Island*, Allen County Park Lodge, Leather Mosaic™ mural, 3'H x 8'W.
Bottom: *Diversity, Unity, Community*, City-County Building, Fort Wayne, IN, Leather Mosaic™ mural, 5'H x 15'W. Photographs: Neal Bruns.

G. BYRON PECK/CITY ARTS

G. BYRON PECK STUDIOS ■ 1857 LAMONT STREET NW ■ WASHINGTON, DC 20010 ■ TEL/FAX 202-331-1966
E-MAIL BYRONPECK@EARTHLINK.NET ■ WWW.PECKSTUDIOS.COM ■ WWW.CITYARTSDC.ORG

230

Top: *Mayan* mural, Washington, DC, 12' x 28'. Bottom: *Duke Ellington* mural, Washington DC, 24' x 44'. Photographs: Greg Staley and Rick Reinhard.

SPOLAR STUDIO

TONY SPOLAR ■ 126 EAST MINERAL STREET ■ MILWAUKEE, WI 53204 ■ TEL 414-672-9847 ■ FAX 414-831-2493
E-MAIL TONY@SPOLARSTUDIO.COM ■ WWW.SPOLARSTUDIO.COM

231

Top: *The Survey* mural, 2001, Miller Park, Milwaukee, WI, digitally designed, printed on archival fine art canvas, 14' × 40'.
Center: *Book Land*, 2004, Wawautosa Public Library Children's Reading Room, Wauwatosa, WI, handpainted on canvas with three-dimensional handmade books, 10' × 28'.
Bottom: Sculpted mural, 2003, Master Lock World Headquarters, Oak Creek, WI, digital imagery with mixed media, 8 murals, 6' × 15' each.   Photographs: Jeff Salzer Photography.

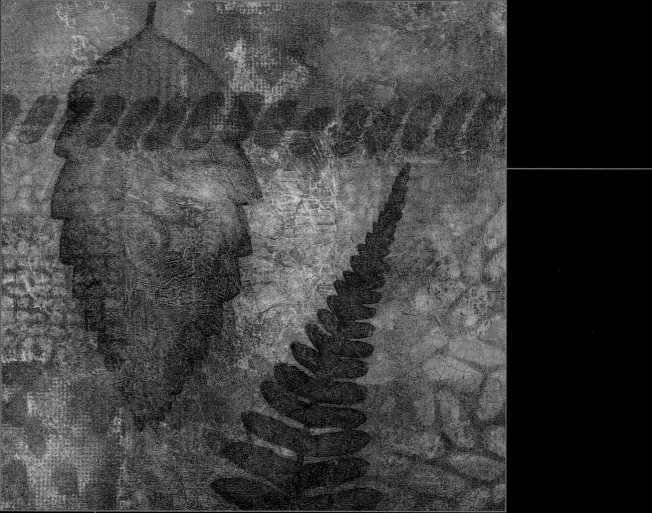

Paintings & Prints

" GUILD artists are serious, professional, and in general just great to work with. You don't need to worry about working over distance, because they're so capable of handling details from beginning to end. "

Jan Thompson
Interior Designer
Houston, TX

FRAN BULL

FRAN BULL STUDIO ■ PO BOX 707 ■ CLOSTER, NJ 07624 ■ TEL 201-767-3726 ■ FAX 201-767-7733
E-MAIL FRANBULL@FRANBULL.COM ■ WWW.FRANBULL.COM

234

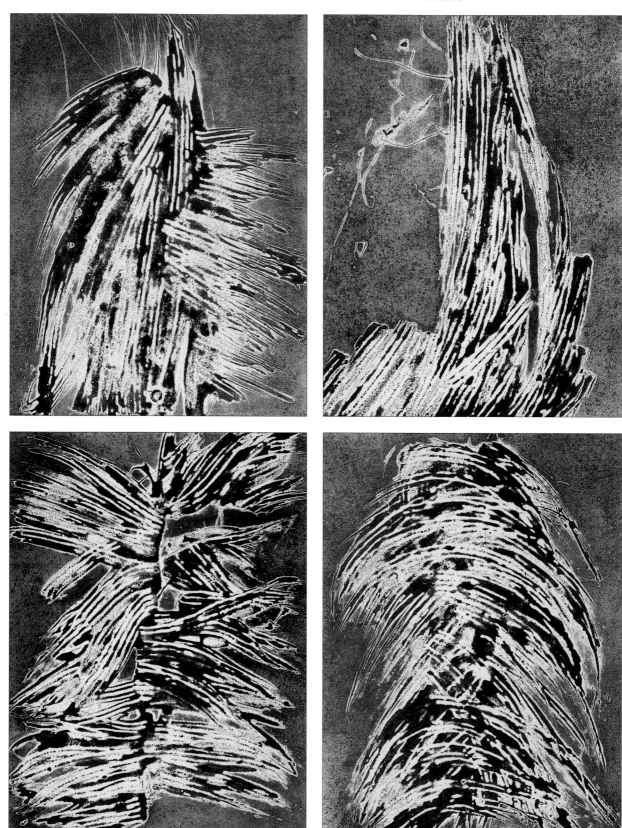

Top left: *Regal,* 2001, etching, paper: 49" × 43", plate: 33" × 25". Top right: *Feste,* 2001, etching, paper: 49" × 43", plate: 33" × 25". Bottom left: *Pa Bo,* 2001, etching, 49" × 43" (paper), 33" × 25" (plate). Bottom right: *Avui,* 2001, etching, paper: 49" × 43", plate: 33" × 25". All etchings from the *Barcelona!* series. Photographs: David Allison.

BARBARA DE PIRRO

370 EAST SOUNDVIEW DRIVE ■ SHELTON, WA 98584 ■ TEL 360-426-6899
E-MAIL BDEPIRRO@IX.NETCOM.COM ■ WWW.DEPIRRO.COM

235

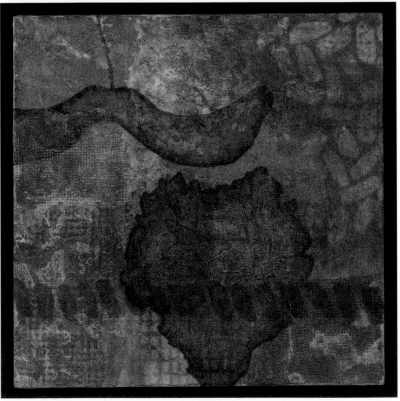

Top: *Drenched*, 2004, acrylic, 20" × 20" × 2". Bottom: *Breath*, 2004, acrylic, 20" × 20" × 2".
Photographs: Dirk Park.

JAMES F. DICKE II

REYNE GALLERY ■ 17 EAST EIGHTH STREET, THIRD FLOOR ■ CINCINNATI, OH 45202 ■ TEL 513-651-4198
E-MAIL REYNEH@AOL.COM ■ WWW.JAMESFDICKE.COM

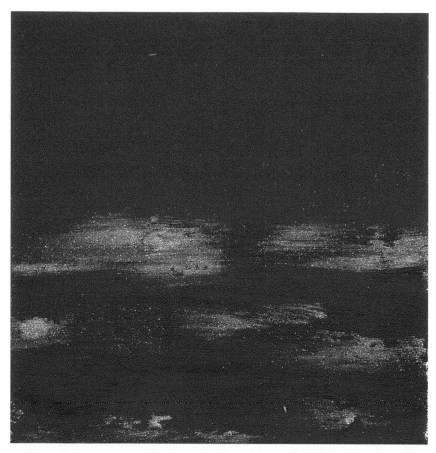

236

Top: *8/13.2/04*, acrylic on canvas, 8" × 8". Bottom: *8/6/04*, acrylic on canvas, 20" × 14.5".

LEMYA EL SOPHIA

EL SOPHIA GALLERY ■ 305 WEST BROADWAY #265 ■ NEW YORK, NY 10013 ■ TEL 212-300-5496
E-MAIL INFO@ELSOPHIA.COM ■ WWW.ELSOPHIA.COM

237

Top: *The Pharaoh*, 2004, oils and mixed media on canvas, 60"H x 36"W. Bottom: *Sergeant*, 2004, oils and mixed media on canvas, 60"W x 36"H. Photographs: F. Abe.

KEN ELLIOTT

250 LEAD KING DRIVE ■ CASTLE ROCK, CO 80108 ■ TEL 303-814-1122 ■ FAX 303-814-1133
E-MAIL ELLIOTTKC@EARTHLINK.NET ■ WWW.KENELLIOTT.COM

238

Top: *Blue Trees at Roadside*, giclée print, image size 20.3" x 39.4", paper size 26.3" x 45.4". Bottom left: *Into the Forest I*, monotype, image size 31.5" x 20.38", paper size 42.5" x 30".
Bottom right: *Clouds over the Foothills I*, monotype, image size 29.5" x 19.88", paper size 42.5" x 30".

JUDY FOWLER

18 EAST JEFFERSON STREET ■ MEDIA, PA 19063 ■ TEL 610-892-9547 ■ FAX 610-892-0482
E-MAIL JUDYMEDIA@ACN.NET ■ WWW.JUDYFOWLERARTIST.COM

239

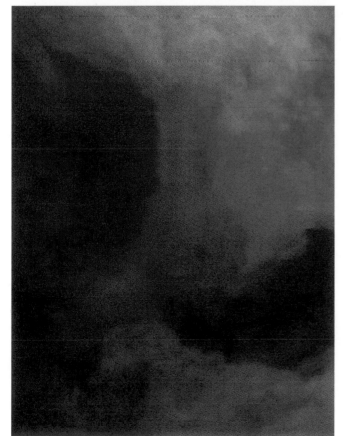 

Top: *Saint Germain*, 2003, oil, 40" × 66".
Bottom left: *Path*, 2003, oil, 60" × 46". Bottom right: *Paris Evening*, 2002, oil, 48" × 32".

YOSHI HAYASHI

YOSHI HAYASHI STUDIO ■ 255 KANSAS STREET #330 ■ SAN FRANCISCO, CA 94103 ■ TEL/FAX 415-552-0755
E-MAIL YOSHIHAYASHI@ATT.NET ■ WWW.YOSHIHAYASHI.COM

240

Full Moon III, 2002, private collection, gold and silver leaf with oil paints, 48" x 48". Photograph: Ira D. Schrank.

KATHRYN JACOBI

WAXWING EDITIONS ■ 654 COPELAND COURT ■ SANTA MONICA, CA 90405 ■ TEL 310-399-8423 ■ FAX 310-399-5350
E-MAIL KATHRYNJACOBI2@MAC.COM ■ WWW.KATHRYNJACOBI.COM

Basket of Garlic and Onions with Lemons, 2004, edition on smooth fine art paper, paper size: 24" x 20" or 36" x 24". Photograph: Chris Staples.

Favorite Images from the Past:
A GUILD Sourcebook Retrospective

Photograph: Anthony Potter.

Marilyn Forth
Tulips
Painted batik
25" × 35"
Published in *Sourcebook 16*

GRANT JOHNSON

STIMULUS LLC ■ PO BOX 170519 ■ SAN FRANCISCO, CA 94117 ■ TEL 415-558-8339 ■ FAX 415-864-3897
E-MAIL GRANT@GRANTJOHNSONART.COM ■ WWW.GRANTJOHNSONART.COM

243

Top: *Rio Fuerte*, No Man's Land series, 2003, archival pigment print on canvas, 48" × 72".
Bottom: *Lake Tahoe #9603300205*, Water Color series, 2004, archival pigment print on canvas, 48" × 72".

S. CHANDLER KISSELL

AMERICAN VELVET MILL ■ 22 BAYVIEW AVENUE
STONINGTON, CT 06378 ■ TEL 860-535-0515

244

Top: *Chill, Still Morning*, 2002, oil, 50" x 26". Bottom left: *Twilight, East Hubbardton*, 2002, oil, 30" x 46".
Bottom right: *Impending Storm*, 2004, oil, 30" x 40". Photographs: Brad Stanton.

SILJA TALIKKA LAHTINEN

SILJA'S FINE ART STUDIO ■ 5220 SUNSET TRAIL ■ MARIETTA, GA 30068
TEL 770-993-3409 ■ FAX 770-992-0350 ■ E-MAIL PENTEC02@BELLSOUTH.NET

245

Top: *The Spirits of the Prairie*, 2003, artist collection, acrylic on canvas, 24" x 24". Bottom: *The Sun Paints the Sky with Fire*, 2003, artist collection, acrylic on canvas, 24" x 24".

BRENT LILLY

BRENTART.COM ■ 10750 RIVER RUN DRIVE ■ MANASSAS, VA 20112 ■ TEL 703-298-2994
E-MAIL BRENTART@GMAIL.COM ■ WWW.BRENTART.NET

246

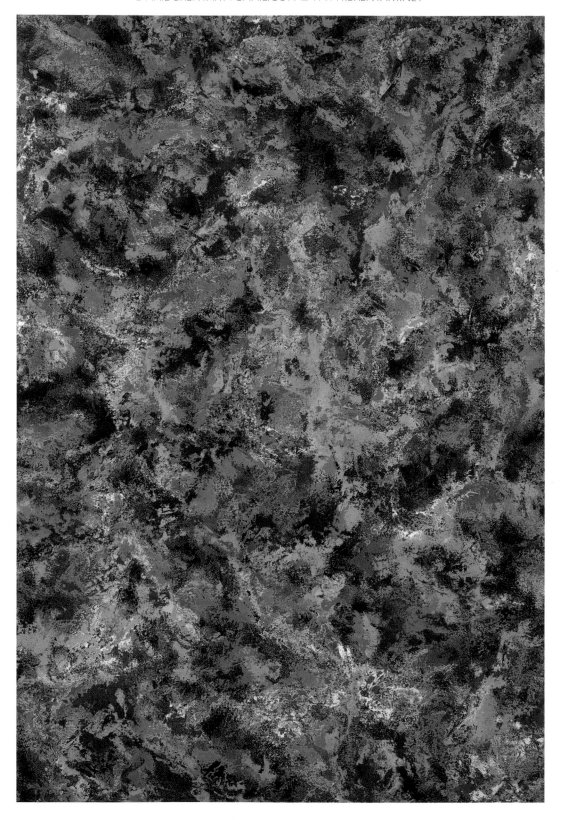

Trade Winds, 2002, modular acrylic on canvas, 60" x 48". Photograph: ABC Photo & Imaging, Inc.

MARY JO MAUTE

2736 ALDERWOOD AVENUE ■ BELLINGHAM, WA 98225 ■ TEL 360-671-1793
E-MAIL STARDUSTMEMORIES@ACCESS4LESS.NET

 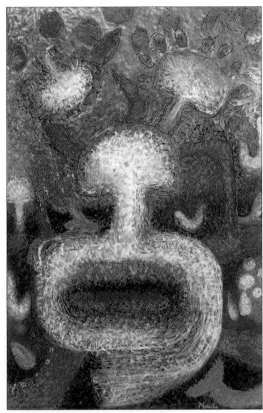

247

Top left: *Fleshy*, 2003, pastel, 18.5" × 15" unframed. Top right: *Spore Release*, 2004, pastel, 40" × 25.5" unframed. Photograph: Brett Baunton.
Bottom: *Shangara 4*, pastel, 23" × 27" unframed.

NANCY "STEVIE" BROWN PEACOCK

NANCY PEACOCK ARTWORKS ■ PO BOX 47346 ■ SEATTLE, WA 98146 ■ TEL 206-242-8884
E-MAIL STEVIEWONDERFUL@COMCAST.NET ■ WWW.NANCYPEACOCK.COM

248

The Pink Martini, acrylic and handmade paper on canvas, 36" x 36".

SCOTT RAYNOR

SCOTT RAYNOR FINE ART STUDIO ■ 1418 MOUNTAIN VIEW CHURCH ROAD ■ KING, NC 27021
TEL 336-972-2261 ■ E-MAIL JSRAYNOR@YAHOO.COM ■ WWW.SCOTTRAYNORSTUDIO.COM

249

Top left: *Studio Interior with Window,* 2004, oil on canvas, 4' × 4'. Top right: *Sunflowers with Pears,* 2004, watercolor and crayon, 11" × 15".
Bottom left: *Daffs and Lemons,* 2004, oil on canvas, 24" × 32". Bottom right: *Still Life with Teapot,* 2004, oil on canvas, 30" × 40". Photographs: Atlantic Studios.

KRISPEN SPENCER

KRISPEN ART ■ 211 KIOWA DRIVE EAST ■ LAKE KIOWA, TX 76240 ■ TEL 866-265-0995
E-MAIL KRISPEN@KRISPENART.COM ■ WWW.KRISPENART.COM

250

Top: *Tres Bliss*, triptych, acrylic, 40" x 78". Bottom left: *Sensation*, acrylic, 48" x 36". Bottom right: *Ambrosia*, acrylic, 48" x 36". Photographs: Harrison Evans.

STEPHANIE STANLEY

SANGITA ART ■ 816 WILSON PLACE ■ SANTA MONICA, CA 90405 ■ 330 NE 129TH STREET ■ MIAMI, FL 33161
TEL 310-924-9630 ■ FAX 305-843-0910 ■ E-MAIL STEPHANIE@SANGITAART.COM ■ WWW.SANGITAART.COM

251

Epiphany, oil, 48" x 48" x .5". Photograph: American Fine Art Photography.

JANE STERRETT

536 GRAND STREET #401 ■ HOBOKEN, NJ 07030 ■ TEL 201-656-5979 ■ FAX 201-656-4355
E-MAIL JANE@JANESTERRETT.COM ■ WWW.JANESTERRETT.COM

252

Top: *Three Fish*, 2004, mixed-media collage, available in various sizes as digital prints. Bottom left: *Sunflower*, 2004, mixed media, available in various sizes as digital prints. Bottom right: *Golden Fern*, 2004, mixed media, available in various sizes as digital prints.

CASSIE TONDRO

1348 GRANT STREET ■ SANTA MONICA, CA 90405 ■ TEL 310-452-2964
E-MAIL CASSIE@CASSIETONDRO.COM ■ WWW.CASSIETONDRO.COM

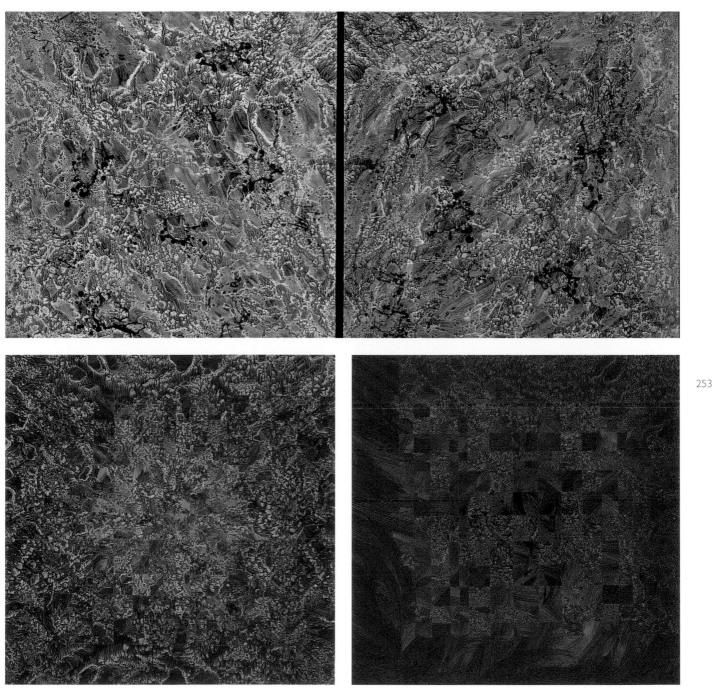

253

Top: *Camellias in the Rain*, 2004, acrylic on canvas, 36" × 72".
Bottom left: *Dare to Dream*, 2004, acrylic on canvas, 36" × 36". Bottom right: *World on Fire*, 2004, acrylic on canvas, 36" × 36".

149 HARBOR SOUTH ■ AMITYVILLE, NY 11701 ■ TEL 631-691-2376 ■ FAX 631-691-1920 ■ E-MAIL LOISVWALKER@AOL.COM

254

Vermont/Fall, 1998, oil on jute, 60" x 42".

LOIS WALKER

149 HARBOR SOUTH ■ AMITYVILLE, NY 11701 ■ TEL 631-691-2376 ■ FAX 631-691-1920 ■ E-MAIL LOISVWALKER@AOL.COM

255

Top: *Habit*, 1989, acrylic on canvas, 36" x 36". Bottom: *Escape*, 1991, oil on canvas, 30" x 48". Photographs: Lisa Hermanson.

Favorite Images from the Past:
A GUILD Sourcebook Retrospective

Silja Talikka Lahtinen
Moon-Vivaldi-Spring
Acrylic on canvas
32" x 32"
Private collection
Published in *Sourcebook 17*

STEPHEN YATES

YATES ARTS ■ PO BOX 744 ■ PORT TOWNSEND, WA 98368 ■ TEL/FAX 360-385-4330
E-MAIL YATESART@OLYMPUS.NET ■ WWW.YATESARTS.COM

257

Top left: *Sienna*, acrylic on panel, 12" x 12". Top right: *Border*, acrylic on canvas, 30" x 30". Bottom: *Swoop*, acrylic on wood panel, 36" x 80".

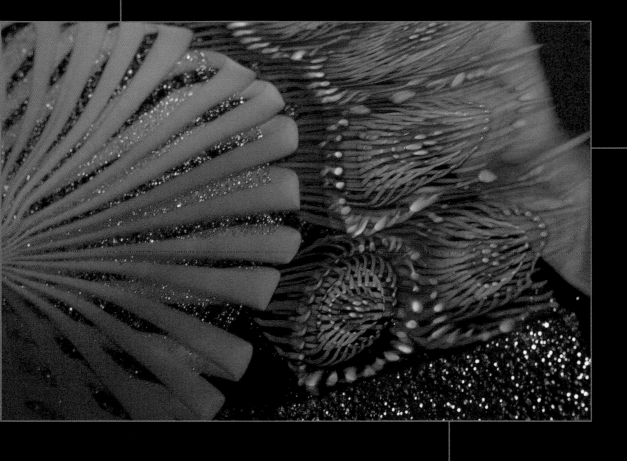

Fine Art Photography

PIA DAVIS

70 NORTH FRENCH PLACE ■ PRESCOTT, AZ 86303 ■ TEL 928-778-1227
FAX 928-443-1929 ■ E-MAIL PIA@PIAPHOTO.COM ■ WWW.PIAPHOTO.COM

260

Photographic interpretations of original glass art by James Nowak.
Top: *Green Glitter*, 2002. Bottom left: *Azure Bouquet*, 2002. Bottom right: *Coral Weave*, 2002.

DAR HORN

UNION ART WORKS ■ 402 WEST FIFTH STREET ■ SAN PEDRO, CA 90731 ■ FAX 310-833-1592
E-MAIL DAR@DARHORN.COM ■ WWW.DARHORN.COM ■ WWW.UNIONARTWORKS.COM

261

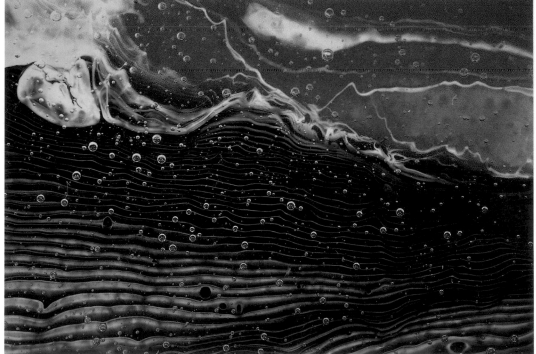

Top: *Crab Nebula*, Ilfochrome print on aluminum panel, 20" × 30". Bottom: *Going to the Light*, Ilfochrome print on aluminum panel, 20" × 30".

MARK IVINS

MARK IVINS PHOTOGRAPHY ■ PO BOX 102 ■ JAMESTOWN, CO 80455 ■ TEL 303-459-0224
E-MAIL MARK@MARKIVINS.COM ■ WWW.MARKIVINS.COM

262

Top: *East River Sunset* (left); *Manhattan Bridge and Empire State Building.* Center: *Adirondack Mountains, New York* (left); *George Washington Bridge.*
Bottom: *Catskill Mountains, New York.*

TALIAFERRO JONES

442 DUFFERIN STREET, UNIT N ■ TORONTO, ON M6K 2A3 ■ CANADA ■ TEL 416-538-3304 ■ FAX 416-538-8272
E-MAIL TALIAFERRO@TALIAFERROJONES.COM ■ WWW.TALIAFERROJONES.COM

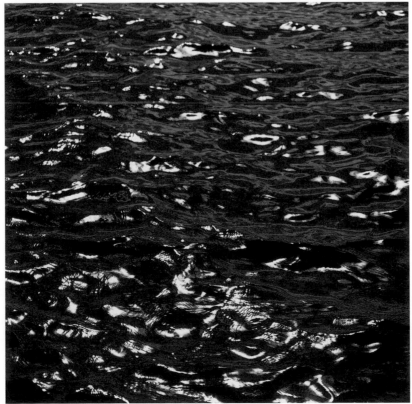

Top: *Still*, giclée print, 16" x 16", edition of 45.   Bottom: *Plunge*, giclée print, 41" x 41", edition of 15.

ANDREA KEMLER

120 FARLOW ROAD ■ NEWTON, MA 02458 ■ TEL 617-243-0590 ■ E-MAIL ANDREA@ANDREAKEMLER.COM
WWW.ANDREAKEMLER.COM

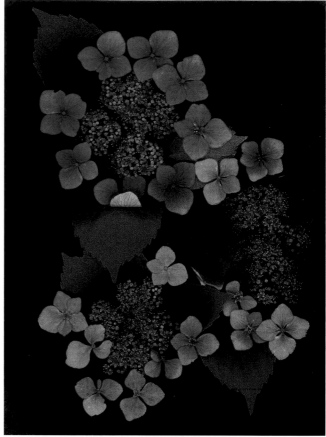

264

Top left: *Early Spring,* 2003, limited edition giclée print, 16.75" x 24". Top right: *Lace Capped Hydrangea,* 2003, limited edition giclée print, 18" x 24".
Bottom: *Ohana-han,* 2005, limited edition giclée print, 36" x 22".

JOYCE P. LOPEZ

JOYCE LOPEZ STUDIO ■ 1147 WEST OHIO STREET #304 ■ CHICAGO, IL 60622 ■ TEL 312-243-5033
FAX 312-243-7566 ■ E-MAIL JOYCE@JOYCELOPEZ.COM ■ WWW.JOYCELOPEZ.COM

265

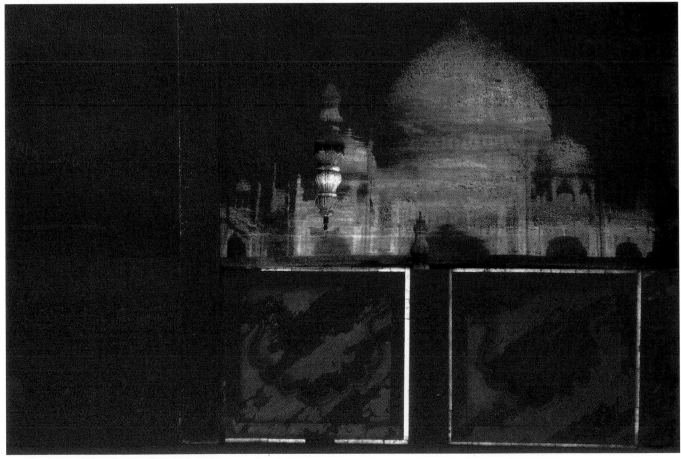

Top left: *Crane with Lilac River*. Top right: Jain Temple *Ceiling with Carp*.
Bottom: *Ochre Wall with Taj*, 22" x 17" (unframed).

MAXWELL MacKENZIE

2641 GARFIELD STREET NW ■ WASHINGTON, DC 20008 ■ TEL 202-232-6686
FAX 202-232-6684 ■ E-MAIL MAXMACKENZIE@VERIZON.NET

266

Top: *Near Pomme de Terre Lake, Grant County, Minnesota, 1997, 32" × 96" (image).* Bottom left: *Maplewood Township Homestead, Otter Tail County, Minnesota, winter 1993, 16" × 48" (image).* Bottom center: *Everts Township Schoolhouse, Otter Tail County, Minnesota, summer 1992, 16" × 48" (image).* Bottom right: *Near Nome, Barnes County, North Dakota, 1998, 32" × 96" (image).*

RON MELLOTT

THE NATURE GALLERY ■ PO BOX 444 ■ BLOOMFIELD, IN 47424 ■ TEL 812-863-2525
FAX 812-863-2424 ■ E-MAIL RON@NATUREGALLERY.NET ■ WWW.NATUREGALLERY.NET

267

Top left: *Loving Arches, Sweetheart Abbey, Scotland,* photograph, 38" x 50". Top right: *Blueberry Fields, Maine,* photograph, 40" x 50".
Center right: *Solemn Grandeur, Sweetheart Abbey, Scotland,* photograph, 23" x 30" (32" x 40" framed).
Bottom: *Far to the West, Sunset on Isle of Skye, Scotland,* photograph, 30" x 60".

GEORGE THOMAS MENDEL

PO BOX 13605 ■ PITTSBURGH, PA 15243 ■ TEL 412-563-7918
WWW.PHOTO-NOW.COM OR WWW.GUILD.COM

268

Top: *Zurich.* Bottom: *New York City.*

TALLI ROSNER-KOZUCH

PHO-TAL, INC. ■ 15 NORTH SUMMIT STREET ■ TENAFLY, NJ 07670 ■ TEL 201-569-3199 ■ FAX 201-569-3392
E-MAIL TAL@PHOTAL.COM ■ WWW.PHOTAL.COM

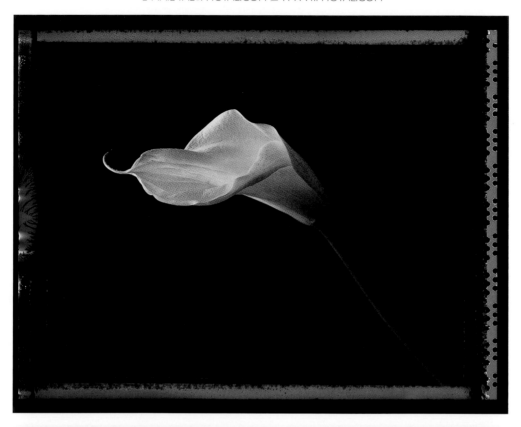

269

Top: *Calla Lily.* Bottom: *2 Tulips Bouquets.*

JULIE BETTS TESTWUIDE

JULIEARTS.COM ■ 482 UNDERHILL AVENUE ■ YORKTOWN HEIGHTS, NY 10598 ■ TEL 914-962-5096
TEL (CELL) 914-672-1897 ■ E-MAIL JBT@JULIEARTS.COM ■ WWW.JULIEARTS.COM

270

Top left: *7 Carries 5.* Top right: *Beachplay on the Riviera.* Bottom left: *Equestrian Landscape #1.* Bottom right: *Monet's Garden.*
All images available as limited edition prints in standard sizes of 8" × 8" and 20" × 20" on Somerset Velvet fine art paper.

JANET VAN ARSDALE

THE ART COLLECTOR ■ 4151 TAYLOR STREET ■ SAN DIEGO, CA 92110 ■ TEL 619-299-3232 ■ FAX 619-299-8709
E-MAIL JANET@THEARTCOLLECTOR.COM ■ WWW.JANETVANARSDALE.COM ■ WWW.THEARTCOLLECTOR.COM

271

Top: *Boat Hull* triptych, sepia prints, 22" × 40". Bottom left: *Koi*, photograph, 24" × 36".
Bottom right: *Villa d'Este*, Polaroid transfer, 30" × 30".

Art for the Wall: Metal

"I often use the GUILD Sourcebook to find that extra ordinary piece of art for my clients."

Greg Thompson
Greg Thompson Fine Art
Little Rock, AK

Favorite Images from the Past:
A GUILD Sourcebook Retrospective

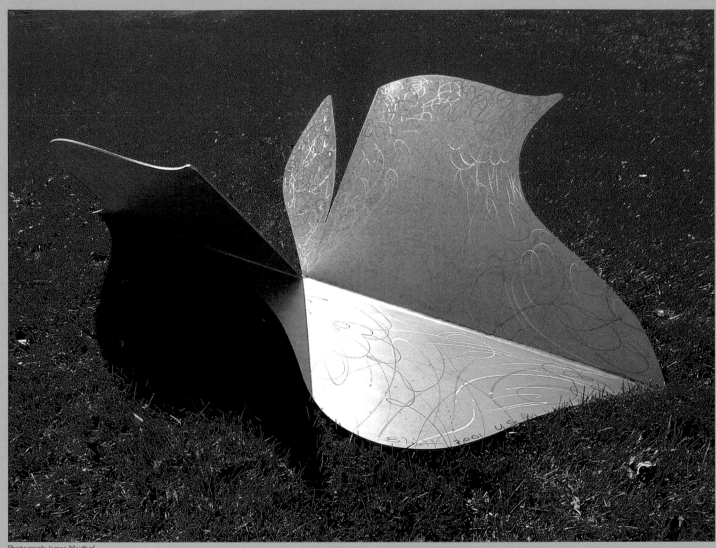

Photograph: James Maidhof.

Rita Blitt
Liberation
Stainless steel
Gold Coast Regional Art Center
Surfers Paradise, Australia
4' x 5' x 10'
Published in *Sourcebook 17*

ARCHIFORMS

NANCY AND RUSSELL THAYER ■ 30735 ADAIR COURT ■ FRANKLIN, MI 48025
TEL/FAX 248-539-0280 ■ E-MAIL THAYER@UMICH.EDU

Top: Wall piece (detail), 2003, Pfizer Corporation, acrylic on aluminum, 22' × 6'. Bottom left: Ceiling piece, 2003, Pfizer Corporation, acrylic on aluminum, 8' × 6'.
Bottom right: Lobby piece, 1992, acrylic on aluminum, 22' × 24'.

LINDA LEVITON

LINDA LEVITON SCULPTURE ■ 1011 COLONY WAY ■ COLUMBUS, OH 43235
TEL 614-433-7486 ■ EMAIL GUILD@LINDALEVITON.COM ■ WWW.LINDALEVITON.COM

276

Eve's Leaves, copper, 24"W x 52"H x 10"D. Photograph: Jerry Anthony Photography.

LINDA LEVITON

LINDA LEVITON SCULPTURE ■ 1011 COLONY WAY ■ COLUMBUS, OH 43235
TEL 614-433-7486 ■ EMAIL GUILD@LINDALEVITON.COM ■ WWW.LINDALEVITON.COM

Top: *Patterns of Nature/Wave* series (square configuration), copper, patina and wood, 31"H x 31"W x 4"D. Photograph: Jerry Anthony Photography.
Bottom: *Patterns of Nature/Wave* series (horizontal configuration), copper, patina and wood, each row 15.5"H x 62"W x 4"D. Photograph: Flashback Photography.

LINING ARTS INC.

WAYNE MANN ■ CAREY THORPE ■ 390 DUPONT STREET, SUITE 200 ■ TORONTO, ON M5R1V9 ■ CANADA
TEL 416-927-0353 ■ FAX 416-922-0820 ■ E-MAIL CTHORPE@LININGARTS.COM ■ WWW.LININGARTS.COM

278

City of Flowers, 2005, bronzed, patinated, and engraved steel, stainless steel, and brass plate, 28" x 28". Photograph: Rafael Goldchain.

SUSAN McGEHEE

METALLIC STRANDS ■ 540 23RD STREET ■ MANHATTAN BEACH, CA 90266 ■ TEL 310-545-4112 ■ FAX 310-546-7152
E-MAIL SUSAN@METALSTRANDS.COM ■ WWW.METALSTRANDS.COM

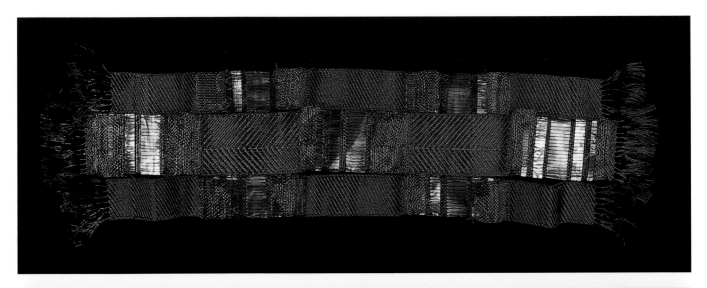

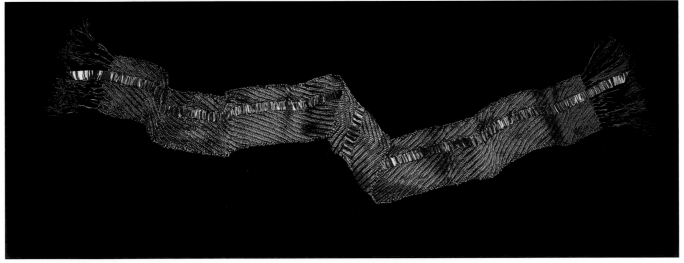

279

Top: *Las Ventanas*, woven anodized aluminum wire and copper, 14" x 58".
Bottom: *Metallic Swirl*, woven anodized aluminum wire and copper, 25" x 70". Photographs: Andrew Neuhart.

DARCY MEEKER

3452 SPUR STREET ■ BLACKSBURG, VA 24060 ■ TEL 540-449-4291
E-MAIL DARCY.MEEKER@JUNO.COM ■ WWW.DARCYMEEKER.COM

280

Top: *Elephant Vine*, 2000, General Electric Company, Schenectady, NY, copper and flexible plywood, 14' × 36' × 2'. Photograph: Jim Pease.
Bottom: *Elephant Vine* (details). Photographs: Glenn Davenport.

BASHA RUTH NELSON

PO BOX 86 ■ LAKE HILL, NY 12448 ■ TEL 845-679-2941 ■ FAX 845-679-4583
EMAIL BASHA@BASHARUTHNELSON.COM ■ WWW.BASHARUTHNELSON.COM

Cascades, 2004, aluminum and copper. Photograph: Jason Zhang.

281

MARSH SCOTT

2795 LAGUNA CANYON ROAD, STUDIO C ■ LAGUNA BEACH, CA 92651 ■ TEL 949-494-8672
E-MAIL MARSH@MARSHSCOTT.COM ■ WWW.MARSHSCOTT.COM

282

Top: *Nature's Lyrics*, 2004, Kaiser Permanente, Downey, CA, seven stainless steel panels, overall size 72"H x 180"W. Photograph: Rick Lang.
Bottom: *Desert Voices*, 2003, Kaiser Permanente, Palmdale, CA, five of six stainless steel panels, 48"H x 48"W each.

JOHN SEARLES

SEARLES METAL ART ■ 13462 RED ARROW HIGHWAY ■ HARBERT, MI 49115 ■ TEL 269-469-1509 ■ FAX 269-469-0129
E-MAIL JS@SEARLESART.COM ■ WWW.SEARLESART.COM

283

Top: *Dancing Shapes*, 2004, copper and brass, 42" x 95" x 5". Bottom: Shaped woven copper rhombus, 2004, 45" x 72" x 3".

Favorite Images from the Past:
A GUILD Sourcebook Retrospective

Photograph: Barry Michlin.

Martin Sturman
Door, 1998
Burnished stainless steel
102"H x 40"W x 2"D
Private collection
Published in *Architect's 15*

MARTIN STURMAN

MARTIN STURMAN SCULPTURES ■ 3201 BAYSHORE DRIVE ■ WESTLAKE VILLAGE, CA 91361 ■ TEL 818-707-8087
FAX 818-707-3079 ■ E-MAIL MLSTURMAN@SBCGLOBAL.NET ■ WWW.STEELSCULPTURES.COM

Flowers & Vines, 56" x 48" x 1.5". Photograph: Barry Michlin.

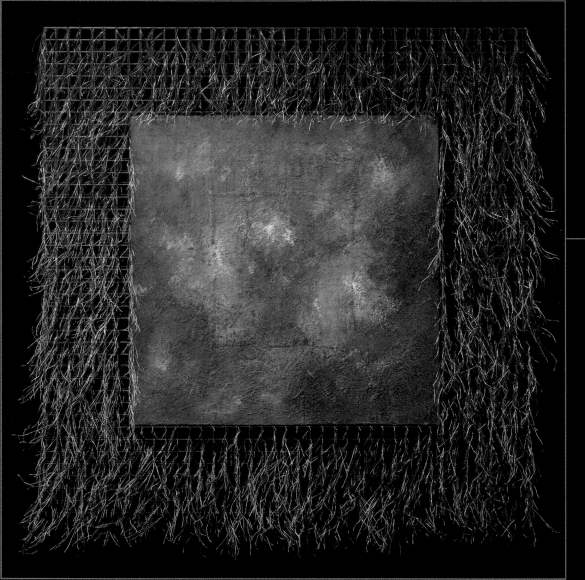

Art for the Wall:
Mixed & Other Media

" As art consultants, we must always have new work to present to our returning clients. "

Francie Kelley
Paragone Gallery
Los Angeles, CA

AMERICAN INDUSTRIAL ARTS

JACK DEMUNNIK ■ 655 THIRD STREET ■ SUITE 302 ■ BELOIT, WI 53511 ■ TEL 608-365-2194 ■ TEL (CELL) 608-295-5130
FAX 608-365-2353 ■ E-MAIL JACK@AMERICANINDUSTRIALART.COM ■ WWW.AMERICANINDUSTRIALART.COM

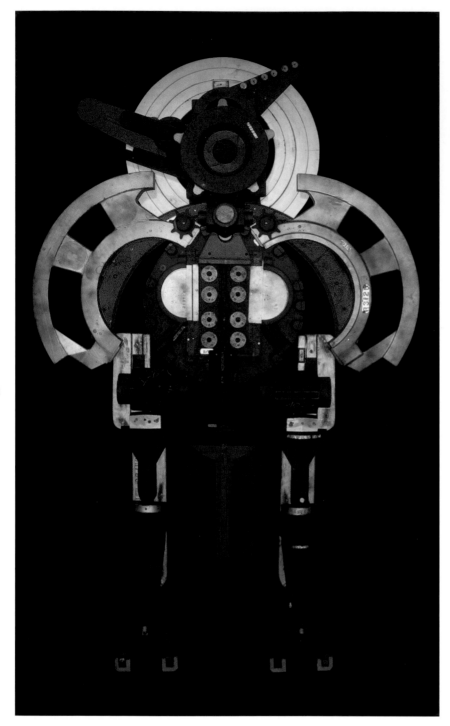

288

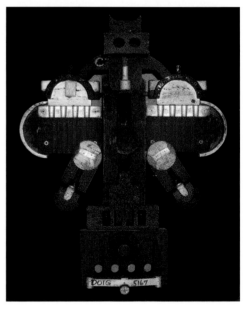

Left: *Aura Bird*, 9.75' × 5.25' × 10". Top right: *Wild Willy*, 3.33' × 5.83' × 11".
Center right: *Apache Thunderbird*, 6.83' × 6.5' × 12". Bottom right: *Batman-Machina*, 3.42' × 2.66' × 10".

BRUCE R. BLEACH

146 COLEMAN ROAD ■ GOSHEN, NY 10924 ■ TEL 845-294-8945
E-MAIL BRBLEACH@FRONTIERNET.NET

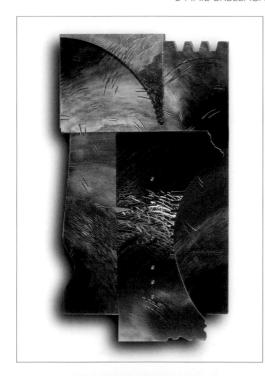 

289

Top left: *Untitled* wall sculpture, Greenleaf Trust, Radisson Plaza, Kalamazoo, MI, bronze with patina, acrylic on wood, 42" x 24". Top right: *High Gear #6*, acrylic on canvas, giclèe edition, part of a suite of 3, edition of 150 each, 24" x 36". Bottom: *Untitled* wall sculpture, The World Bank, Washington, DC, mixed media on aluminum, welded aluminum framing, 30" diameter each, 10' x 2.5' overall. Inset: *Wall sculpture* (detail).

MYRA BURG & LIZ CUMMINGS

171 PIER AVENUE #353 ■ SANTA MONICA, CA 90405 ■ TEL 310-399-5040 (MYRA) ■ TEL 877-249-2552 (LIZ)
WWW.MYRABURG.COM ■ WWW.LIZCUMMINGS.COM

290

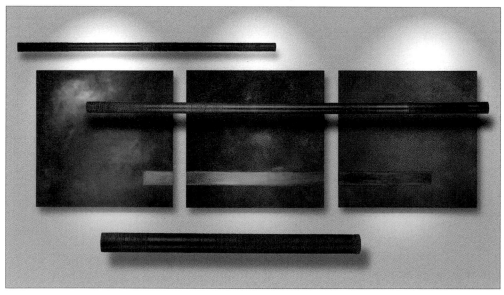

Top: *Transitions*, mixed media, approx. 60"H x 120"W. Bottom left: *Theory*, mixed media, approx. 48"H x 18"W.
Bottom right: *Beginning*, mixed media, approx. 72"H x 180"W. Photographs: Barry Blau Photography.

TERESA CAMOZZI

THE CAMOZZI ART STUDIO ■ 1190 A SHAFTER AVENUE ■ SAN FRANCISCO, CA 94124
TEL 415-822-6222 ■ WWW.TERESACAMOZZI.COM

Left: *Morning, Noon & Evening*, Marriott's Harbor Beach Resort, Fort Lauderdale, FL, 72 modular panels composed of resin with imbedded natural elements, photo-based encaustic wax and acrylic paintings, 8' × 8' × .5' each. Insets: *Morning, Noon & Evening* (details). Photographs: Lieslie Bauer.

RENE CULLER

RENE CULLER GLASS LLC ■ 540 EAST 105TH STREET #122 ■ CLEVELAND, OH 44108 ■ TEL 216-851-5149
E-MAIL GLASS@RENECULLER.COM ■ WWW.RENECULLER.COM

292

Top: *Abstraction in Red,* 2005, Flaster Greenberg PC, Cherry Hill, NJ, fused glass with enamel, 21" × 21" each.
Bottom: *Abstraction in Red* (detail). Inset: *Abstraction in Red* (detail). Photographs: Daniel Fox.

ELLEN KOCHANSKY

EKO ■ 1237 MILE CREEK ROAD ■ PICKENS, SC 29671 ■ TEL/FAX 864-868-4250
E-MAIL EKOCHANSKY@GMAIL.COM ■ WWW.EKOCHANSKY.COM

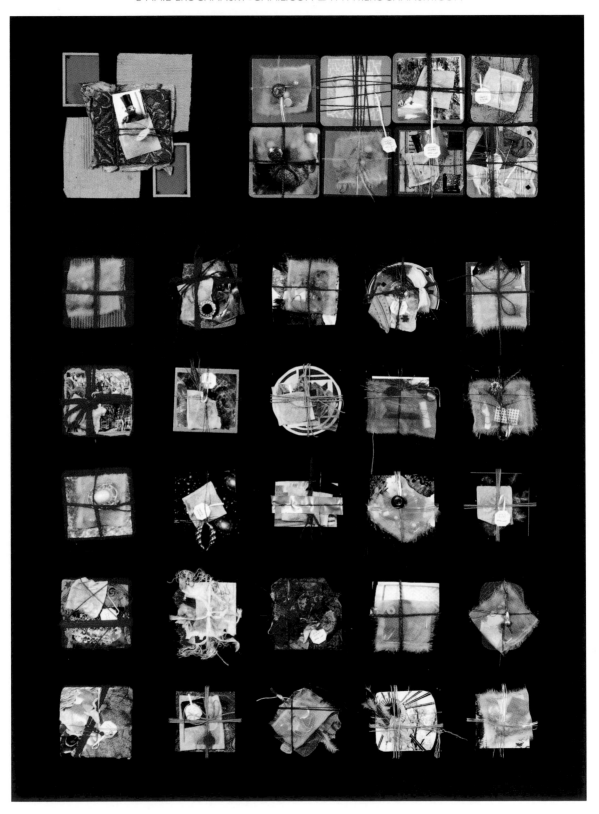

293

Page #1/Family Album, 2004, Mint Museum of Craft + Design, Charlotte, NC, mixed media, 34"W x 48"H.
A related piece is on view at the Mecklenburg County Library, Charlotte, NC

IG MATA

IG MATA STUDIO ■ 43-01 22ND STREET #351 ■ LONG ISLAND, NY 11101 ■ TEL/FAX 212-979-7921
E-MAIL INFO@IGMATA.COM ■ WWW.IGMATA.COM

294

Top: Group Panels, glass panels and stainless steel hardware, pinhole photographs exposed on photosensitive material hand-applied on glass surface, 24" × 30" each.
Bottom: *Brazil*, glass panel and stainless steel hardware, pinhole photograph exposed on photosensitive material hand-applied on glass surface, 24" × 30".

TERRY DAVITT POWELL

1424 MILLS AVENUE ■ REDLANDS, CA 92373 ■ TEL 909-793-8141
E-MAIL TERRY@TDPOWELL.COM ■ WWW.TDPOWELL.COM

295

Top: *Meet and Greet*, mixed media on panel, 14" x 25" x 1.75". Bottom: *Street Smart*, mixed media on panel, 20" x 24" x 1.75".

Career-building Projects:
Commissions Generated Through GUILD Sourcebooks

SUSAN VENABLE
Firemirage, 1993
Steel and copper wire
18"H x 12"W
Hillman Properties, San Francisco, CA

Photograph: Charles Callister.

Firemirage was made over twelve years ago, and I'm still really proud of it. Since it is in a very public lobby, I have received many comments about it over the years. I love sending out the tear sheets from *GUILD 9* which featured *Firemirage*, although now I save them for special clients because I have only a few left!

This commission came through a gallery in San Francisco whose staff saw my ad in THE GUILD; I presented drawings to the architect and owners, who made the final selection. I did three more commissions with that gallery before its partners retired. I was sad to see them go.

My work has changed very little over the years; I have developed a language that is my own. But *Firemirage* took my work to a very large scale, which was phenomenal for me. At that time collaborating with an architect on an installation was a new adventure. The challenge of transporting and installing an eighteen-foot-tall piece of my work was daunting—and the ultimate thrill!

PRISCILLA ROBINSON
Fields and Fog, 2004
Acrylic on handmade paper
7'H x 18'W
Stafford Performing Arts Center, Houston, TX

I've developed a long-term working relationship with Charles White, the art consultant for this project. He knows he can depend on me to meet deadlines and really listen to what he and the client want. The rather sterile environment of this lobby needed color, texture, and pattern, which is what my work is all about. Charles also knew I'd be comfortable working in a large format, although *Fields and Fog* is the largest "flat" piece I've done.

I was curious to see whether my embossed surfaces would read at this scale, and they definitely did. I divided the piece into four panels for visual effect. Five panels would have been easier, more cost-effective in terms of materials, and wouldn't have required such a big truck to transport, but the visual strength of four wound up being a good decision. Sometimes on big projects, the decisions you make early on aren't as important as you think they will be in the end. But this time, it made a real difference in the success of the piece.

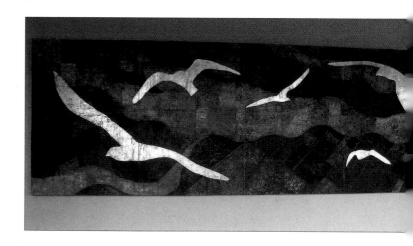

PRISCILLA ROBINSON

2811 HANCOCK DRIVE ■ AUSTIN, TX 78731 ■ TEL/FAX 512-452-3516 ■ TEL 505-758-2608
E-MAIL PJR@PRISCILLAROBINSON.COM ■ WWW.PRISCILLAROBINSON.COM

Left: *Vertical Garden Series #106*, 2004, acrylic and cotton on panel, 72" × 30".
Right: *Vertical Garden Series #105*, 2004, acrylic and cotton on panel, 72" × 30".

LEE SILTON

972 HILGARD AVENUE ■ LOS ANGELES, CA 90024 ■ TEL 310-824-0051 ■ FAX 310-824-1671
E-MAIL LEECLECTIC@VERIZON.NET ■ WWW.LEESILTON.COM

298

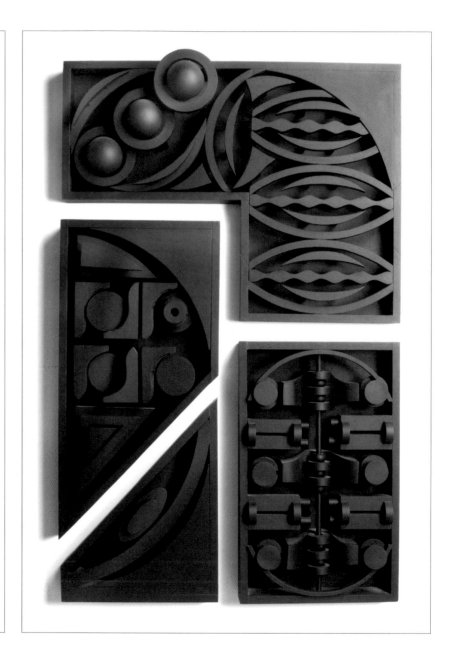

Left: *Space New York*, 2003, wood, 78" × 24" × 3". Right: *Third Connection*, 2003, wood, 48" × 60" × 3". Photographs: Roger Marshutz.

LEE SILTON

972 HILGARD AVENUE ■ LOS ANGELES, CA 90024 ■ TEL 310-824-0051 ■ FAX 310-824-1671
E-MAIL LEECLECTIC@VERIZON.NET ■ WWW.LEESILTON.COM

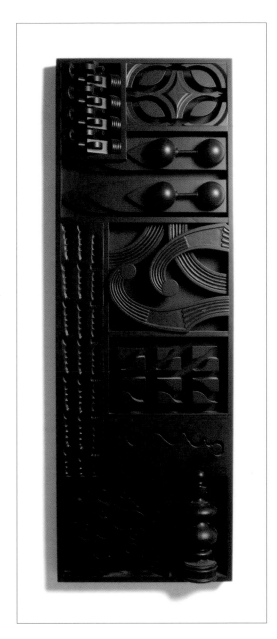

299

Left: *Mozart,* 2003, wood, 72" × 30" × 3". Photograph: Roger Marshutz. Right: *Zen Door,* 2003, wood, 138" × 81" × 4.5".

SUSAN VENABLE

VENABLE STUDIO ■ 2323 FOOTHILL LANE ■ SANTA BARBARA, CA 93105 ■ TEL 805-884-4963 ■ FAX 805-884-4983
E-MAIL SUSAN@VENABLESTUDIO.COM ■ WWW.VENABLESTUDIO.COM

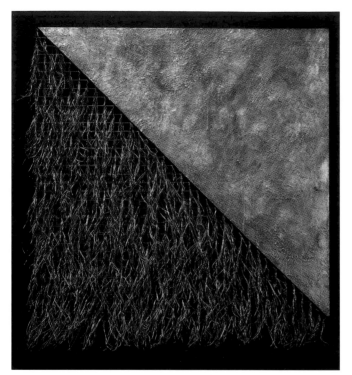

300

Top left: *Sundara,* mixed media, 34" × 34". Top right: *Transcendental Bleu,* mixed media, 40" × 40".
Bottom: *SierraSOL,* mixed media, 28" × 84". Photographs: William Nettles.

VITRAMAX GROUP

116 SOUTH TENTH STREET ■ LOUISVILLE, KY 40202 ■ TEL 502-589-3828 ■ FAX 502-589-3830
E-MAIL CDAVIS@VITRAMAX.COM ■ WWW.VITRAMAX.COM

301

Top: *Brittas Bay*, 2004, Priestap residence, illuminated wall sculpture, cast, bent, etched, and leafed glass, 24"H x 96"W.
Bottom: *Brittas Bay* (detail). Photographs: Doug Decker Photographics.

WKRP, INC.

MANOSE STUDIOS, INC. ■ 407 ASPEN OAK DRIVE ■ ASPEN, CO 81611 ■ TEL 970-920-4098
FAX 970-920-2242 ■ E-MAIL MANOSE@ROF.NET ■ WWW.WKRPINC.COM

302

Top: women's bathroom wallpaper, 2004, Aspen Art Museum, dimensions variable.
Bottom: men's bathroom wallpaper with painting *Legal Tender*, 2004, Aspen Art Museum, dimensions variable.

ERNEST WILMETH

1521 BRYN MAWR NE ■ ALBUQUERQUE, NM 87106 ■ TEL 505-266-0391 ■ FAX 505-255-4920
E-MAIL WILART@SWCP.COM ■ WWW.ERNESTWILMETH.COM

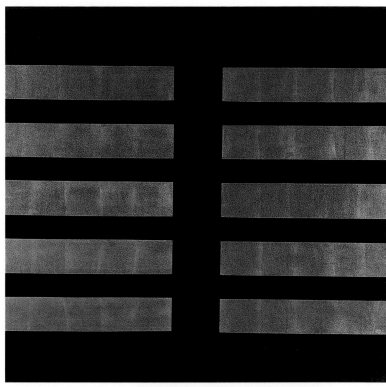

303

Top left: *Infinity*, 2004, mixed media acrylic and metal leaf on canvas, 48" × 36". Top right: *Garden Entrance*, 2004, mixed media acrylic and metal leaf on canvas, 48" × 48". Bottom left: *Red Sky Rising*, 2004, collage paper, 22.5" × 20". Bottom right: *Japanese Tea Garden*, 2003, collage canvas, 48" × 36". Photographs: Norman Johnson.

Art for the Wall: Fiber

" *My company works with the architectural and interior design community for the purpose of integrating custom art within the structural design of a building. I have found the GUILD Sourcebooks to be an invaluable source over the years, and often use GUILD editions, present and past, to locate artists for commissioned projects!* "

Jan Prokopenko
Fine Arts West, Ltd.
Longmont, CO

BIRDWORKS FIBER ARTS ■ 2633 REYNARD WAY ■ SAN DIEGO, CA 92103 ■ TEL 619-294-7236 ■ FAX 619-294-6873
E-MAIL CBIRD2400@AOL.COM ■ WWW.BIRDWORKS-FIBERARTS.COM

306

Life's Amazing, 2004, art quilt, 58" x 45". Photograph: Gary Conaughton.

LAURA MILITZER BRYANT

PRISM ARTS, INC. ■ 3140 39TH AVENUE NORTH ■ ST. PETERSBURG, FL 33714
TEL 727-528-3800 ■ FAX 727-528-3308 ■ E-MAIL LAURA@PRISMYARN.COM

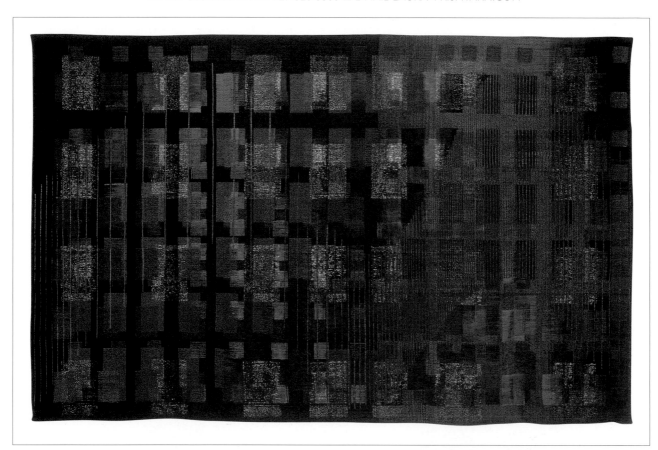

307

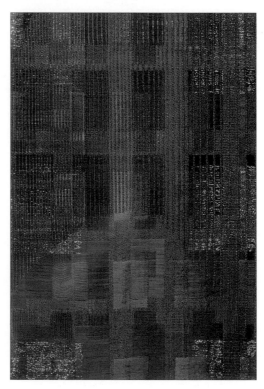

Top: *Odyssey*, weaving, 48.25" x 75.25". Bottom left: *Earth/Sky Grid*, weaving on copper, 20" x 20". Bottom right: *Odyssey* (detail). Photographs: Rob Moorman.

MYRA BURG

171 PIER AVENUE #353 ■ SANTA MONICA, CA 90405
TEL 310-399-5040 ■ WWW.MYRABURG.COM

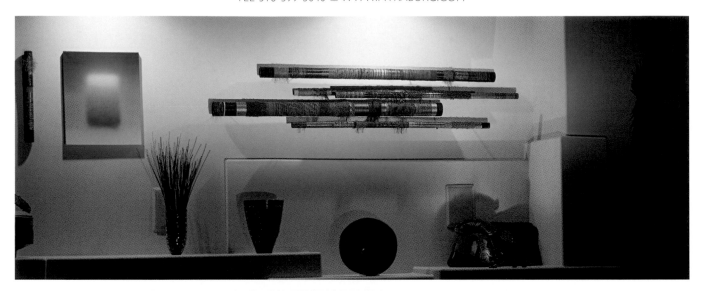

308

Top: *Quiet Oboes*, wrapped fiber, overall size 2.5' × 7.5'. Bottom left: *Indonesian Oboes*, wrapped fiber, overall size: 8' × 7'.
Bottom right: *Jenny*, wrapped fiber and burnished aluminum, 12' × 3'. Photographs: Ron Luxemburg.

309

Finland - Path to Lake Saimaa, 2004, handmade wool felt, sisal, and acrylic, 60"H x 39"W x 3.5"D, (framed). Photograph: Cindy Momchilov.

MARILYN FORTH

BAYBERRY ART STUDIO ■ 7658 HAYLAGE CIRCLE ■ BALDWINSVILLE, NY 13027 ■ TEL 315-638-3666
FAX 315-458-4828 ■ E-MAIL MFORTH@TWCNY.RR.COM

310

Essence of Honor, painted batik, 58" x 28".

MARILYN FORTH

BAYBERRY ART STUDIO ■ 7658 HAYLAGE CIRCLE ■ BALDWINSVILLE, NY 13027 ■ TEL 315-638-3666
FAX 315-458-4828 ■ E-MAIL MFORTH@TWCNY.RR.COM

311

Soft Rock Symphony II, St. Vincent's Hospital, Erie, PA, painted batik, 72" x 45".

MARILYN HENRION

505 LAGUARDIA PLACE, #23D ■ NEW YORK, NY 10012 ■ TEL 212-982-8949
E-MAIL MARILYNHENRION@RCN.COM ■ WWW.MARILYNHENRION.COM

312

Top left: *A Vivid Air*, hand-quilted silks, 35"H x 52"W. Bottom: *Remains of the Day*, hand-quilted silks, 39"H x 57"W. Photographs: Karen Bell.

CHRISTINE L. KEFER

OUT OF THE MAINSTREAM DESIGNS, INC. ■ 107 SOUTH SECOND STREET ■ GENEVA, IL 60134
TEL 630-232-2419 ■ FAX 630-232-2491 ■ E-MAIL C.KEFER@ATT.NET

313

Top: Handwoven silk panel with twisted fringe on stitched suede, resting on silk cloth.
Bottom: Handwoven Italian silk textured panel over suede with antique and vintage Italian glass beads. Photographs: Barbara Collins.

CAROL LeBARON

2278 HIGHWAY 91 ■ ELIZABETHTON, TN 37643 ■ TEL 423-474-2729
E-MAIL CLEBARON@EARTHLINK.NET ■ WWW.CAROLLEBARON.COM

314

Left: *Aral Sea,* wool, acid dye, clamp resist, hand-pieced, 14.83'H × 4.66'W. Top right: *Stony Creek September,* wool, acid dye, clamp resist, hand-pieced, three panels, 108"H × 30"W each. Center right: *Surrender to Confusion,* wool, acid dye, clamp resist, hand-pieced, three panels, 108"H × 30"W each.
Bottom right: *Disintegration* (detail of *Surrender to Confusion,*), 2004.

GAIL RUTTER-VₐNSLYKE

PERPENDICULAR TO THE WIND STUDIO ■ PO BOX 268 ■ 320 WEST 200 SOUTH ■ MOAB, UT 84532 ■ TEL 435-259-0088
FAX 435-259-1992 ■ E-MAIL GVSFIBERART@CITLINK.NET ■ WWW.PERPENDICULARTOTHEWIND.COM

 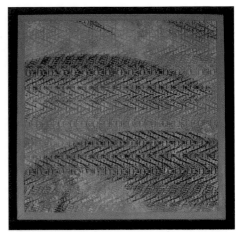

Top left: *Blowin' in the Wind,* from the *TextTILES* series, 2001, acrylic paint on handwoven canvas, 4' × 8' × .75" (18 16" × 16" tiles). Top right: *Blowin' in the Wind* (detail).
Bottom: *Solstice Reflection,* John C. Flanigan Police Department Headquarters Building, Anchorage, AK, handwoven rayon, linen, and jute fabric panels, 17.33'H × 29.33'W.

RAMONA SAKIESTEWA

RAMONA SAKIESTEWA LTD. ■ 7198 OLD SANTA FE TRAIL ■ SANTA FE, NM 87505
TEL 505-982-8282 ■ FAX 505-820-7130 ■ E-MAIL RAMONA@RAMONASAKIESTEWA.COM

316

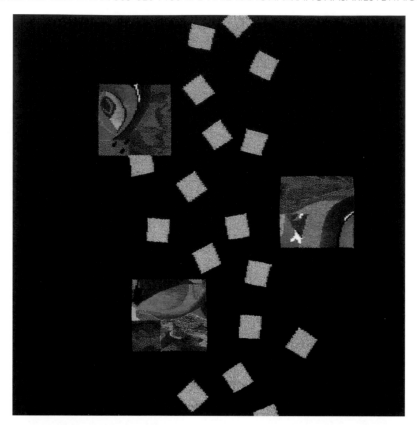

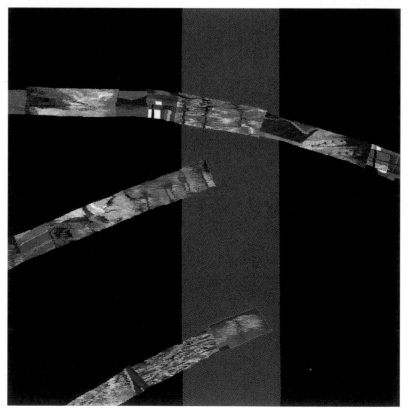

Top: *Urban Galaxy 2*, 2003, wool, 36" x 36" framed. Bottom: *Urban Galaxy 3*, 2004, wool, 45" x 45" framed. Photographs: A. Doty

JOAN SCHULZE

808 PIPER AVENUE ■ SUNNYVALE, CA 94087 ■ TEL/FAX 408-736-7833
E-MAIL JOAN@JOAN-OF-ARTS.COM ■ WWW.JOAN-OF-ARTS.COM

317

Top: *Dream the Sun*, 2004, pigment print, 15" × 42". Bottom: *Haiku 119, Haiku 125, Haiku 15*, collages, images approximately 9" × 9", 11" × 11" mounted, 15" × 15" framed.
Photographs: Sharon Risedorph.

SUSAN SINGLETON

AZO ■ PO BOX 39 ■ ORCAS, WA 98280 ■ TEL 360-376-5898 ■ FAX 360-376-5519
E-MAIL AZO@ROCKISLAND.COM ■ WWW.AZOART.COM

318

Ziggurat, 2005, washi paper stitched and dyed with copper leaf, 7' x 7'.

KAREN URBANEK

314 BLAIR AVENUE ■ PIEDMONT, CA 94611-4004 ■ TEL 510-654-0685
FAX 510-654-2790 ■ E-MAIL KRNURBANEK@AOL.COM

Up 1, 2005, naturally dyed silk fiber, polymer, 53"H x 40"W. Photograph: Don Tuttle Photography.

ALICE VAN LEUNEN

VAN LEUNEN STUDIOS ■ 9025 SE TERRACE VIEW COURT ■ AMITY, OR 97101 ■ TEL 503-835-7717 ■ FAX 503-835-7707
E-MAIL AVANLEUNEN@MSN.COM ■ WWW.ALICEVANLEUNEN.COM

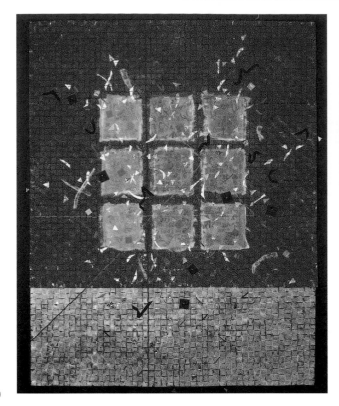

320

Top left: *Ain Soph Aur: Limitless Light*, 2005, woven paper with paint, metallic foil, fabric, stitchery, and collage, 40" x 32". Top right: *Log Cabin Study IV*, 2004, woven paper with paint, metallic foil, fabric, and collage, 23" x 22". Bottom left: *Book of Days*, 2005, woven paper with paint, iridescent metallic foil, fabric, collage, stitchery, and mother-of-pearl, 48" x 40". Bottom right: *Makura No Sōshi: Pillow Book*, 2005, woven paper with paint, metallic foil, fabric, stitchery, collage, beads, and dichroic glass, 48" x 40".

ALICE VAN LEUNEN

VAN LEUNEN STUDIOS ■ 9025 SE TERRACE VIEW COURT ■ AMITY, OR 97101 ■ TEL 503-835-7717 ■ FAX 503-835-7707
E-MAIL AVANLEUNEN@MSN.COM ■ WWW.ALICEVANLEUNEN.COM

321

Log Cabin III, 2005, woven paper with paint, fabric, collage, and stitchery, 40" × 32".

Career-building Projects:
Commissions Generated Through GUILD Sourcebooks

JOAN SCHULZE
Gateway Scrolls, 1999
Mixed-media fiber
72"H x 24"W; 96"H x 24"W; 120"H x 24"W
Spieker Properties, San Jose, CA

Anytime you have a successful project to show clients, it gives you a better chance of being selected for their commission. I have a very productive relationship with Travis White of White Sheff Associates, which has placed many of my prints. He used a tearsheet from *GUILD 13* to show to representatives from Spieker Properties how my scrolls could be oriented vertically to fit the space they had in mind.

I kept the feeling and color scheme of my earlier scrolls for this commission, although they changed a bit during execution. The space was dramatic and could accept bold accents, so I altered the scale. We also had to anticipate the challenge of airflow across the open lobby. My solution, which worked well, was to weight the scrolls by slipping pieces of archival mat into hidden pockets.

322

My GUILD pages chronicle the development of my work over time. I get many calls about the page with my scrolls, and I always send visuals of the *Gateway Scrolls* when responding. As a result, I've received several commissions for similar pieces through other consultants.

Photograph: Sharon Risedorph.

JOYCE LOPEZ
Quiet in Red, 2000
French thread, chromed steel
31" x 31" x 1"

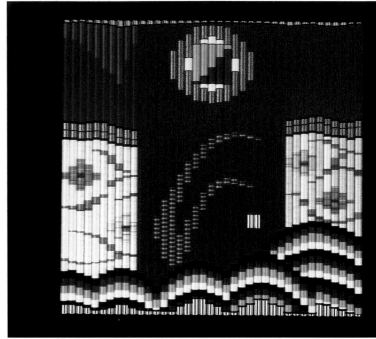

Photograph: Mark Belter.

When the letter from China arrived, inviting me to exhibit my work in a tapestry exhibition called *From Lausanne to Beijing*, I couldn't imagine how representatives would have seen my work. It wasn't until months later that I learned they had found it in a GUILD Sourcebook.

Feeling honored and very surprised, I decided to send *Quiet in Red*, the design of which is based on Japanese kimonos. Although it is not tapestry, my work has a similar feeling and appears both traditional and contemporary. I think this, along with my use of chromed steel, intrigued the curators.

For the opening in Beijing, I was hosted by an extraordinary group of people from Tsinghua University's fiber department, who staged a fabulous show with a beautiful catalog. Thanks to THE GUILD, it was the experience of a lifetime. Through contacts made in China, I was also invited to exhibit in Latvia in 2001. Being part of the international art community has been an amazing experience. I have made connections with many people with whom I share only the language of art, which always speaks from the heart.

BARBARA WEBSTER

STARFOREST QUILTS ■ 1610 LICKSKILLET ROAD ■ BURNSVILLE, NC 28714 ■ TEL 828-682-7331 ■ FAX 828-682-7987 (CALL FIRST)
E-MAIL BARBARA@STARFORESTQUILTS.COM ■ WWW.STARFORESTQUILTS.COM

323

The Chimneys, Great Smoky Mountains National Park, 100% cotton fabric printed with a dyejet printer, machine pieced, hand appliquéd.
Machine quilted by Rachel Reese, 53" x 70". Photograph: Tom Mills.

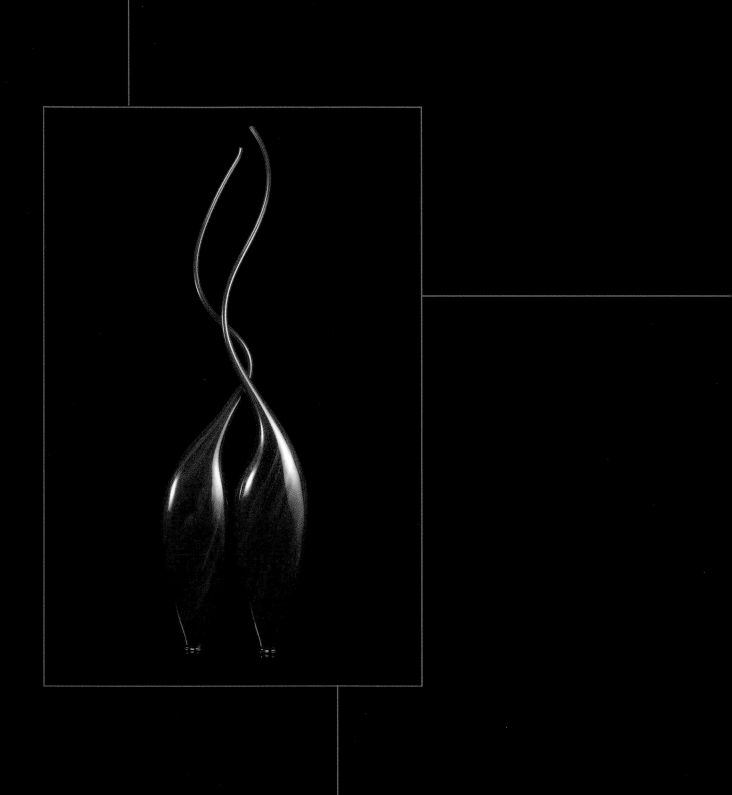

Resources

The Custom Design Center
A Project of GUILD.com

GUILD Sourcebooks give architects, designers, and art consultants the essential tools to find and commission original works of art. Within these pages you can find photographs showing a range of products, media, and art forms, as well as contact information so that you can connect directly with the artists who offer them.

But GUILD offers another avenue to find hundreds more artwork options: the Custom Design Center, an online complement to GUILD's paper-and-ink sourcebooks. Best of all, it's free to use!

Available through the GUILD.com website, the Custom Design Center features additional images of work by artists who have advertised in this sourcebook and others. In addition to artwork appropriate for corporate, public, and liturgical spaces, the Custom Design Center also features hundreds of unique residential pieces.

USE GUILD'S CUSTOM DESIGN CENTER TO:

- Search for the perfect work of art by art category, medium, or artist's name
- Post your project specifications to hundreds of artists through our online form
- Create an online presentation for a client by saving images or links
- Get help from one of our trade sales consultants by e-mail or phone

Visit the GUILD Custom Design Center at **www.guild.com/cdc**, or call 877-344-8453 to discuss your idea with one of our consultants. They can recommend candidates for a specific job, assess the qualifications of individual artists, or help draft letters of agreement.

Above: Jeff Smith, *The Five Books of Moses*, Washington Hebrew Congregation, Washington, DC. Photograph: Anice Hoachlander.

ARTIST STATEMENTS

The pages that follow provide important information on the artists featured in *The Sourcebook of Architectural & Interior Art 20.* ■ Listings in the Artist Statements section are arranged alphabetically according to the heading on each artist's page. These listings include their contact information as well as details about materials and techniques, commissions, collections, and more. References to past GUILD sourcebooks are also included, so that you can further explore the breadth of a particular artist's work. Each listing includes a reference to the artist's page within the book. ■ As you explore *The Sourcebook of Architectural & Interior Art 20*, use the Artist Statements section to enrich your experience. If something intrigues you while perusing the sourcebook—a shape, a form, an exotic use of the commonplace—we hope you'll give the artist a call. Serendipity often leads to a wonderful creation.

Favorite Images from the Past:
A GUILD Sourcebook Retrospective

Photograph: J. Wadian Photography

Kevin Robb
Shibumi
Upper Iowa University
Fayette, IA
Published in *Architect's 13*

ARTIST STATEMENTS

SUSAN AHREND
Architectural Ceramics, Mosaics & Wall Reliefs
Page 56

I began Cottonwood Design in 1987, specializing in bas-relief patterned tiles for kitchens and baths. Since 2000, I have focused on creating tile murals for residential, commercial, and public environments. I work in the traditional *cuerda seca* (dryline) technique with color palettes ranging from vibrant, full-color transparencies to soft, warm mattes. Within each palette I mix and play with the glazes to give my work a painterly or watercolor appearance. Frequent designs include florals, *plein air* landscapes, animals, and sea life. My murals can be found throughout California, enhancing kitchens and baths and enlivening once-sterile hospital corridors. They have also been used as fundraisers for nonprofit organizations.

COMMISSIONS: Vista Grande Elementary School, 2004, Palos Verdes, CA; Los Angeles Orthopedic Hospital, 2000, Los Angeles, CA; American Heart Association, 2000, Irvine, CA; Rancho Los Alamitos, 1998, Long Beach, CA; Barlow Respiratory Hospital, 1999-2005, Los Angeles, CA

AIRWORKS, INC.
Atrium Sculpture
Page 84

The works we have created over a span of more than thirty years have been primarily influenced by aerial and atmospheric themes. As an artist team we have installed many large-scale commissions both nationally and internationally for public spaces and corporate buildings. We strive to make works that have a voice and character that uplift and reflect the positive aspects of human vision. We work with the client to develop integrated solutions for a unique proposal. We refine the ideas through three-dimensional modeling to fit the work with the interior architecture or exterior site.

COMMISSIONS: Washington Metro Area Transit Authority, DC, 2004; Iowa City Library, IA, 2004; San Diego Port Authority, CA, 2004; McGraw/Hill Companies, London, 2003; AstraZeneca Pharmaceuticals, Wilmington, DE, 2003

GUILD SOURCEBOOKS: *Architect's 13, 14, 15; Architectural & Interior Art 16, 17, 19*

MARY LOU ALBERETTI
Architectural Ceramics, Mosaics & Wall Reliefs
Page 57

Throughout my career as a sculptor, I have lived, taught, and studied the architecture of Spain, Italy, France, and Ireland, looking for clues and insight from the fragments left behind. My creative impulse and curiosity has found expression in clay sculptural reliefs . . . a fusion of classical features that capture the light, textures, and colors of ancient walls, arches, and other architectural forms from history and my imagination. Through these multi-layered works, I seek to evoke the depth and mystery of the human experience. My works are freestanding or wall-hung in individual or multiple groupings and are designed for residential and corporate settings. Original works are available, and commissions are welcomed.

COLLECTIONS: Mint Museum of Art, Charlotte, NC; HBO World Headquarters, NYC

EXHIBITIONS: Currier Museum of Art, Manchester, MA

GUILD SOURCEBOOKS: *Designer's 14, 15; Architectural & Interior Art 16, 17, 18, 19*

AMERICAN INDUSTRIAL ARTS/ JACK DEMUNNIK
Art for the Wall: Mixed & Other Media
Page 288

My "Mythical Patterns" evolved from patinaed, hardwood patterns handcrafted at the Beloit Ironworks' papermaking machine complex from the mid-19th through the 20th century. Pushed aside by the techno-laser era, these haunting icons represent an incredible blend of American craftsmanship and historic industrial ingenuity. Hundreds of thousands of these patterns, now serve as an archeological treasure trove. I am honored to create new purposes for these unique industrial artifacts. These new forms, or "machinas," seem to build themselves. Patterns "speak out" as obvious tails or heads or wingspans and, once joined together, emerge as animate objects. The pieces are in pairs, and evoke a call to symmetry and balance. Each pattern was originally color-coded, and many are adorned with engraved tin labels. The patinas form an incredibly rich and vibrant palette requiring little supplementation. The fusion of symmetry/color, historic context/contemporary design, and industrial precision/mythical animation work together to honor a proud American heritage while forging ahead towards new horizons. For a virtual tour, visit www.AmericanIndustrialArts.com.

ARCHIFORMS
Art for the Wall: Metal
Page 275

For the past thirty years we have worked with galleries, agents, architects, designers, and individual clients creating site-specific works for corporate, public, and residential spaces. These works for the wall, floor, or pedestal, many placed in large indoor and outdoor sites, range in scale from 3' to 24'. Prices begin at $4,000.

RECENT PROJECTS: Pfizer Corporation, Ann Arbor, MI; Cobo Hall Convention Center, Detroit, MI; St. Mary's Hospital, Saginaw, MI; St. Joseph Medical Center, Grand Rapids, MI; Huron Valley/Sinai Hospital, Commerce, MI; School for the Performing and Visual Arts, Detroit, MI; Comerica Park, Detroit, MI; Dearborn Community and Performing Arts Center, Dearborn, MI

COLLECTIONS: Detroit Institute of Arts; Daimler Chrysler Corporation; Ford Motor Corporation; General Motors Corporation; Hyatt Corporation; Compuware Corporation; Dow Chemical; Blue Cross/Blue Shield; Nikko Corporation; Shell Oil Corporation

ART ON A GRAND SCALE
Murals & Trompe L'Oeil
Pages 220-223

Richard Solomon's "Art on a Grand Scale™" is a unique showcase for the work of today's most sought-after artists, muralists, and emerging stars. Our new agency division is designed as a one-stop shop for fine art digitally reproduced on a grand scale. It's a concept that lets art buyers commission, reproduce, and apply fine art to any space, at record speed and budget-conscious cost. With over 100 prestigious awards, our artists are accustomed to working collaboratively with a design team, from client to architect and installation crew. Our team guides each client through the entire process, from selecting an artist to recommending fabrication and installation experts. Whether the project is a monumental work for a hotel lobby or an identifying design for a chain of restaurants, "Art on a Grand Scale™" can create art that transforms any space from mundane to memorable.

ARTIST STATEMENTS

A. E. TED AUB
Public Art
Page 96

Public commissions are an important aspect of my artistic endeavors. Among my commissioned works are historic monuments that pay homage to the women's rights movement. In pieces such as these I have sought to incorporate messages and symbolism without overly sentimentalizing the subject matter, though I find a certain level of romanticization appropriate. I seek creative ways to draw viewers into the process of looking and participating in the meaning of a work by making history more relevant. The cast bronze works have a traditional appeal, but are also a product of our time.

RECENT PROJECTS: *Elizabeth Blackwell, M.D.*, Hobart and William Smith Colleges, Geneva, NY; *When Anthony Met Stanton,* Seneca Falls, NY; *Paraiso Invierno,* Village of Merrick Park, Coral Gables, FL; *No Bird Soars Too High,* Nazareth College, Rochester, NY

BSK DEVELOPMENT
Representational Sculpture
Page 170

We strive to create lasting sculpture characterized by strong form, careful detailing, and harmonious siting. Grounded by years of experience in commercial and fine arts applications, we approach a project from multiple perspectives. We continue to work both representationally and non-representationally, creating commissions for public spaces and private locations.

RECENT PROJECTS: Westerville Firemen's Memorial, Westerville, OH

COMMISSIONS: Owner's Suite, Great American Ballpark, Cincinnati, OH; St. Mary's Hospital, Huntington, WV; Children's Hospital, Cincinnati, OH; Wheeling Health and Wellness Center, Wheeling, WV; Turley Park, Carbondale, IL; Indiana University Library, Fort Wayne, IN

COLLECTIONS: Columbia Pictures; Disney; Dream Works; 20th Century Fox; Lucas Film Ltd.; Universal Studios; Warner Brothers Studios

GUILD SOURCEBOOKS: *Architectural & Interior Art 19*

LAURIE BRECHEEN BALLARD
Representational Sculpture
Page 171

I have prepared for this work my entire life. I have always been fascinated by athletic form, from the flicker of a young thoroughbred's ear to the subtle distinctions between the 120 and 140 Jaguar Drophead Coupes. I've studied anatomy by riding hundreds of horses in varied disciplines, stitching up ranch dogs shredded by Javelina, and wrapping the legs of my polo horses. My mother and Cherokee great-grandfather will always be remembered for their exceptional abilities in communicating with animals. I hope I have inherited this. I have great respect and empathy for animals' fear, courage, and inherent grace. Animals show us the best in ourselves, the essence of our being. Sculpture brings me great joy. Thank you for your interest in my work.

MICHAEL BAUERMEISTER
Non-Representational Sculpture
Page 126

I think of these tall vessels as figures. As such, I'm interested in their personalities and how they relate to one another. These vessels are made from cabinet-grade hardwoods and are finished with lacquer so they will not warp or crack. Most range in price from $1,000 to $3,000.

EXHIBITIONS: Smithsonian Craft Show, 2003, 2002, Washington, DC; Wood Turning Invitational, 2000-2003, American Art Co., Tacoma, WA; Turned Wood Invitational, 2002, 1999, 1998, Del Mano Gallery, Los Angeles, CA; Nuances d'ete, 2001, Carlin Gallery, Paris, France

AWARDS: 25th Annual Contemporary Crafts Purchase Award, 2003, Mesa Arts Center, Mesa, AZ; Best of Wood, 2002, American Craft Exposition, Evanston, IL; Niche Award, 2002; Award of Excellence, 2000, American Craft Council, Baltimore, MD

PUBLICATIONS: *Wood Art Today,* 2003; *Scratching the Surface,* 2002; *Object Lessons,* 2001; *American Craft,* June 1995

GILBERT BEALL
Representational Sculpture
Page 172

My mother and grandmother were artists. I can remember making small sculptures with my mother before I was of school age. My work is realistic figurative sculpture with a specialty in portrait sculpture. Through the use of accents and shadow, my sculpture has movement and represents the personality of the subject. I work quickly, so I have never missed a deadline. My sculpture has been collected by churches, corporations, individuals, universities, and government agencies.

RECENT PROJECTS: Eight-foot bronze of *The Rancher* for a private collection; bronze bas-relief for the east wall of Darryl Royal Stadium, University of Texas, Austin; bronze bas-relief of Baseball Hall of Fame recipient Willie Wells for the State of Texas, Texas State Cemetery, Austin.

BEAR CREEK GLASS
Architectural Elements
Page 74

After earning a Master of Science degree from Ohio State University, I worked as an engineer and businessman for twenty years. I then took a course at the world famous Pilchuck Glass School that would change my life. After the first day, I knew my future was in glass art. I returned home and built a glass studio that enabled me to pursue my passion. My main focus is creating functional art that can be used and enjoyed. My lavatories and chandeliers have won critical acclaim, have been featured in numerous local and national publications, and are enjoyed in homes and businesses across the country.

ARTIST STATEMENTS

CHRIS BENNETT
Public Art
Pages 97, 194

I specialize in classically rendered sculptures of human figures, animals, and wildlife. Works include more than fifty public works of art for parks, colleges, liturgical settings, memorials, corporate headquarters, hospitals, and private residences. Each design is personal and poignant to present a poetic and enduring perspective of those commemorated or of the idea portrayed. Site-specific works relate to and inspire the community of origin. I have successfully worked in collaboration with architects and other professionals to implement large-scale designs and site developments. All budgets are accommodated; recent projects have ranged from $25,000 to $250,000.

RECENT PROJECTS: Military Memorial, Ames, IA; Iowa Events Center, Des Moines, IA; Riverside Park, Elgin, IL

COMMISSIONS: *Street Scape Project*, Clinton, IA; Upper Iowa University, Fayette; Des Moines Area Community College, Ankeny, IA

COLLECTIONS: Various private collections

EXHIBITIONS: Kavenaugh Gallery, 2005, West Des Moines, IA

AWARDS: Pollock-Krasner Foundation grant, 1999

SANDRA CHRISTINE Q. BERGÉR
Non-Representational Sculpture
Pages 21, 127, 152

Glass design for specific locations is my passion. Thirty years of experience proves that whether I create unique two-dimensional installations or limited-edition sculptures, I am captivated by glass art for any application. I bring contemporary style to the timeless material of glass for corporate, commercial, residential, and retail environments with precision engineering and skillful execution. I provide effective responses to projects of any scale, with timely worldwide service and delivery.

RECENT PROJECTS: *Towers of Glass,* limited edition; Bird of Freedom, Liberty Museum, Philadelphia, PA

COMMISSIONS: Concert Theatre, Minot, ND; Tanforan Business Center, San Francisco, CA; White House, Washington, DC; Thermo King Corporation, Minneapolis, MN; other public and private commissions

PUBLICATIONS: *Designing Interiors* textbook; *Women in Design International; Facets Magazine*

GUILD SOURCEBOOKS: *THE GUILD 1, 2, 3, 4, 5; Architect's 6, 7, 8, 10, 11, Architectural & Interior Art 16, 17; Designer's 8, 11, 13, 14, 15; Artful Home 1*

CHARLOTTE BIRD
Art for the Wall: Fiber
Page 306

Cadenced stories come alive in colorful textile works for public or private spaces. English and Spanish images and language enchant children of all ages and the adults who love them. My lifelong studies of color, pattern, and anthropology turn children's stories, rhymes, and poetry into vivid, intimate, touchable art. I have been featured on "Telling Stories with Tomie de Paola" on the Odyssey channel and "The Carol Duvall Show" and "Simply Quilts" on HGTV. Commissions are welcome. Prices range from $100-$250/square foot.

COLLECTIONS: Neutrogena; Luce Forward; Del Thomas Contemporary Quilt Collection; various private collections

EXHIBITIONS: *Quilt Visions,* 2004, San Diego, CA; John Wayne Airport, 2004, Santa Ana, CA; Rocky Mountain Quilt Museum, 2003, Golden, CO; Children's Museum of San Diego (Museo de los Niños), 2002, CA

GUILD SOURCEBOOKS: *Architectural & Interior Art 19*

BRUCE R. BLEACH
Art for the Wall: Mixed & Other Media
Page 289

I work independently as an artist, teacher, and part-time musician. My career as a fine artist spans 28 years. My work includes etchings and monoprints, paintings, and large wall sculpture in etched bronze, aluminum, and wood. Listed in the *Who's Who in American Art*, my work has appeared in numerous solo and group exhibitions, galleries, publications, and collections throughout the country and abroad. Two of my etchings have recently been selected by the Smithsonian Institute, Library of Congress Print Collection.

COMMISSIONS: Johnson & Johnson; Xerox headquarters; Lucent Tech.; IBM; Dupont; British Airways; Pfizer; Intel; Lockheed Martin; AOL; The World Bank; Motorola; Hyatt; RCA Americom

COLLECTIONS: Merrill Lynch; Bristol-Meyers; Blue Cross Blue Shield; Hilton Hotels; World Business Council, DC; General Electric; MCI; Trump Tower; Empire State Building; World Trade Center; General Foods World Headquarters; Sheraton Hotels; Radisson Hotels; Yamaha World Headquarters

RITA BLITT
Non-Representational Sculpture
Pages 128-129, 274

My work celebrates nature, my love of music, dance, and the spontaneous flow of movement captured in the drawn gesture. My monumental, pedestal and wall sculptures, drawings and paintings are in public and private collections and museums worldwide, including Australia, Germany, Israel, Japan, Singapore, Taiwan, and many states in the U.S.

Rita Blitt: The Passionate Gesture (2000, RAM Publications), my website www.ritablitt.com, and the videos *dancing hands: Visual Arts of Rita Blitt* and *Caught in Paint* (a collaboration with the Parsons Dance Company) are all award winners.

EXHIBITIONS: Florence Biennale, 2005; Ezair Gallery, 2005, New York, NY; Marion Meyer Contemporary Art, 2005, Laguna Beach, CA; 4 Star Gallery, 2005, Indianapolis, IN; Walton Arts Center, 2006, Fayetteville, AR; Jacqueline Casey Hudgens Center for the Arts, 2006, Atlanta, GA

KATHY BRADFORD
Architectural Glass
Page 27

Sandblasting, carving, and etching remain the major forces in my art glass. Over twenty years I have created many unique techniques to achieve imagery not found anywhere else. Much of my work is imagery derived from nature. In the last few years I have combined etched and sandcarved design with independent laminated elements such as dichroic and sandblasted flashed glass. These contemporary compositions are unique, whimsical, energetic, and powerful. I continually work with architects, designers, and contractors to ensure successful installations in many locations throughout the country. See other GUILD publications for examples of realistic nature scenes as well as contemporary works.

RECENT PROJECTS: Northwest Medical Center, Oro Valley, Tucson, AZ; Oakhill Park Warming House, St. Louis Park, MN; St. Patrick's Catholic Church, Sidney Nebraska; Aurora Firehouse #3, Aurora, CO

GUILD SOURCEBOOKS: *Architect's 12, 13, 14, 15; Architectural & Interior Art 16, 17, 18, 19*

ARTIST STATEMENTS

BRIAN RUSSELL STUDIO
Non-Representational Sculpture
Pages 130, 162

I create works that will live harmoniously in the world as independent functionaries of society. I draw inspiration from forms and rhythms in nature, the human body, ancient artifacts, mathematics and science, distilling these influences into abstract points of intersection. My aim on a public scale is to involve the viewer, to interject into the world points of beauty, interest and spontaneity. I want people to use my sculpture as an excuse to mentally shift to another level of consciousness, above the daily hubbub, even for a moment, and to reconnect with themselves via that primal, emotional, cortex-controlled spasm of an encounter with an unexpected oasis in a visual desert.

COLLECTIONS: Cafesjian Museum, Minneapolis, MN; Rhodes College, Memphis, TN; Tennessee State Museum, Nashville

EXHIBITIONS: Solo exhibitions at Eleonore Austerer Gallery, Palm Desert, CA, 2005; Tobin Hewett Gallery, Louisville, KY, 2005; Jerald Melberg Gallery, Charlotte, NC, 2004; David Lusk Gallery, Memphis, TN, 2005

NICHOLAS BRUMDER
Architectural Metal
Pages 72, 75

I have been designing and producing hand-wrought ornamental and sculptural metalwork since 1972. Working in collaboration with clients, architects, designers, and artists from a variety of disciplines, I offer design services including drawing, model making, and sample work. Brochure and references are available upon request. Through apprenticeship and studies, I have joined traditions of craftsmanship traceable to the Middle Ages. Perhaps the greatest service I can offer is the development of design and craft to suit the clients' application. My body of work shows a breadth of style, period, and technique. I love to explore the crafts past, present, and future. I work primarily in steel and bronze.

CARL & SANDRA BRYANT
Architectural Ceramics, Mosaics & Wall Reliefs
Page 58

We are a mosaic artist team that uses vitreous and stained glass, ceramic, and semi-precious stones to create beautiful art that will last indefinitely. We love the medium for its durability, resistance to graffiti, ability to withstand all kinds of weather, and its suitability to so many settings. Mosaics can add unique style and color as both indoor fine art and outdoor installations. It's wonderful the way a piece will change as the glass absorbs the light that plays across its surface.

EXHIBITIONS: *A More Perfect Union: Mosaic Aspirations*, 2005, Ellipse Gallery, Arlington, VA; *Madonnas and Mosaics*, 2005, Arts of Snohomish, WA; *Opus Veritas: Fragments of Truth*, 2004, Museo ItaloAmericano, San Francisco, CA

332

LAURA MILITZER BRYANT
Art for the Wall: Fiber
Pages 204, .307

I create richly layered and detailed complex double weaves of wool, rayon, nylon, and Lurex. All threads are hand-painted and dyed by me with high-quality light-fast dyes. Enhanced by patinated copper backings or floating on a wall, these landscape-inspired geometric images provide an enticing environment for home or office.

RECENT PROJECTS: Northrup Grumman IT Headquarters, McLean, VA

AWARDS: Recipient of the NEA and Florida State Artist grants

GUILD SOURCEBOOKS: *Designer's 10, 11, 12, 13, 14, 15; Architectural & Interior Art 16, 17, 18, 19*

FRAN BULL
Paintings & Prints
Page 234

My art has been exhibited in the United States and abroad for several decades. Recently I had two exhibitions of etchings in Plsen, Czech Republic, where I conducted art workshops at the University of West Bohemia. I work in a variety of media including painting, printmaking, and performance art. Most recently, as a set designer, I created a series of murals for a production of the opera Carmen. I travel each year to Barcelona where I make etching editions in the famed studio of master printer Virgili Barbara, a place where Picasso, Miro and others have also worked.

AWARDS: The American Institute of Graphic Arts, the New Jersey Council on the Arts, and the New Jersey Printmaking Association.

COLLECTIONS: The Museum of Modern Art, The National Museum of Women in the Arts, Princeton University, and Johnson and Johnson Corp.

PUBLICATIONS: *Photorealism* by Louis K. Meisel.

MYRA BURG
Art for the Wall: Fiber
Pages 23, 290, 308

Somewhere between tapestry and jewelry, my "quiet oboes" and sculptural installations adorn space in a free-floating, peaceful way. Hand-wrapped fiber and burnished metals are combined to create inspired sculptural pieces that meet clients' needs and wants within the requirements of the space. The bigger the challenge, the more the fun. Collaborations are welcome.

RECENT PROJECTS: *Japonaise*, Universal Studios, Japan; *Galactic Curve*, Universal Studios, Japan; *Quiet Oboes*, Caribé Hilton, Puerto Rico; Travelocity, Dallas, TX

EXHIBITIONS: SOFA, Chicago; Los Angeles County Museum of Art, CA; Howard Hughes Center, Los Angeles, CA; Orange County Museum of Art, CA

AWARDS: First place, 2002, *Artfest of Henderson, NV*; first place, 2001, 1999, 1998, *Beverly Hills Affaire in the Gardens*, CA

GUILD SOURCEBOOKS: *Designer's 10, 13, 14, 15; Architect's 14, 15; Architectural & Interior Art 16, 17, 18, 19; Artful Home 1, 2, 3*

ARTIST STATEMENTS

MYRA BURG & LIZ CUMMINGS
Art for the Wall: Mixed & Other Media
Pages 23, 290

At long last, we have done it! We are now celebrating our collective fifty years of artistic experience by producing a whole new art form that begins on the wall and blooms, becoming spatial elements as well. Liz, with twenty-five years experience as an artist painting romantic architectural and scenic images, and Myra, recovering from the practice of architecture by creating wrapped fiber elements, have joined efforts in their respective specialties. We are combining lustrous oils on canvas, creating two-dimensional color fields that provide an environment for sumptuous wrapped fiber. The planar canvases and dimensional cylinders work in tandem, engaging one another in this brand new and highly versatile mixed-media format. Somewhere between the image and the imagination, these combinations give new life to the act of placing color in a living space.

RUTH BURINK
Representational Sculpture
Page 173

Stone is a truly beautiful and satisfying medium in which to work. I never force my sculptures; instead, I allow them to emerge gracefully from the magnificent stone. The abstract nature of my work engages the viewer, instigating a dialogue between art and viewer. I collaborate closely with clients to design and create original sculpture—from tabletop to monumental—that meets their needs. I usually carve directly in stone and often cast bronze from a stone original.

RECENT PROJECTS: Penrose Hospital, Colorado Springs, CO; St. Theresa Parish, Houston, TX

COLLECTIONS: St. Joseph Hospital, Denver, CO; Sammy Yu, Sidney, Australia; Loveland Arts Commission, Loveland, CO

EXHIBITIONS: Biennale Internazionale dell'Arte Contemporanea, Florence, Italy; Colorado Governor's Invitational

PUBLICATIONS: *Sculptural Pursuit Magazine*

GUILD SOURCEBOOKS: *Architectural & Interior Art 18, 19*

RIIS BURWELL
Non-Representational Sculpture
Pages 106, 131

The dynamic balance between order and chaos in nature serves as the inspiration for the abstract metal sculpture I create. Each piece, from wall sculpture to tabletop to large-scale work, is hand-fabricated. I primarily use bronze, steel and stainless steel for both indoor and outdoor sculpture. My work can be found in private and corporate collections within the United States and abroad.

COMMISSIONS: The District in Green Valley Ranch Resort, Henderson, NV; Suffolk Construction Company, Boston, MA; Hyatt Vineyard Creek Hotel Spa & Conference Center, Santa Rosa, CA; Burbank Airport Plaza, Burbank, CA

COLLECTIONS: Fresno Museum of Art, Fresno, CA; Kaiser Permanente, San Diego, CA; Hotel Vue Plage, La Baule, France; Williams Corporation, Tulsa, OK; SAS Institute, Inc., Cary, NC

EXHIBITIONS: Bronze in Paradise, 2004, Paradise Ridge Winery Sculpture Grove, Santa Rosa, CA

GUILD SOURCEBOOKS: *Architect's 13, 14, 15; Architectural & Interior Art 16, 17, 18, 19*

333

BARBARA CADE
Art for the Wall: Fiber
Pages 304, 309

Collectible rocks, luscious vegetation, textured trees, and dramatic skies: two- and three-dimensional sculptural landscape elements inspired by your geographic location, maybe using your favorite photograph. I use elements together or individually. I continue to be inspired by themes in nature, translating my photographs into tapestries of woven and felted wool, often incorporating other fiber techniques.

RECENT PROJECTS: Trip to Finland to study felt-making

COMMISSIONS: St. Luke's Hospital, 2003, The Woodlands, TX

COLLECTIONS: Weyerhaeuser Company, Tacoma, WA; Tacoma Art Museum, WA

EXHIBITIONS: One-person show, 2005, Arts & Science Museum, Pine Bluff, AR; Reality Check, 2001, Ohio Craft Museum, Columbus

AWARDS: Scholarship, 2004, Arkansas Committee National Museum of Women in the Arts

GUILD SOURCEBOOKS: *Designer's 8, 9, 10, 11, 12; Architectural & Interior Art 17, 18, 19; Artful Home 1*

TERESA CAMOZZI
Art for the Wall: Mixed & Other Media
Page 291

Inspiration for my work is drawn from a passion for ecological ideals. In collaboration with architects and art and design professionals, I create intimate to monumental scale commissions for hospitals, hotels and corporate collections. Combining nature photography, sculptural elements and painting, I am able to achieve a unique complexity that leaves a lasting impression. My process incorporates the use of polyresin sculptures imbedded with natural elements that are then superimposed over photo-covered wood panels. These photo panels are made permanent with encaustic wax, and then are complemented by oil painting. My desire is to draw interest to environmental concerns. I offer lectures regarding health and the environment, rebuilding our ecology, and living harmoniously with compassion for our planet.

COLLECTIONS: Four Seasons Hotels; Nemacolin Woodlands Resort, Farmington, PA; Fluor Daniel; Bellagio Hotel, Las Vegas, NV; Kaiser Permanente; Canon Corporation; Mills-Peninsula Health Services, Burlingame, CA

BOBBIE K. CARLYLE
Representational Sculpture
Pages 175, 184

I create monumental bronze sculptures that capture bold strength and provocative intelligence. My figures go beyond first impressions to challenge the intellect and cause the viewer to look within themselves for greater meaning. My work reflects my love of classic sculpture, while presenting a modern approach with its presentation and a psychological appeal for connection to the struggles and triumphs of life.

COLLECTIONS: University of North Carolina-Charlotte; Public Library, Pueblo, CO; City of Grand Junction, CO; City of Batavia, IL; Emir, Saudi Arabia; Lay Center, St. Louis University, Louisiana, MO; Columbus University, Picayune, MS; Manchester Grand Hyatt, San Diego, CA; City of Chinandega, Nicaragua; Westernbank, PR; MBI Institute, Austria

ARTIST STATEMENTS

KATHY CARTER
Liturgical Art
Page 200

For me every study, from theoretical physics to psychology, is a study in my relationship to God. These studies, together with my choice to follow Christ, inform my work. My inspiration comes from questions surrounding our concept of the physical universe and the nature of spirituality. I love working with light and with the figure, most commonly using clay or beads. Using transparent beadwork to 'paint' a picture seems appropriate because understanding the image is dependent on lighting and the viewer's position in relation to the work. My work is ephemeral, seemingly solid, but made up of particles that reflect, refract, and transmit light to produce an image that moves in its stillness. I like the idea of the viewer being aware of the image only in the right conditions, which seems to me an accurate reflection of our life experiences.

COMMISSIONS: Baptist Hospital, Nashville, TN; St. Thomas Hospital, Nashville, TN

EXHIBITIONS: The Renaissance Center, 2004, Dickson, TN; Faculty exhibition, 2000, Watkins Institute of Art & Design, Nashville, TN

334

WARREN CARTHER
Architectural Glass
Pages 6, 17, 28-29

Through glass, I explore light in varied ways, manipulating the quality of light as it is filtered through the translucent layers of my work. My respect and understanding of the structural capabilities of glass, combined with my interest in working sculpturally within the architectural environment, has lead me to produce unique work that crosses the boundaries between art and architecture. Innovative techniques in structure, abrasive blast carving, laminations, and color application distinguish my often large-scale work. Numerous commissions and publications throughout the world have helped me create a reputation for producing strikingly unique work for public and private spaces.

COMMISSIONS: Canadian Embassy, Tokyo, Japan; Swire Group, Hong Kong; Charles de Gaulle International Airport, Paris, France; Anchorage International Airport, AK

GUILD SOURCEBOOKS: *Designers 6, 15; Gallery 2; Architect's 6, 7 ,9 ,10 ,11 ,13 ,15; Architectural & Interior Art 16, 17, 18, 19; Commission 16*

JOSEPH L. CASTLE, III
Non-Representational Sculpture
Page 132

Pushing the contrast between dynamic energy and reflective contemplation, and exploring the nature in which they are defined, is the basis of my work. With minimal line, outside influences are removed and a forum for testing shade and the interconnectedness of inner spaces is discovered. My sculptures are kept purposefully simple, stripped of detail, and require exact attention to proportion. The sculptures are sensitive to the slightest alteration. This invites exploration from many angles, mimicking the juxtaposition of individual serenity and collective activity.

RECENT PROJECTS: 9/11 Project, Garden on the Rocks, Bellingham, WA

COMMISSIONS: Mr. Timothy Reynolds, 2004, Northfield, IL; Mr. John Sullivan, 2003, Chicago, IL

COLLECTIONS: The Secretary and Mrs. Donald Rumsfeld, Washington, DC; Mr. and Mrs. Thomas Reynolds, Northfield IL; Mr. Dean Hanley, Berkley, CA; Mr. John Fix, Chicago, IL

EXHIBITIONS: Group show, 2004, Tapestry Gallery, Sun Valley, ID; 2004, Absolute Gallery, Pasadena, CA; 2004, William Traver Gallery, Seattle, WA; 2004, Chestnut Hill Academy, Philadelphia, PA

CHARLES STRAIN SCULPTURE
Public Art
Page 98

I draw my imagery from nature and from life experience. The human figure and human emotions are the basis of my compositions. Happiness, sadness, a moment in time, a familiar experience, a celebration—these events and emotions serve as catalysts for my sculptures. My dedication, mastering of the lost wax method of casting bronze, and a "labor of love" approach to art-making, serve to transform each bronze into a timeless statement. My sculpture can be installed indoors or outdoors. I enjoy working with clients who have the creative vision to transform outdoor spaces into works of art. I accept commissions in a range of sizes and can install sculpture on bases, or in fountains or ponds.

COMMISSIONS: University of Florida, Gainesville, FL, 2003; City of Northville, Northville, MI, 2002; Westminster College, Fulton, MO, 2001; Northwestern College of Chiropractic, Bloomington, MN, 2001

L.T. CHEROKEE
Non-Representational Sculpture
Page 133

I have been expressing my vision of form for more than 20 years. My work in bronze, stone, wood, and fiberglass, combined with elements of water/mist, are represented at galleries internationally and are widely held in private collections. I am most renowned for my ability to breathe a gamut of emotions into the medium and for the subsequent impact on the living environment, bringing fluidity and substance together into graceful, lyrical forms. Pieces can be designed to site-specific requirements, integrating well with outdoor or indoor spaces. I prefer close collaboration with architects and designers to achieve optimal impact. Brochures are available.

COMMISSIONS: Terry Farrell Park, 2004, NY; Bald Hill Cultural Center, 2003, NY

COLLECTIONS: Art Mode, Ottawa and Calgary, Canada; Spinnato Gallery, NY

PUBLICATIONS: *New York Times*, 2003, 1999, 1998; *Art Business News*, 2001

GUILD SOURCEBOOKS: *Architect's 15; Architectural & Interior Art 16, Artful Home 2*

JEREMY CLINE
Non-Representational Sculpture
Pages 134, 324

My glasswork reflects my love for the medium, my fine craftsmanship, and an ongoing endeavor to better my working processes. I started working with glass in 1987 at Santa Monica College, and then furthered my education at the California College of Arts and Crafts and Pilchuck Glass School. In 1991 I apprenticed with Pino Signoretto, master glass artist, in Murano, Italy. I opened Incline Glass in 1992. My work examines the vessel as an art form, taking cues from the glass itself as well as from antiquity and contemporary sources. In addition to creating my own work, I also use my facility to produce pieces for other artists and designers, including custom lampshades for the lighting industry, Venetian-style stemware, sculptures, and various prototypes. I continue to expand my abilities, techniques, and methodology in pursuit of excellence in glass.

ARTIST STATEMENTS

CLOWES SCULPTURE
Atrium Sculpture
Pages 18, 85-86

We have been creating sculpture together for over thirty years. We design for healthcare, corporate, hotel, cruising, and academic settings as well as for private homes. We enjoy collaborating with clients, architects, designers, and art consultants and find the results to be a balanced solution of space and sculpture. In short, we are adept at developing site-specific designs. Our distinct shapes and flowing curves formed in wood, metal, or composite, contrast with the color and texture of blown glass, stone, and other materials. We intend our work to invoke the presence of serene seas, soft winds, and gracious gestures.

COMMISSIONS: White County Medical Center, Searcy, AR; Phelps Dunbar, Jackson, MS; Hope Hospice, Ft. Myers, FL; Pfizer, Groton, CT; Royal Caribbean International, Oslo, Norway; Tokyo Hilton Hotel, Tokyo, Japan; Indianapolis Museum of Art, Indianapolis, IN; Visalia Convention Center, Visalia, CA; Monadnock Paper Inc., Bennington, NH; Manchester District Courthouse, Manchester, NH; Antioch New England Graduate School, Keene, NH

GESSO COCTEAU
Representational Sculpture
Pages 176-177

I design sculpture for public, corporate, and private settings and I work with architects and designers. My work truly enhances and defines everything from architectural elements to wide open spaces. All technical, design, and installation issues are handled from start to finish by Cocteau Studios. Meeting deadlines and staying within budget is of utmost concern to us. We will deliver your project.

BRENT COLLINS
Non-Representational Sculpture
Page 135

I've been inspired to create sculpture of significant geometric originality, at once subtle in analytical rigor and seamless in organic coherency. This has given my work a mathematical dimension that has both special resonance for scientists and mathematicians and eloquent clarity accessible to lay audiences. Most moving of all has been the enthusiasm shown by schoolchildren. For work that is essentially an aesthetic expression of visual mathematics, dramatically engaging both schoolchildren and elite scientists is an achievement I'm proud of.

COMMISSIONS: American Association for the Advancement of Science, Washington, DC; Hyatt Regency Convention Center, Shanghai, China

COLLECTIONS: Yves and Helga Piaget, Paris, France

EXHIBITIONS: Cooper Union School of Design, 2000, New York, NY

AWARDS: Represented the United States at the UNESCO World Conference on Science: *Science in the Arts* exhibition, 1999, Budapest, Hungary

PUBLICATIONS: *Scientific American,* February 2000

335

J. GORSUCH COLLINS
Architectural Glass
Page 30

I produce works in leaded, fused, carved, cast, laminated, and beveled glass for corporate, public, and residential settings. Commitment to excellence and extensive dialogue with the client are distinguishing aspects of my work. Creative design solutions, often involving unique combinations of other materials with glass. A fresh approach to design and technique for each project can result in a complete departure from prior work.

RECENT PROJECTS: Kaiser Permanente Rock Creek, Lafayette, CO; Marriott Hotel, Denver, CO; cast glass bar top, Denver, CO; cast glass doors, Denver, CO; entry and surround, Colorado Springs, CO

COMMISSIONS: Berger Fund, Denver, CO; Hoffman Reilly Pozner & Williamson, Denver, CO; TeamMates, Denver, CO; Charles Schwab, Englewood, CO; Wells Fargo Building, reception wall piece, Denver; Avon Public Library, Beaver Creek, CO

PUBLICATIONS: *Architecture & Design of the West,* Spring 2004, Fall 2003; *Colorado Homes and Lifestyles,* August 2003; *The Art of Stained Glass,* 1998

GUILD SOURCEBOOKS: *THE GUILD 4, 5; Architect's 7, 8, 9, 10, 11*

JONATHAN COX
Non-Representational Sculpture
Pages 136, 166

My father gave me my first toolbox when I was four. He cleared the trees from the land that he bought from my grandmother and used them to build the house in which I was raised. Before I was fourteen, we had built five boats together. The process of creating my large-scale sculptures begins with wood and skills that I learned as a child. Then I add the materials that will best communicate the idea: marble, granite, bronze, clay, and polyester.

COMMISSIONS: Avampato Discovery Museum, Charleston, WV; Art Source L.A. for Western Assets Management Co., Pasadena, CA

COLLECTIONS: Huntington Museum of Art, WV; Marshall University, Huntington, WV; Dr. Susan C. Power; Ms. Jean M.K. Miller

AWARDS: Sasakawa Fellowship Award, 2005, American Association of State Colleges and Universities; West Virginia Individual Artist Fellowship, 2002, WV Commission on the Arts; Florida Individual Artist Fellowship, 1999, FL Department of State

GUILD SOURCEBOOKS: *Architectural & Interior Art 19*

DWAYNE S. CRANFORD
Furniture & Lighting
Page 210

My rock chairs have been compared to something found on the set of "The Flintstones," but great care is taken to ensure they are both aesthetically pleasing and comfortable. The stone added to discarded steel results in functional furniture inspired by Mother Nature. My furniture is built for public areas; not only is it vandal-proof, but it never requires any maintenance. I have built it to be extremely durable and withstand all weather conditions. An important advantage of my furniture is that it integrates easily into landscapes and cityscapes without intruding on the surrounding beauty.

COLLECTIONS: Old Town Fort Collins, CO; Red Feather Lakes, CO; Sedona, AZ

EXHIBITIONS: Aspen Art Show, 2004, CO; 2004, Telluride, CO; Fountain Hills, AZ; and Sedona, AZ; 2004, 2003, Lincoln Center, CO

PUBLICATIONS: *Log Home Design Ideas,* 2004; *Fort Collins Weekly,* 2003

ARTIST STATEMENTS

RENE CULLER
Art for the Wall: Mixed & Other Media
Page 292

I work with glass because absorbed light animates and enlivens my compositions. Many layers of color or pattern, created by fusing and slumping, yield dimension and dynamism. High-fire enamel painting, scrafitto, and line drawing embellish the surface and interior of the glass. I enjoy working with clients to create meaningful projects. Prices start at $1,000.

RECENT PROJECTS: Flaster Greenberg PC, Cherry Hill, NJ; Cleveland Clinic Intercontinental Suite Hotel, OH; The Blackwell Hotel, Columbus, OH

COMMISSIONS: Distinguished Service Award, Cleveland Orchestra, OH; Cuyahoga County Public Libraries multiple branches, OH

COLLECTIONS: The Renwick Gallery, Smithsonian Institution, Washington, DC

AWARDS: Ohio Arts Council Individual Fellowship Grant, 1998, 2005; Ohio Arts Council Professional Development Grant, 1999, 2000

PUBLICATIONS: *Women Working in Glass*, 2003; *International Glass Art*, 2003

GUILD SOURCEBOOKS: *Architectural & Interior Art 19*

336

DAVID B. DAHLQUIST
Public Art
Page 99

The emphasis of our work is the design and creation of artwork for public spaces. Through the understanding of a particular subject, history, or event, we develop concepts relevant to the people living and working in a given place and community. Our process combines insight with research and documentation. We represent a wide range of talents and expertise, orchestrating many different sculptural elements in a variety of materials: terra cotta, laser and plasma-cut steel, lighting, tile murals, epoxy-terrazzo, and more. Mindful of the "experience," we make meaningful connections between architecture and the landscape.

RECENT PROJECTS: Charlotte Convention Center, NC; Iowa Department of Transportation Art-In-Transit Program; St. James Church, Newport, CA

COMMISSIONS: Numerous installations since 1990, including collaborations/associations with other artists and design professionals

COLLECTIONS: Represented in over 50 corporate, public, and private collections nationally

PUBLICATIONS: *Public Art Review*, 2004; *Ceramics Monthly*, 2003; "Modern Masters," HGTV, 2003

DALE ROGERS STUDIO
Non-Representational Sculpture
Page 137

I believe in simple truths and enduring value. My work is an exercise in blending lines with contemporary flair. My sculpture is an extension of my theory that art can be both creative and highly functional. I prefer working with a variety of metals, including stainless steel, steel, and aluminum. These metals offer me the flexibility to design creative, high quality, and beautiful pieces that will last for many years to come. My work includes sculptures for the home and garden and fine furnishings, which are on display at fine galleries and included in private and corporate collections. My large sculpture has also found its place in public displays. I love to collaborate with individuals and organizations to add the classic yet cutting-edge look of metal to their homes, offices, and gardens. I have done many private commissions for homeowners across the U.S. and abroad.

COMMISSIONS: Aveda Haircare Training Center, 2001, Worcester, MA; Mizan Day Spa, 2001, Haverhill, MA; Glory Restaurant, 2002, Andover, MA

EXHIBITIONS: Somerby's Landing, 2004, Newburyport, MA; Essex Art Center, 2005, Lawrence, MA

ALLEN DAVID
Public Art
Page 100

Glass is the most sustaining and spiritual of all the media I have worked with as a painter, sculptor, and designer. The rich color and transparency of glass change with every variety of natural and artificial light. I respect and love the medium and strive for an inner vision that will give my glass sculpture its life and energy. The technique I have used combines laminated glass and Lucite to make the glass sculpture permanent and suitable for outdoor locations. Each new site is a challenge requiring an appropriate work that will enhance the space. Works of art enrich our cities and our lives.

COMMISSIONS: La Trobe University, Melbourne, AUS; Aldermanbury Square, City of London Corporation, UK; *The Magician*, Municipality of Tel Aviv, ISR; Burns, Summit, Rovins & Feldman, New York, NY

COLLECTIONS: Sir Roland Penrose, London, UK; Mrs. Margaret Carnegie, Melbourne, AUS

DAVID WILSON DESIGN
Architectural Glass
Pages 20, 24, 31

My work seeks to reinvent the ancient craft of stained glass and place it in the context of contemporary architecture as a visually integrated building component. Simplicity, restraint, changing light, projected image, and night view all inform design development. Together with architect and client, I encourage a reciprocal dialogue in a collaborative design process and offer, in association with WRW Studio LLC, a complete service of design, fabrication, and installation.

COMMISSIONS: College of Education Building, Rowan University, 2005, Glassboro, NJ; Fairlight Hall, 2005, Fairlight, East Sussex, U.K., St. John the Evangelist Catholic Church, 2004, Rochester, MN; St. Ignatius Chapel, University of Detroit Mercy, 2004, Detroit, MI

GUILD SOURCEBOOKS: *THE GUILD 1, 2, 3, 4, 5; Architect's 6, 7, 8, 9, 11, 13, 14, 15; Architectural & Interior Art 16, 17, 18, 19*

DARRELL DAVIS
Representational Sculpture
Page 178

Composition is what drives my work. After receiving a B.F.A. from the University of Texas at Arlington, I enrolled in the Graduate School of Architecture's landscape architecture program. My works can be seen in major exhibitions and collections throughout the U.S. and Mexico. Recently I have installed a life-size multi-figure commission for the City of Frisco, TX, and I am currently working on a sculpture of larger than life-size black bears for the Lincoln Park Zoo in Chicago, which will be installed in May 2005.

EXHIBITIONS: Birds in Art, 2004, at the Leigh Yawkey Woodson Art Museum, Wausau, WI; Society of Animal Artists Exhibition, Hiram Blauvelt Art Museum, Oradell, NJ; American Society of Marine Artists Exhibition, 2004, Vero Museum of Art, Vero Beach, FL; Wings of Hope, Wings of Peace, 2003, National Sculpture Society, New York, NY

COLLECTIONS: City of Gaithersburg, MD; Dallas Zoo, TX; City of Loveland, CO

PUBLICATIONS: "A Portfolio of Sculptors" *Southwest Art*, July, 2002; "Carved in Stone and Bronze and Steel and . . .," *Wildlife Art*, July/August, 2003

ARTIST STATEMENTS

PIA DAVIS
Fine Art Photography
Pages 258, 260

Capturing patterns and saturated colors on film has been a quest of mine for many years, particularly in floral images and landscapes. More recently, my exploration of art glass through a macro lens has yielded uniquely beautiful perspectives of glass and color, resulting in great richness and unusual, magical topographies. My photography is a labor of love. I am always in search of the beauty of nature; in the glass collection my mission is to capture nature as interpreted by man. I work with 35mm and medium format equipment. A self-taught photographer, I prefer shooting in natural light. Slides are scanned at high resolution, resulting in precisely rendered giclée prints, using archival materials. Various sizes are available. My work has been exhibited in Europe, the U.S., and Israel.

DORA De LARIOS
Architectural Ceramics, Mosaics & Wall Reliefs
Page 54, 59

The work shown in this book took 15 months to complete. The project was a challenge that became a crucible of all the knowledge I had accumulated about clay and, in particular, glaze technology. In order to attain the magnificent turquoise glaze, over 150 glaze tests were made. The mural was fired to C/10 2385 degrees Fahrenheit. I hired seven artists to complete the work. Their dedication and generosity of spirit is reflected in the final piece. The mural is a masterpiece.

COMMISSIONS: Montage Resort and Spa, 2003, Laguna, CA; Marriott Resort, 2000, Maui, HI; Bonaventure, 1997, Los Angeles, CA; Trammell Crow, 1993, Santa Fe Springs, CA

EXHIBITIONS: Lois Neiter Fine Art group shows with various themes, 2000-2004; solo exhibition, 2000, Japanese American Cultural & Community Center, Los Angeles, CA; several one-person exhibitions as well as group and juried exhibitions

BARBARA De PIRRO
Paintings & Prints
Pages 232, 235

Nature and its workings, its seasons, its weather and its manifestations in the world around us, deeply affect the ways in which we all live. I am fascinated with the overlapping patterns found in nature and human kind. We create in response to our environment both internal and external, so it shouldn't be a surprise to find organic influences in all cultural symbols and patterns. My art is a celebration of the inspiration, enlightenment and harmony that can be found simply by opening your eyes to your surroundings. Acrylic is my predominant medium; it allows me to create depth and texture within the many transparent layers. Looking into my paintings is very much like peering into a pool of water.

RECENT PROJECTS: Allenmore Medical Plaza, Tacoma, WA; Dayton Hudson, Chicago, IL

ANN DeLUTY
Representational Sculpture
Page 179

I strive to express the essence of natural objects in stone and wood. My work ranges from abstract to extremely realistic. My textures and carving techniques give an air of realism to any object. A graduate of the School of the Museum of Fine Arts, Boston, I am also known for my portraits of people and pets in bronze, clay, and cold-cast bronze. I have numerous works in private collections, and commissions are welcome. Because of the variety of colors available in alabaster, I can carve to match any color scheme.

RECENT PROJECTS: neon sculpture for dentist office, Lawrence, MA

GUILD SOURCEBOOKS: Architect's 15; Designer's 15; Architectural & Interior Art 16, 17, 18

JAMES F. DICKE II
Paintings & Prints
Page 236

A photographer from the age of five, I first painted at Culver Military Academy in 1963 under the late Warner Williams, a realist bas-relief artist. Later I studied with Nelson Shanks of Pennsylvania. My work has been heavily influenced by my fascination with nature, surfaces, and modern artistic materials. I believe that a work of art should engage your mind and draw you into its surface, sharing with the viewer the experience and wonder of the artist with the viewer's own experiences, curiosity, and exploration of ambiguity.

COLLECTIONS: Mandarin Hotel, 2004, Washington, DC; NASA, Washington, DC; Las Vegas Museum of Art; National Museum of American Art, Washington, DC; Long Beach Museum of Art, Long Beach, CA; Minster Bank, Minster, OH; Crown Equipment Corporation, New Bremen, OH; Eli Wilner Collection, New York, NY; Relocation Strategies, Inc., Cincinnati, OH; Congressman Lamar Smith; Senator Joe Tydings

JUDY DIOSZEGI
Atrium Sculpture
Pages 86-87

Since 1976, we have specialized in designing and fabricating banners, tapestries and mobiles for corporate, residential, liturgical and public spaces. Collaborating with architects, designers and individual clients, we produce site-specific creations that enhance environments through color, shape and attention to architectural surroundings. Materials range from richly textured fabrics in tapestries to durable, vibrant nylon for mobiles and atrium pieces. Projects are unique, and prices vary according to design and complexity. Inquiries are welcome.

AWARDS: Industrial Fabrics Association International: Award of Excellence, 2004; Outstanding Achievement Award, 2002; two Outstanding Achievement Awards, 2001; Design Award, 1998, 1994; Modern Liturgy Bene Award, 1996-97

GUILD SOURCEBOOKS: Architect's 8, 10, 12, 14; Architectural & Interior Art 17, 19

ARTIST STATEMENTS

JACOB DOBSON
Representational Sculpture
Page 180

"Edifying the lives of thousands" has been my charge since a young artist. It is my reward to create compelling work that benefits people's lives. By striving for sincerity and avoiding the predictable stale statue, the viewer is able to feel the figure's life. I enjoy finding the life I am asked to convey in a sculpture. My ability to weave anatomy and design with emotion was strengthened while receiving my M.F.A. from the New York Academy of Art. I specialize in bronze sculptures that include portrait, relief, animals, and monuments for both public and private spaces.

COMMISSIONS: Memorial Sculpture for Joshua Chamberlain, 2000.

EXHIBITIONS: 80th Annual Hoosier Salon, 2004, Indiana State Museum; Diploma Show, 2004, NYAA, New York, NY; "Parables" solo show, 2002, JFS Gallery, Laie, HI

AWARDS: Best Sculpture Award, Hoosier Salon, 2004

PHILIP S. DRILL
Non-Representational Sculpture
Page 138

I am intrigued by natural forms. My sculpture combines structural integrity with the sensual curvilinear grace of found natural objects, such as leaves, shells, or bone fragments. A walk in the woods, a stroll on the beach or a city street, and even the remains of a meal have served as catalysts for my designs. An engineer by training, I began my career as an artist working with welded metal. My interest in organic form led me to explore the expressive possibilities of more plastic media such as clay, wax, or plaster, then casting each sculpture in bronze, acrylic, or stainless steel. My work has been exhibited in juried exhibitions, one-man shows, art festivals, museums, and universities. To view more of my sculpture, please visit my website at www.psdrill.com. I welcome the opportunity to discuss commissions.

DWIGHT WILLIAM DUKE
Representational Sculpture
Page 181

My works do not tell a single story, but rather reveal a process of change or state of being. Each piece invites the viewer to consider their relationship to nature, art, time, and space. I enjoy exploring the tactile qualities of metal and the way surfaces interact with light. Through the application and removal of multiple layers, I can achieve these interactions and reveal to the viewer the process and struggle through which the work evolved. My work has been installed in many public spaces, private residences, and museums.

COMMISSIONS: *North, South, East, West,* 2001, Donner Trust, Hollywood, CA; *Artifacts,* 2003, Ojai Memorial Project, CA

COLLECTIONS: Lambiel Museum, Orcas Island, WA; Orcas Historical Museum, Orcas Island, WA; Bell Group, Monterey, CA; The Hemingways, Palm Desert, CA

338

JEROME R. DURR
Architectural Glass
Page 32

I have been designing, fabricating, and installing architectural glass artworks using the techniques of painting, etching, carving, slumping, fusing, and leading since 1973.

COMMISSIONS: National Baseball Hall of Fame, Cooperstown, NY; Carlisle Corporation, Syracuse, NY; Blair Academy, Blairstown, NJ; Christian Dior Retail; Lehman Bros., NYC

AWARDS: Best of Show, Atlanta Art Glass Guild; Best of Show, Cooperstown Art Open

PUBLICATIONS: Custom Home, 2000; Upstate Living magazine, 1997

GUILD SOURCEBOOKS: *THE GUILD 4, 5; Architect's 6, 7, 8, 9, 10, 14, 15; Designer's 6; Architectural & Interior Art 16*

SKIP DYRDA
Murals & Trompe L'Oeil
Page 225

My trompe l'oeil murals are intended to surpass expectations by including subject matter that individualizes the work, making it significant to the site. My vision for public art is to provide a piece that the community and its visitors can view, appreciate, and identify with. By including elements that symbolize the region and providing a visual commentary on its history, a mural can unify that vision.

RECENT PROJECTS: Two murals, Rosemary Beach, FL; two murals, Lake Mary, FL; thirteen custom-painted rugs, Lutz, FL

COMMISSIONS: Commercial Building mural, Sarasota, FL; Rivolta 90 custom yacht, Sarasota, FL; public buildings, Stuart and Sarasota, FL

COLLECTIONS: Mr. & Mrs. Dick Vital, FL; Rivolta Group, USA, Italy; Mr. Jeno Paulucci, FL

PUBLICATIONS: *Sarasota Magazine,* 2002; *American Style,* 2003; *Style Magazine,* 2002, 2004; *Floorcloth Magaic,* 2001; Home & Garden TV (HGTV) *Modern Masters,* 2003, 2004

GUILD SOURCEBOOKS: *Architectural & Interior Art 16, 17, 18*

LEMYA EL SOPHIA
Paintings & Prints
Page 237

In my paintings texture is actually utilized—not simulated—to build up relief from the surface of the canvas. A work of art is a triple experience: visual, emotional and intellectual. Everything is understood in its essence, and the essential quality is expressed by the most effective degree of emphasis; in the case of my work, utilizing textural contours. There is nothing more personal than touching something with your hands, manipulating it, making it exact. It is my intimate connection with each of these paintings.

ARTIST STATEMENTS

KEN ELLIOTT
Paintings & Prints
Page 238

I am a landscape artist who focuses primarily on color and composition. My works are direct, showing the lessons of both the Impressionist and Modern schools. I work primarily in oils, pastels, and monotypes, and I reproduce some of my images as editioned giclée prints. My alternative method of making more original-looking giclées has attracted national attention.

COLLECTIONS: Coopers and Lybrand; Raychem; Hewlett Packard; Kaiser-Permanente; Panhandle Eastern; National Dairy Board; Pinnacol; First Data; Visa; Blue Shield; Hitachi; The David and Lucile Packard Foundation; Marriott Hotels

PUBLICATIONS: *Pastel Journal; New York Times on the Web; Artweek; U.S. Art*

GUILD SOURCEBOOKS: *Architectural & Interior Art 18*

BILL & SANDY FIFIELD
Furniture & Lighting
Page 211

We have worked together for over 38 years, at times collaborating, and at others, working on our separate projects in stained glass and wood.

Sandy: The intricacy in my stained glass is facilitated by my background as a jeweler and by my use of the copper foil method of construction. This is combined with my technique of beveling Dalles de Verre glass to produce a sculptural effect.

Bill: My work has been influenced by folk art from around the world. Over 95% of our work is commission. We love the challenge of new projects, incorporating wood and glass together or separately. Please visit www.macfifield.com to see more of our work.

EXHIBITIONS: Western Design Conference, 2004, Cody, WY

GUILD SOURCEBOOKS: *Artful Home 1, 2*

ROB FISHER
Atrium Sculpture
Pages 19, 88-89

I am an internationally recognized sculptor with commissions in Japan, Saudi Arabia, St. Thomas, VI, and throughout the U.S. Working primarily in stainless steel, aluminum, and light, I create pieces for private residences, corporations, hospitals, and public spaces. I am a Distinguished Fellow of the STUDIO for Creative Inquiry at Carnegie Mellon University and a member of the Board of Directors of the International Sculpture Center.

RECENT PROJECTS: University of Utah, Salt Lake City; Florida Atlantic University; Penn Stater Conference Center Hotel, State College, PA; Two West Liberty Building, Malvern, PA; Christ Hospital, Cincinnati, OH; WakeMed Hospital, Cary, NC

COMMISSIONS: International Arrivals Hall, Philadelphia International Airport, PA; National Education Association, Washington, DC; Harbor Branch Oceanographic Institution, Fort Pierce, FL; AstraZeneca Visitor Center, Wilmington, DE; Gateway Center, Columbia, MD; Booz Allen Hamilton, McClean, VA

GUILD SOURCEBOOKS: *Architect's 9, 11, 12, 13, 14, 15; Architectural & Interior Art 16, 17, 18, 19; Artful Home 1*

339

CAROL FLEMING
Non-Representational Sculpture
Page 139

Since 1988, I have been a full-time studio artist, selling large ceramic sculptures. I make nine-foot, slab-built stoneware columns and three-foot eggs of coiled clay. I specialize in site-specific projects, working with architects and private clients. My work includes fountains, seating, tables, and garden focal points. My artwork is durable and waterproof and will enhance any site.

RECENT PROJECTS: Stephens Lake Park, Columbia, MO

COMMISSIONS: River Port Commons, Magellen Health Services, St. Louis, MO; Daum Museum of Contemporary Art, Sedalia, MO; People's Project with Enterprise Sponsorship; BJC Children's Hospital; Creve Coeur Community Center; Maritz Inc., Fenton, MO

COLLECTIONS: Hilton Hotel, Dedham, Boston, MA; Andrew's Bar and Grill, La Quinta, CA; First Hawaiian Bank, Honolulu, HI; Central Institute for the Deaf, St. Louis, MO; numerous private collections

EXHIBITIONS: Udinotti Gallery, 2005, Scottsdale, AZ; solo exhibition, 2003, New Harmony Gallery of Contemporary Art, IN

STEVE FONTANINI
Architectural Elements
Page 76

I am a designer and builder of forged metalwork for home and business. My crew and I create architectural metalwork such as stair railings, gates, fireplace accessories and even furniture. Bronze, stainless steel, mild steel or aluminum can be forged, cast, machined, or welded into any shape or design. I will design items to fit your environment, taste, and style. My work is found throughout the US.

AWARDS: Silver award, 2002, National Ornamental & Miscellaneous Metals Association

PUBLICATIONS: *Teton Home* magazine, Spring/Summer 2003, Fall/Winter 2001-2002, premiere issue 2000; *Cowboys & Indians* magazine, January 2002, Summer 1996

MARILYN FORTH
Art for the Wall: Fiber
Pages 242, 310-311

My batik paintings light up a room with nature's wonder. Add natural foliage to the mix and inside merges with outside. I have exhibited for the past twenty years and have created paintings for corporate and residential clients. I have also taught fiber courses at Syracuse University.

Satisfied clients are a must for me. Photos of completed commissions are sent to the client for final approval. My art is light-fast, framed, and ready to hang.

GUILD SOURCEBOOKS: *Architect's 16, Designer's 6, 7, 9, 10, 11, 12, 13, 14, Architectural & Interior Art 16, Artful Home 2*

ARTIST STATEMENTS

JUDY FOWLER
Paintings & Prints
Page 239

My paintings are memories of places: the light, color, movement, thoughts and feelings of a specific time. They portray the harmonies and rhythms of color and forms that have the energy of life and encompass its joys and sorrows. I am interested in what makes colors work: how they move, how they interact, and especially what makes them sing and convey feelings. I investigate the way color and shape come together, overlap and stay apart. My work explores losing edges while maintaining the separateness of shape and color. I paint in layers, building them up until the colors make a harmonious whole that has depth and luminosity. Prices range from $2,000 to $4,000.

STEPHANIE GASSMAN
Murals & Trompe L'Oeil
Page 226

I create commissioned, site-specific paintings and wall reliefs. My work can be found in public, corporate, and residential environments around the U.S. I enjoy the challenge of making an original statement for a client or a community using a variety of materials. A diverse portfolio reflects my ability to handle both large and small projects while maintaining contemporary visual excitement. A commission list, slides, and pricing are available upon request.

RECENT PROJECTS: Mosaic panel on outside face of Marion County Public Library, Ocala, FL; wall relief for Florida A & M University, Tallahassee, FL, for the Art in State Buildings Program

GUILD SOURCEBOOKS: *Designer's 13, 14, 15; Architectural & Interior Art 16, 17*

GLASSIC ART
Architectural Glass
Pages 26, 33

True connoisseurs, collectors, curators, and the most discriminating buyers appreciate the outstanding quality of Glassic Art's creations—unique glass products developed from 23 years of experience. Our studio offers completion within deadlines, service beyond compare, and unique one-of-a-kind pieces that have been receiving rave reviews from investors and viewers for years. The "glassic art" created at the studio is a multi-dimensional medium in glass made by sandblasting, painting, welding, fusion, kiln-formed glass, metal, and bonding techniques. From fine art to functional, Our pieces are used for murals; bars and countertops; staircases; room dividers; entries; freeform sculptures; and floor, shower, and swimming pool tiles. The possibilities for projects are limitless.

340

GOLDSTEIN & KAPELLAS STUDIO
Atrium Sculpture
Pages 82, 90

We have collaborated with architects and designers for over twenty years on public, private, and corporate commissions of all sizes. Our site-specific sculptures and mobiles are lightweight, durable, and reflective. The kinetic pieces move gracefully and require minimal air currents to set them in motion.

COMMISSIONS: mobile for Sallie Mae Corporation, Reston, VA; mobile for California Department of Health Services, Richmond, CA; mobile for AstraZeneca, Wilmington, DE

COLLECTIONS: Fine Arts Museums of San Francisco, CA; Art Institute of Chicago, IL; Brooklyn Museum, NY; California Department of Health Services, Richmond, CA; AstraZeneca, Wilmington, DE; Sallie Mae Corporation, Reston, VA

EXHIBITIONS: Durka Chang Gallery, 2002, San Francisco, CA; Brauer Museum of Art, 2000, Valparaiso, IN; Museum of Contemporary Religious Art, 1998, St. Louis, MO

PUBLICATIONS: *Beyond Belief: Modern Art and the Religious Imagination,* 1998; *Reliquaries,* 1994

GUILD SOURCEBOOKS: *Architect's 7, 8, 10, 13, 14, 15*

LYNN GOODPASTURE
Public Art
Page 101

I design, fabricate, and install site-specific art, including large-scale clocks, for national and international clients. Working closely with architects and designers, I have created projects for diverse settings: hospitals, schools, transportation center, animal shelter, cruise ship. Projects include mosaic and architectural glass installations; clocks made of mosaic, glass, and metal. Because clocks demand precise planning and meticulous execution, I work with skilled teams of engineers and fabricators who are able to produce and install accurate timepieces that are also works of art. Public and private commissions welcomed.

COMMISSIONS: University of Chicago Comer Children's Hospital, IL, lobby clock, 2005; Los Angeles Cultural Affairs Department, CA, architectural glass, 2005; West Hollywood Fine Arts Commission's Urban Art Program, CA, tower clock, 2003; Good Samaritan Hospital, Puyallup, WA, mosaic mural and architectural glass, 2000; Royal Caribbean International Cruise Line, three mosaic murals, 2000; Glendale Transportation Center, CA, suspended clock, 1999

GUILD SOURCEBOOKS: *Architectural & Interior Art 17, 18*

JANE B. GRIMM
Architectural Ceramics, Mosaics & Wall Reliefs
Page 60

Texture, repetition of form, and subtle color variations are the themes of my handmade ceramic sculptures. The small sculptures are mounted on wood, while the large sculptures are installed directly on the wall. Freestanding sculpture and handmade tiles also are available.

COMMISSIONS: Lucent Technologies, Inc., San Carlos, CA; Temple Isaiah, Orinda, CA

COLLECTIONS: Nora Eccles Harrison Museum of Art, East Logan, UT; University of California—Berkeley Art Museum

EXHIBITIONS: *Subtraction & Addition: Ceramic Sculpture and Installation;* San Francisco Museum of Craft and Folk Art, CA; *The Chess Set,* 2005, Oakland Museum Sculpture Court, Oakland, CA

AWARDS: Award of Merit, 2004, Valley Sculpture; Award of Merit, 2000, 1999, 1994, California State Fair; ACGA Award, 1999; Murphy Fellowship, San Francisco Foundation, 1991

PUBLICATIONS: *Artweek,* July/Aug 2004, vol. 35; *American Art Collector,* 2004, vol. 1; *Art of Northern California,* 2003; *The Museum of California,* Summer 99, vol. 23, no. 3

ARTIST STATEMENTS

CHRISTOPHER GRYDER
Architectural Ceramics, Mosaics & Wall Reliefs
Page 61

The lineage of my hand-carved ceramic reliefs can be traced to the tradition of organically-inspired terra cotta architectural panels, which have formed the intricate facades of buildings around the world. My work reinterprets natural objects and processes into a new language of form. The tiles, suitable for both indoor and outdoor applications, have been installed in residential and corporate settings, including the headquarters of a corporate office in Ann Arbor, Michigan. My skills as an architect allow me to seamlessly integrate the unique needs of each client and space with my own artistic sensibilities. From the production of detailed study drawings and images to the creation of one-of-a-kind tiles, I have perfected a process that leads to artwork of extraordinary beauty.

COMMISSIONS: Kalina residence, 2005, St. Louis, MO; St. Joseph Mercy Hospital, 2004, Ann Arbor, MI; Edelstein residence, 2004, New York, NY

EXHIBITIONS: *Outrageous Home*, 2004, Hunterdon Museum of Art, Clinton, NJ

GUILD SOURCEBOOKS: *Artful Home 2*

MARK ERIC GULSRUD
Architectural Glass
Pages 16, 26, 34

Primarily site-specific, my commissions range internationally and include public, private, corporate, and liturgical settings. My media include custom hand-blown leaded glass; sand-carved, laminated and cast glass; handmade ceramic; stone; and carved wood. I encourage professional collaboration and am personally involved in all phases of design, fabrication, and installation. My primary concern is a sympathetic integration of artwork with environment.

GUILD SOURCEBOOKS: *GUILD 3, 4; Architect's 7, 8, 9, 10, 11, 12, 13, 14, 15; Architectural & Interior Art 16, 17, 18, 19*

SARAH HALL
Architectural Glass
Page 35

Art can open doors, illuminate the possible, and forge a connection with the spiritual. There is a point in every design project when all of the separate elements—material, intellectual, artistic, and spiritual—coalesce. The design takes on a life of its own and becomes a delicate bridge between ideas and feelings, physical thresholds, and intuitive dimensions. I believe windows are pathways to the spirit of a building. Within the last year, we have completed a massive stained glass skylight at St. Marguerite d'Youville in Toronto and a vast window wall for the Kuwait Embassy in Ottawa, and are also pioneering new work in photovoltaic art glass.

JOAN ROTHCHILD HARDIN
Architectural Ceramics, Mosaics & Wall Reliefs
Page 62

My award-winning hand-painted ceramic art tiles add interest and richness to corporate, public, and residential settings. Over the years, I have developed methods of layering glazes on tiles to create depth and variety not usually seen in the medium.

COMMISSIONS: Lobster kitchen backsplash, New York, NY; nudes for a bedroom wall, Indianapolis, IN; three veterinary hospitals, New York, NY; *al benessere*, New York, NY

COLLECTIONS: AMACO, Indianapolis, IN

AWARDS: Architecture Award, Fourth Silverhawk Fine Craft Competition

PUBLICATIONS: *A Glaze of Color*, 2004; *Ceramic Tile Art for the Home*, 2001

GUILD SOURCEBOOKS: *Designer's 14, 15; Architectural & Interior Art 16, 17, 18, 19; Artful Home 3*

LUTZ HAUFSCHILD
Architectural Glass
Pages 36-37

I am captivated by the shaping of glass and light, and consider light my true medium. By combining innovative fabrication methods with sensitive aesthetic treatments, I strive to create distinctive and harmonious work that possesses a timeless beauty.

RECENT PROJECTS: *Crucifixion*, Emmaus Chapel, Church of St. John the Divine, Victoria, BC; *Holy Spirit*, Holy Spirit Chapel, St. Ignatius Church, San Francisco, CA; Legacy Salmon Creek Hospital, Portland, OR; *Emerald Laminata*, Rapid Transit Station, Kaohsiung International Airport, Taiwan

COMMISSIONS: Bata Shoe Museum, Toronto, ON; Lynnwood Civic Center Fire Station, WA; City Hall, Taunusstein, Germany; East 21 Hotel, Tokyo, Japan

COLLECTIONS: Canadian Museum of Civilization, Ottawa, ON/Hull, QC; Museum for Contemporary Glass, Langen, Germany

PUBLICATIONS: *Stained Glass*, Virginia Chieffo Raguin, Harry N. Abrams; *The Art of Glass*, Stephen Knapp, Rockport; *Contemporary Stained Glass*, Andrew Moor, Mitchell Beazley

SARAH HAVILAND
Public Art
Page 102

My sculptures and public art projects strike a balance between abstract form and human or natural presence. Art historian Irving Sandler has described how "the abstract and the figurative, and the organic and the crystal-like are played off against each other" in my work. Life-size and monumental projects are designed for indoor and outdoor settings using fabricated and cast metals, wood, or fiberglass composites. Tactile surfaces may be richly colored or activated with mirrors, water, or transparent metal mesh. Commissions include single figures, interactive groups, fountains, and architectural environments.

COMMISSIONS: Grounds for Sculpture, Hamilton, NJ; National Endowment for the Arts, Arts Exchange, White Plains, NY; Crittenden Middle School, Armonk, NY; New York City Parks Department; The Dormitory Authority of the State of New York, Albany, NY

EXHIBITIONS: Hudson River Museum, Yonkers, NY; L&B Viewing Room, Seattle, WA; Harvard University, Cambridge, MA; Chesterwood, Stockbridge, MA; PepsiCo Gallery, Purchase, NY; Queens Museum, New York, NY

ARTIST STATEMENTS

JARRETT HAWKINS
Non-Representational Sculpture
Page 140

Embodied as precious objects, these works are a personal exploration of visual perception. Visual mechanics, light passage, its resultant retinal patterns (the original figure-ground), its conversion to spatial information, are all the focus of my abstract sculpture. I choose traditional media for this work because they provide discrete objects for interaction. I try to manipulate form in terms of geometrical transformations of volumes. This process has an inherent beauty and variability of scale in common with Nature. Though emphatically non-representational, many people nonetheless see figurative intentions. I expect the work to be widely accessible. In a culture of forced obsolescence, I mean this work to endure.

COLLECTIONS: Bridge Worldwide, Cincinnati, OH; Fidelity Investments, Covington, KY; City of Hamilton, Hamilton, OH; City of Deer Park, Deer Park, OH; Middletown Arts Center, Middletown, OH; Miami University, Oxford, OH

YOSHI HAYASHI
Paintings & Prints
Pages 17, 240

I was born in Japan and learned the rigorous techniques of Japanese lacquer art from my father. I carry the spirit, history, and inspiration of this process with me today as I reinterpret the ancient lacquer tradition for my screens and wall panels. My designs range from delicate traditional 17th-century Japanese lacquer art themes to bold, contemporary geometric designs. By skillfully applying metallic leaf and bronzing powders, I add both illumination and contrast to the network of color, pattern, and texture. Recent commissions include works for private residences in the United States and Japan.

COMMISSIONS: Restaurant, 2003, San Diego, CA

EXHIBITIONS: *Lost Art for the Modern World,* 2004, San Francisco, CA; *Japanese Screens Revisited,* 2003, San Francisco, CA

GUILD SOURCEBOOKS: *THE GUILD 4, 5; Designer's 6, 7, 8, 9, 10, 11, 12, 13, 14, 15; Architectural & Interior Art 16, 17, 18, 19; Artful Home 1*

CHRISTIAN HECKSCHER
Architectural Elements
Page 77

I have been creating and producing a unique range of etched metal artwork since 1971. Whether a one-of-a-kind piece for public space or a large series suited for corporate spaces, my work provides original details for any environment. My craftsmanship embraces many styles suitable for elevator or entry doors, murals, and furnishings such as conference or dining room tables. Working on the East and West Coasts, I welcome collaboration with architects and interior designers on major residential and commercial projects.

342

ARCHIE HELD
Non-Representational Sculpture
Page 141, 166

I work primarily in bronze and stainless steel, with water as a central element. I enjoy incorporating contrasting materials, surfaces, and textures in my work.

RECENT PROJECTS: *Dedication to Special Education,* The Village Shopping Center, Corte Madera, CA; Bellagio Hotel and Casino, Las Vegas, NV; City of Stockton, CA; The Crossing, San Bruno, CA; California Department of Health Services, Richmond, CA; City Hall Plaza, Sacramento, CA

COMMISSIONS: SCSI Corporation, Australia; Alliant Energy World Headquarters, Madison, WI; Louis Vuitton Moet Hennessey Group, San Francisco, CA; SAP Labs, LLC, Palo Alto, CA; T Mimarlik, Istanbul, Turkey; ChevronTexaco World Headquarters, San Ramon, CA; Sacramento Metropolitan Arts Commission, CA; Playboy Mansion, Los Angeles, CA; Robert Mondavi Winery, Napa, CA; WW Grainger, Inc. World Headquarters, Chicago, IL; Howard Hughes Corporate Headquarters, Las Vegas, NV; Midway Trading, Montreal, Canada; Sky Tokyo Club, Japan; Harrah's Resort Casino, Reno, NV; Los Angeles Department of Water and Power, CA; Krups, Solingen, Germany

MARILYN HENRION
Art for the Wall: Fiber
Page 312

I use color, line, and form much as a poet employs words to convey a particular emotion or idea. As in poetry, the images are meant to resonate, being both themselves and something they may suggest to the viewer. The works transcend the impersonal objectivity of geometric abstraction through the sensuousness of materials with which they are constructed, revealing a blend of reason and passion. My pieced constructions include silks from India and Japan, Chinese brocades, metallic weavings, and exotic printed cottons. Paying homage to traditional techniques of hand piecing and hand quilting, these materials are transformed into expressive works of art.

COMMISSIONS: Carnegie Abbey Country Club, 2003, Portsmouth, RI; Valley Hospital, 2004, Ridgewood, NJ

EXHIBITIONS: *Cornwall: Inside/Outside—Works by Marilyn Henrion,* 2004, Noho Gallery, New York, NY

GUILD SOURCEBOOKS: *Designer's 11, 13; Architectural & Interior Art 17, 19; Artful Home 1, 3*

LAUREL HERTER
Architectural Glass
Page 38

We incorporate traditional and innovative methods of glass crafting for public, commercial, liturgical, and residential sites. Since 1975 we have drawn on natural forms to enhance the geometric and linear expression of architecture. Extensive collaboration with designers and fabricators of glass, metal, and wood throughout the country assures an inspired level of detail and quality. Our techniques include carved sandblasted, stained and leaded, cast and slumped, and jeweled and beveled glass. We also provide antique mirror, verre églomisé, and brilliant-cut work.

COMMISSIONS: Five entry windows depicting Arts, Education, Community, Youth, and Environment for the Arthur M. Blank Family Foundation, 2004, Atlanta, GA; Skillets Restaurant, 2004, Hilton Head Island, SC

PUBLICATIONS: *Carolina Architecture & Design,* 2004; *HGTV Modern Masters,* 2003

GUILD SOURCEBOOKS: *Architect's 14; Architectural & Interior Art 16*

ARTIST STATEMENTS

KAREN HEYL
Architectural Ceramics, Mosaics & Wall Reliefs
Pages 18, 63, 70

My award-winning mural relief sculpture combines old world stone carving techniques with contemporary design, lending itself to a variety of architectural applications, both monumental and small. Using varied textural surfaces I create aesthetic sophistication with simplified sensual forms.

RECENT PROJECTS: *Ecological Sampler*, six limestone panels at 5' x 3.5' x 3" mounted on 30' high steel easel, Orange County Convention Center, Orlando, FL; *Nature's Guardians*, two limestone panels at 4'x 8'x 10" flanking entryway into housing development, privately funded public art project for the City of Brea, CA

COMMISSIONS: *Organic Life Forms*, courtyard sculpture, 2002, private residence, Ft. Thomas, KY; *Parrots*, 2002, garden sculpture, private residence, Mason, OH; *Cellular Micrographs*, 2000, Vanderbilt University Medical Research Center, Nashville, TN

GUILD SOURCEBOOKS: *Architect's 9, 12, 13, 14, 15; Architectural & Interior Art 16, 17, 18, 19; Artful Home 1, 2*

ERIC HIGGS
Public Art
Page 103

Utilizing various combinations of stone, metal, and concrete, I strive to create impeccable-quality, intriguing, and architecturally bold sculpture. My designs embody abstract symbolism inspired by the history, context, and purpose of the locale. I focus on site-specific commissions for public, corporate, and private clients, and welcome collaborations of all types.

RECENT PROJECTS: Whole Foods Market, 2004-05, Sarasota, Palm Beach Gardens, and Coral Gables, FL; The Arts Center/American Express Grant, 2004, Saint Petersburg, FL; City of Pleasanton/Charles Schwab Corporate Park, 2002, Pleasanton, CA

EXHIBITIONS: *Transitions*, Aqui Siam Gallery, Vallauris, France; *International Sculpture Exhibition*, Meguro Museum, Tokyo, Japan; *Shriek from an Invisible Box*, 2004, Rack and Hamper Gallery, New York, NY

COLLECTIONS: Chateau Musee de Vallauris, 2004, Vallauris, France; private collections in the U.S., Japan, and France

GUILD SOURCEBOOKS: *Architect's 14, 15*

CLAUDIA HOLLISTER
Architectural Ceramics, Mosaics & Wall Reliefs
Page 64

Using hand-built colored porcelain, I create site-specific architectural wall pieces for public, corporate, and residential environments. Highly textured and richly colored, my work is set apart by the combination of such intricate techniques as inlaying, embossing, and hand-carving three-dimensional elements on tiles.

RECENT PROJECTS: Comer Children's Hospital, University of Chicago; Bristol-Myers Squibb Children's Hospital at Robert Wood Johnson University Hospital, New Brunswick, NJ; Takashima residence, Portland, OR

COMMISSIONS: Air Pax, Indianapolis, IN; Beth-El Zedick Synagogue, Indianapolis, IN; General Instrument, Horsham, PA; Hewlett Packard, Fort Collins, CO; Humana Medical, Cincinnati, OH; Kelsey Seybold Clinic, Houston, TX; Longmont United Hospital, Longmont, CO; Marriott Denver Tech Center, Denver, CO

GUILD SOURCEBOOKS: *Designer's 8, 10, 11, 13, 14, 15; Architectural & Interior Art 16, 17, 18*

343

ERLING HOPE
Liturgical Art
Pages 198, 201

" . . . to take a closed space of very limited proportions, and, by no other means than the play of colors and lines, give it infinite dimensions."
- Henri Matisse

RECENT PROJECTS: Sanctuary furnishings and artwork, Good Shepherd Church, Silver Springs, MD

COMMISSIONS: Bronze freestanding sculpture, 2005, Trinity Lutheran Church, North Bethesda, MD; Freestanding bronze sculpture and fourteen Stations of the Cross, 2003, Immaculate Heart of Mary Catholic Church, Grand Junction, CO

COLLECTIONS: Insurance Board, UCC and Disciples of Christ, Georgetown, MD

AWARDS: Merit award, 2003, *Inform* magazine; AIA's Religious Arts Award, 2002 (IFRAA), BENE honorable mention, 2005

GUILD SOURCEBOOKS: *Architect's 13; Architectural & Interior Art 16, 19*

DAR HORN
Fine Art Photography
Page 261

These images are taken from my glass sculptures. The intensely saturated colors and richly detailed forms combine to engage viewers and draw them into the image—and seemingly into vistas and worlds not even imagined. These Ilfochrome prints are laminated to a UV protectant film and mounted on aluminum panels. Additional sizes (to 40" by 60") are available.

COLLECTIONS: Boeing Co., Huntington Beach, CA; LoringCruz, Long Beach, CA

AWARDS: Finalist, the 2004 Philip and Sylvia Spertus Judaica Prize Competition

GUILD SOURCEBOOKS: *Architectural & Interior Art 18, 19*

PAUL HOUSBERG
Architectural Glass
Pages 18, 39

We at Glass Project create art glass features for hospitality, corporate, religious, and public spaces. Central to our work is the power of light, color, and texture to shape and define a space. We welcome inquiries regarding any planned or contemplated project. Please visit our website to view additional projects and information.

RECENT PROJECTS: Four Seasons Hotel, Boston, MA; Logan International Gateway, Boston, MA; Le Meridien Hotel, Minneapolis, MN; Temple Habonium, Barrington, RI; Peninsula Hotel, Chicago, IL; William J. Nealon Federal Building and U.S. Courthouse, Scranton, PA

GUILD SOURCEBOOKS: *Architect's 6, 7, 8, 9, 10, 11, 13, 15; Architectural & Interior Art 16, 17, 18, 19*

ARTIST STATEMENTS

HOWDLE STUDIO INC.
Architectural Ceramics, Mosaics & Wall Reliefs
Page 65, 70

I have been a ceramic sculptor since 1976. I have produced work ranging from thrown forms up to six feet in height to 50-foot relief murals utilizing nine tons of clay. I fire with a sodium process that melts the clay surface, preserving the integrity of the media and creating a very durable piece. My work is suitable for freestanding or installed wall locations. My pieces are in large public institutions, banks, corporations, private offices and homes. Prices range from $1,500 to $150,000. I collaborate closely with clients and provide detailed drawings of my proposed projects.

GUILD SOURCEBOOKS: *Architect's 7, 9, 10, 11, 12, 13, 14, 15; Architectural & Interior Art 16, 17, 18*

HUBBARDTON FORGE
Furniture & Lighting
Page 212

Thirty years ago, Hubbardton Forge® was founded as a two-person craft studio located in an old barn in Hubbardton, Vermont. At that time products were one of a kind, sold at craft fairs throughout New England. Though we've outgrown the barn, our products are still hand-forged by skilled craftsmen. Our designs are truly timeless—simple, classic, elegant, original—form and function inseparable in every piece. By blending time-honored black-smithing techniques with new, environmentally friendly technology, Hubbardton Forge® creates wrought-iron lighting and home accessories that sell through retail showrooms throughout North America. Visit us at www.vtforge.com. You can also find a selection of Hubbardton Forge® products through THE GUILD's Artful Home catalog. Visit their website at www.artfulhome.com.

HUCK FISHER METALWORKERS
Architectural Elements
Page 78

We combine finely detailed, traditional artistic black-smithing with contemporary design. Our motto, "Attention to detail adds strength to design," is apparent in all of our work, which includes large static and kinetic sculptures, whimsical garden sculptures and weathervanes, heirloom home furnishings and lighting, and exterior and interior railings and gates.

RECENT PROJECTS: Design of hand-forged wrought iron and copper perimeter fencing and central gateway for the sculpture court of the Art Gallery of Nova Scotia; design and creation of 44 hand-painted aluminum fish which hang from light standards throughout the seaport of Lunenburg, Nova Scotia, a UNESCO World Heritage Site.

COMMISSIONS: Bronze and stained glass grand entrance chandelier, for the Government of Canada; large forged and fabricated aluminum hand-painted signage for McKelvie's Restaurant, Halifax, Nova Scotia.

344

INDIANA ART GLASS
Architectural Glass
Page 40

Our artisans and craftsmen produce unique, high-end custom architectural glass products to meet or exceed our clients' visual communication needs by adapting the medium of glass to any circumstance. Specializing in cast glass, we enjoy the challenge of diverse projects, including developing new ideas with glass. We can also include other materials such as metal and stone to produce quality pieces of functional glass art.

RECENT PROJECTS: Blackford Community Hospital, Hartford City, IN; Clarian West Medical Center, Avon, IN; Fantasy Springs Resort Casino, Palm Springs, CA; Margaret Mary Community Hospital, Batesville, IN

COMMISSIONS: Firefighters Credit Union of Greater Indianapolis, IN

EXHIBITIONS: AIA National Convention and Design Expo, 2004, Chicago, IL; NeoCon World's Trade Fair, 2004, Chicago, IL; Hospitality Design Exposition, 2002, Las Vegas, NV

PUBLICATIONS: *Glass* magazine, 2004

GUILD SOURCEBOOKS: *Architect's 8; Architectural & Interior Art 19*

MARK IVINS
Fine Art Photography
Page 262

I refer to myself as a "lunch-bucket artist." There are no underlying big ideas, themes, or messages in my work, although many viewers find their own. I hope to inspire the reaction, "That's just how I remember it," and to create a sense of awe of a place and moment in time. I call my artistic process "when the magic happens;" the magic of light, form, and the intangibles coming together like an orchestra, while I am privileged to be there with my camera. My original photographs are made using large format cameras, ranging in size from 2.25" x 2.75" to 8" x 10", primarily 4" x 5". This allows for large-scale prints of unparalleled detail and color fidelity.

RECENT PROJECTS: Four New York City bridge photographs on permanent display in the lobby of 909 Third Avenue, New York, NY; fourteen New York City scenes, private corporation; twenty-two New York City scenes, Bear Stearns' Corporate Offices, New York, NY

KATHRYN JACOBI
Paintings & Prints
Page 241

I am a classically trained realist painter who has been working professionally for over 35 years, exhibiting in galleries and museums throughout the United States, Canada, and Europe. I have over 50 solo shows to my credit and scores more group exhibitions. My still lifes are painstakingly painted in oil on panel from direct observation. I have now created four new giclée prints of my still lifes. They are in editions limited to 175, signed and numbered copies, and printed on heavyweight fine art paper. To see all four images and an extensive overview of my work and for further information including my resume, please visit my website at www.kathrynjacobi.com.

GUILD SOURCEBOOKS: *Architectural & Interior Art 19; Artful Home 3*

ARTIST STATEMENTS

STEVE JENSEN
Non-Representational Sculpture
Page 142

My metal work is constructed from the highest quality aluminum for artistic uses. My images are based on waves, water, or the natural world. The tradition of carving is a universal cultural dialogue, and through this primitive form a number of images can be explored. I come from a long tradition of Norwegian fishermen and boat builders; the chisel I use has been passed from my grandfather. This body of work intends to honor our natural resources. This work can also be cast in bronze.

RECENT PROJECTS: *Compass*, four 12'H aluminum sculptures depicting North, South, East, and West for a traffic roundabout, City of Bend, OR; *Aqua Heart*, 13'H aluminum sculpture, memorial to a fallen officer, Pierce County Sheriff Office, Tacoma, WA; *Crane*, 16'H aluminum sculpture, Hekinan City, Japan; Edmonds Arts Commission, WA

JOAN OF ART GALLERY
Representational Sculpture
Page 182

I create limited-edition bronze sculptures. I begin with a mood and craft my art with that in mind. I find joy in my silliness and pride myself on getting people to smile. With human nature as my subject, the possibilities are endless! Prices range from $80 to $80,000.

RECENT PROJECTS: Laguna Beach, CA; *Art in the Streets*, Colorado Springs, CO; Waukegan Public Library, IL; Batavia Public Library, IL; Fountain Hills Public Library, AZ; Main Street, Mesa, AZ

COMMISSIONS: Huddleton & Co., 2004, Houston, TX; Emil Fischer, 2004, Loveland, CO; Diana Fuller, 2003, Tampa, FL; Barbie Benton, Aspen, CO; Tony Hawk, 2001, CA

COLLECTIONS: University of St. Thomas, St. Paul, MN; City of Red Wing, MN; City of Colorado Springs, CO; City of Mesa, AZ; Regions Hospital, St. Paul, MN

JOHN LEWIS GLASS
Architectural Glass
Page 41

I have been exploring the potential of cast glass since 1969, when I opened my first hot glass studio. My inspiration derives from my ongoing desire to manipulate this material into new shapes and applications. My work includes cast glass sculptures, decorative and functional tables, and architectural components. A variety of materials are used to form the molds that shape the molten glass, such as graphite, steel, iron, and hardened sand. The finished castings often receive additional handcrafting, including cutting, grinding, and polishing with diamond tooling. Surface treatments such as gold leaf, patinas, and tinted epoxies are also applied to enhance the visual impact of the cast glass.

345

GRANT JOHNSON
Paintings & Prints
Page 243

A fascination with form dominates my work, specifically the evolution of form resulting from the interaction of natural and human forces with the landscape. My art is environmental and celebrates nature as the abiding intelligence at work in the universe. I currently use reconnaissance image processing technology to interpret my terrestrial and high altitude aerial photographs as large prints on canvas and watercolor paper. I personally produce each print in my studio. Trained as a painter and photographer before becoming involved with new media, I received the first graduate degree in experimental video awarded by the Rhode Island School of Design in 1975. My work has been shown worldwide and is found in numerous private collections. Visit www.grantjohnsonart.com for series, portfolios, and more information.

GUILD SOURCEBOOKS: Architectural & Interior Art 19

PATTIE & MARK JOHNSON
Non-Representational Sculpture
Page 143

Inspired by the beauty of the Sonoran Desert and the Petroglyphs etched in its canyons, our collection offers an array of expertly crafted sculptures and glass designs utilizing stained, blown, fused, cast, and sand carved glass. Whether for commercial, residential, interior, or exterior applications, our designs are unparalleled. We have been working in our studio located in Tucson, AZ for 14 years, always putting our clients first. Custom design services are available. Sculptures range in size from one foot to 15 feet and $500 to $25,000.

RECENT PROJECTS: *Ancient*, head office of First Magnus Financial Corp., Tucson, AZ; *Energy*, Bancroft and Associates, Tucson, AZ

COMMISSIONS: *Sonoran Sunset*, private collection, Scottsdale, AZ; *Arizona State Flag*, private collection, Tucson, AZ

GUILD SOURCEBOOKS: *Artful Home 3*

BARRY WOODS JOHNSTON
Representational Sculpture
Page 183

My job is to visualize and then breathe life into an appropriate concept for a client. I seek to capture the client's vision. I strive to grasp the heart of what makes life worthwhile, to transcend materialism, exploring questions about who we are as we consider where we've been and where we are going. My sculptures are often light and lively in feeling. My subjects are generally upbeat, both imaginative and realistic. Clothing is rendered in faithful detail, but with flowing movement and compositional unity. My training in architecture gives me a high regard for its aesthetics and a desire to integrate art into architectural settings. Many of my pieces incorporate micro and macro symbolism. In other words, an overall design, as a macro expression, is often symbolically extracted from a micro observation in nature. I look for an abstract form that symbolically embodies the overall vision and then integrate that abstraction into a realistic statement in the finished sculpture.

COLLECTIONS: Virginia's Outdoor Gallery; The Vatican; Georgetown University; James Michener Museum of Art

GUILD SOURCEBOOKS: *Architect's 13, 14, 15; Architecture & Interior Art 16, 18, 19*

ARTIST STATEMENTS

TALIAFERRO JONES
Non-Representational Sculpture/Fine Art Photography
Pages 144, 263

Utilizing texture, form and light, I explore the essence of balance from the physical to the spiritual in the glass sculptures and Giclée prints. My sensual photographs of macro patterns of sand, water, grass and other natural elements carry on a dialogue with my minimal glass sculptures; I currently have a particular affinity towards using water. My photographic prints range form single images to multi image prints, while my vibrant glass sculptures vary in size form one foot to nine feet. Both the glass and the photography come in a variety of textures and vivid colors. I enjoy working with clients to create dynamic commissions.

EXHIBITIONS: Sandra Ainsley Gallery, 2005, Toronto; Canadian Glass Show, 2005, Andora Gallery, Carefree, AZ.; Lamont Gallery, 2004, Exeter, NH

COMMISSIONS: CordeValle Resort, San Martin, CA, USA; Georgina Fantoni, England; NorthWater, Toronto, Canada; Collins, HI, USA; St. Regis Spa, Aspen, CO, USA; Goya Films, Madrid, Spain

PUBLICATIONS: *International Glass*, Richard Yelle; *Craft of Northern California*; *American Art Collector*

GUILD SOURCEBOOKS: *Artful Home 2*

346

PAMELA JOSEPH
Architectural Ceramics, Mosaics & Wall Reliefs
Pages 9, 66, 302

Designing bathroom environments is one of my specialties. I have created murals for bathrooms that have dealt with water themes, Japanese prints, and reinterpretations of Van Gogh paintings. The image for the tiles of the mural on my page is from a study by the Dutch master Hendrick Goltzius (1558-1617) entitled *Fountain in the Form of a Water Nymph or Goddess* and was created for an Aspen, Colorado guesthouse. The handmade tiles were airbrushed in a soft spray pattern that resembles speckled stone. After a preliminary firing, the tiles were then brushed with layers of transparent pigments. Finally, the mural was sprayed with a durable topcoat glaze and refired. The mural is 8' × 4.5' and would cost approximately $8,500. Commissions would be to a design of the client's specifications. You, too, can have a Matisse painting or Tiepolo's cherubs in your bathroom.

BARNEY JUDGE
Murals & Trompe L'Oeil
Pages 218, 227

Each of our projects is created to reflect the unique vision of our clients and the characteristics of the environments where they will be displayed. Whether large-scale, high-impact murals for corporate settings and public arenas or modest graphics and paintings for private residences and small businesses, we work closely with clients from day one to ensure that the desired effect is achieved. The defining characteristic of our art is not found in a single style, but in the detail and artistry each individual work achieves. We have been creating commercial works of art since 1989 and can complete projects on site or in our Ann Arbor, MI, studio.

RECENT PROJECTS: Twelve paintings and two murals, CompuWare corporate headquarters, Detroit, MI; six murals, Comerica Park, Detroit, MI; two murals, Stir Crazy Café, Cleveland, OH; mural and painting, Thomas A. Duke Corporation, Farmington Hills, MI

JUSTIN LAWYER FINE ART
Representational Sculpture
Page 184

We offer an extensive variety of commissioned and museum-quality fine art for public places, corporations, and private collections. We represent a diverse range of styles, sizes, and prices, ranging from contemporary architectural abstracts to figurative or wildlife works. Unique pieces can be commissioned upon request for specific interior or exterior locations, with sizes ranging from desk or wall pieces to monumental works designed for public spaces or large atriums. We recognize that art reflects the uniqueness of an individual and will work with you to find the perfect piece for your image, tastes, clients, and guests. Please call or e-mail us for more information.

K DAHL GLASS STUDIOS
Furniture & Lighting
Page 213

Having worked in stained, blown, and fused glass for more than twenty years, we are a husband and wife team creating exciting new glasswork for lighting applications. The kiln-formed glasswork shown on our page ranges from pendants and sconces to large-diameter chandeliers and glass panels suspended with steel cable. We look forward to discussing design and color for your project. We value working closely with the client to create custom glass that fits the space for which it is designed. A designer recently told us: "I have truly enjoyed working with you and benefiting from your many talents! Thanks so much for taking my design to the next level of perfection!"

RECENT PROJECTS: "Floating" glass light fixture suspended with steel cable, private residence, Thunderbird Cove, Palm Springs, CA

COMMISSIONS: Private commissions nationwide; One Percent for Art public art commissions in Kotezbue, Dillingham, and Chugiak, AK

VARA KAMIN
Furniture & Lighting
Page 214

Replicated from my original works of art, *Impressions of Light®* images provide a powerful visual element to counterbalance highly technical and stressful healthcare environments. The images, used in backlit ceiling and wall installations, are selected from an extensive collection of my paintings that have been placed throughout the United States. *Impressions of Light®* are cost-effective, durable, environmental, and architectural enhancements that create a positive point of focus. The emotive and interpretive nature of my work allows viewers to tap into their own internal resources by providing access to the realm of active imagination. Installations have included hospitals and healthcare facilities, dental clinics, as well as private and commercial settings throughout the country. Commissions for original works of art are accepted for private, public, and liturgical settings.

GUILD SOURCEBOOKS: *Designer's 14*

ARTIST STATEMENTS

CHRISTINE L. KEFER
Art for the Wall: Fiber
Page 313

I have been designing and weaving for twenty-five years and work with many traditional and non-traditional techniques. My focus for most of the last fifteen years has been commissioned tapestries and rugs. I enjoy research in historic textiles and graphic designs of the past century. Each piece is created with the client's needs, location, and architectural space in mind. Framed wall pieces usually include layered fabric (hand-dyed or felted), as well as handwoven bands of silk and antique buttons or beads. Please contact my studio for slides, pricing, and additional information. I am currently designing woven pieces for private and corporate clients and a series of Renaissance inspired fabrics in bold colors for use in home or office settings.

RECENT PROJECTS: Textile installations for corporate and private clients in Illinois and surrounding states

GUILD SOURCEBOOKS: *Artful Home 2, 3*

ANDREA KEMLER
Fine Art Photography
Page 264

In my images I try to capture and accentuate specific characteristics of the natural material that I am working with—color, shape, depth, and texture. Each image is a purposeful arrangement that I create using a large-format scanner. Placing materials directly on the flatbed captures precise details and vivid colors. The dramatic chiaroscuro emphasizes the vibrancy of my subjects and underscores the balance and rhythm of the composition. I have lived and studied in Japan, and I was trained in and practiced architecture. My artistic sensibilities are reflective of both backgrounds. Many of my images are serene and contemplative, others are lush confections, and all are striking and crisp. They are available as limited edition giclée prints. My work is held in private collections throughout the Northeast, Japan, and Europe.

GUY KEMPER
Architectural Glass
Pages 42-43

An architectural painter working primarily in blown glass, my work is distinctive for its warmth and expressiveness. My fascination lies in understanding the relationship between composition, architecture and the perception of the composition by the users of the building as they move through the space. My sensitivity to these three aspects of architectural art, combined with the development of new techniques that have pushed the material and the field of architectural glass itself into a new direction, has made my work substantially different than anyone else's in the world. Internationally recognized and a winner of several prestigious design awards, my strength lies in listening to the client, the architect, and the space itself. My projects are installed on time and on budget. Using only the finest materials, I strive for a design of harmonious essentials that will outlast fashion. I guarantee my work for my lifetime.

GUILD SOURCEBOOKS: *Architect's 9, 10, 11, 14, 15; Architectural & Interior Art 16, 17, 18, 19*

KESSLER STUDIOS, INC.
Architectural Glass
Page 44

For twenty-five years we have designed contemporary stained glass windows that soften and humanize the built environment. Our dramatic influence on the ambience within a space is achieved by designing works that touch the human spirit, while respecting the architectural character of each site.

COMMISSIONS: Central DuPage Hospital, Chicago, IL; Florida Department of Transportation, Miami; Old St. Mary Catholic Church, Chicago, IL; Wheeling Hospital, Wheeling, WV; University Place Retirement Center, West Lafayette, IN; Ohio Department of Agriculture, Reynoldsville; St. Michael the Archangel Parish, North Canton, OH; University of Cincinnati, OH; Good Samaritan Hospital, Cincinnati, OH

AWARDS: Religious Art Awards, 2004, 1994, American Institute of Architects; Visual Art Awards, 2004, 2003, 2002, *Ministry & Liturgy* magazine; Best of Show Bene Visual Art Award, 2003, *Ministry & Liturgy* magazine; Ohio Individual Artist Fellowship, 1998, Ohio Arts Council

RAIN KIERNAN
Non-Representational Sculpture
Page 145

I love using form to express my vision: the human quest for an independent spirit. While some of the works are free-form, many are abstractions of the female form, and speak to a continuing theme of sensuality and courage. I create sculpture in marble, bronze, stainless and alternative media, including fiberglass and cement. My abstracts include both large-scale outdoor works, and smaller interior sculpture, and are characterized by a unique style which features powerful but sensuous curves, relieved by supporting planes. I work both in my Connecticut studio and Pietrasanta, Italy, have won several awards of merit for sculpture, and am represented by various U.S. galleries. I have been showing my work professionally since 1990, and work with architects, designers, and art consultants to create work for public parks, commercial property and private residences.

COLLECTIONS: Portland Community College, OR; Bristol Community College, Fall River, MA; Waveny Park, New Canaan, CT; private homes and businesses in New York, NY, Atlanta, GA, Palm Beach, FL, Greenwich, CT and Southampton, NY

GUILD SOURCEBOOKS: *Architectural & Interior Art 17, 18; Artful Home 1*

BRYAN KING
Murals & Trompe L'Oeil
Page 228

Artifice, Inc. is a decorative arts studio with a reputation for producing the finest quality handpainted murals. For eighteen years we have created artworks in a wide variety of media and styles, from small interior pieces to large-scale public art. We pride ourselves on bringing innovative solutions to each project and bringing each job to completion on schedule.

RECENT PROJECTS: Mural, Constitution Avenue, Washington, DC, 8' × 150'; Mural, Marriott Corporation, Rosslyn, VA, 10' × 70'; Mural, private residence, Washington, DC, 5' × 54'

ARTIST STATEMENTS

S. CHANDLER KISSELL
Paintings & Prints
Page 244

My media are oils and watercolors. My passions are the exploration of luxurious paint and the building of depth and color intensity through many layers. My subjects are most often landscapes or portraits and usually representational, though not necessarily conventional. Yet while painting is freedom, painting is also discipline. Previous years in advertising have given me the ability to work easily with interior designers and art consultants on commissions.

EXHIBITIONS: Thirty-nine juried national and regional shows since 2001, including Allied Artists and Salmagundi Club, New York, NY; New England Watercolor Society; Connecticut Society of Portrait Artists; and the South Carolina Watercolor Society.

ELLEN KOCHANSKY
Art for the Wall: Mixed & Other Media
Pages 19, 293

For 20 years I've guided an orthodox quilting business, creating works in both two and three dimensions, for corporate and residential clients. I have tuned lately to exercises and objects that celebrate community and sustainability, using the humble debris generated by our lives on this planet. Individual and group projects are designed to energize public spaces, convene community spirit, and encourage the awareness that we have what we need. Specific ideas can be developed for any group and site, within most budgets. I have a substantial history with over 20 major collective works, as well as hundreds of public and private commissions, teaching, lectures, and workshops.

RECENT PROJECTS: Bank of America Gateway Center, Charlotte, NC; Mill Memory, for Hub City Writer's Project

COLLECTIONS: White House Collection; Museum of Art and Design, NY; Mint Museum, NC; SC Arts Commission

ANTHONY KRAUSS
Non-Representational Sculpture
Page 146

In my exploration of the precise power of the triangle, I have evolved my sculptural concepts into pyramidal forms on the diagonal, creating dynamic kinetic illusions. By using mirrored surfaces, the sculptural forms are at once solid and transitory as they reflect changing light patterns and abstract glimpses of the rural and urban landscapes. The viewer is also captured in the reflective surfaces, thus becoming an integral part of the sculpture.

I have had numerous exhibitions of my work throughout the world.

COMMISSIONS: Miyagi University, Sendai, Japan; The Daimaru, Inc., Kobe, Japan; Frontier Insurance Co., Rock Hill, NY; Nancy Kalodner, Monterey, MA; Dr. Alan Winner, New York, NY

COLLECTIONS: Whitney Museum of American Art, NYC; Hirshhorn Museum and Sculpture Garden, Washington, DC; JPMorganChase NA, New York, NY; Metro Goldwyn Mayer, New York, NY

AWARDS: Lorenzo IL Magnifico Sculpture Medallion, Biennale Internazionale, Florence, Italy; First Prize, Outdoor Sculpture Competition, Woodstock, NY

PUBLICATIONS: *New Art International* 2004, 2006

348

SILJA TALIKKA LAHTINEN
Paintings & Prints
Pages 245, 256

My work draws from the myths, landscape, folk songs, and textiles of my native Finland. I am especially inspired by Lapland Shamanism in my paintings, collages, wall panels, prints, and drums. I am always trying to do a better painting today than what I did yesterday. Prices range from $400-$30,000.

EXHIBITIONS: Nuutti Galleria, 2003, Virrat, Finland; Kennesaw College, 2003, Atlanta, GA; Elevations Gallery, 2003, Atlanta, GA; Ward-Nasse Gallery, 2003-2004, New York, NY

AWARDS: Award of Merit, *Not Just Another Pretty Face*, WCA Show, 2003, Sanford, FL

PUBLICATIONS: *Print World Directory*, 2002; *Encyclopedia of Living Artists*, 2002; *Who's Who of American Artists; Who's Who of Women Artists*

GUILD SOURCEBOOKS: *Gallery 1, 2, 3; Designer's 9, 10, 11; Architectural & Interior Art 17, 19*

TUCK LANGLAND
Representational Sculpture
Pages 174, 185

After forty years of creating figurative sculptures and portraits, my list of museum collections and public sculptures is considerable. I enjoy the give and take of working with creative design teams of architects, landscape architects, and others. My recent work ranges from small indoor figures to heroic multiple-figure groupings that interpret the message I am asked to convey. Most recently, I have designed a fountain for the center of a university, a group called *Circle of Care* for Hillman Cancer Center, four figures on columns for Bronson Hospital, and many smaller figures for private or public gardens. Recent portraits include the Mayo brothers for the Mayo Clinic and the former president of Indiana University for a new mall on the campus.

EXHIBITIONS: *Changing the American Landscape Through Sculpture*, 2003, Indiana University South Bend; *Langland Sculptures from the Permanent Collection*, 2003, Midwest Museum of American Art, Elkhart, IN

ERIC DAVID LAXMAN
Furniture & Lighting
Page 215

I enjoy shaping steel into sensuous curves that invite the eye and have a sense of harmony and balance. My current designs are influenced by African sculpture and Early Modern art. I am drawn to the elegant lines and vital energy that infuses both of these genres. As a sculptor working in a range of materials, I am able to translate my clients' functional needs into durable works of art that complement and enhance their living environments. In addition to custom tables, my recent commissions include garden sculpture, fountains, decorative wall sculpture, chairs and lighting. I was featured on the cover of the May 2004 *Home & Design* magazine for the *Journal News*, a Gannett newspaper that serves the New York metropolitan area.

ARTIST STATEMENTS

CAROL LeBARON
Art for the Wall: Fiber
Page 314

My work is an exploration in color from memory and observation. I transform remembered light to imagery by collecting fragments from both the landscape of my experience and my observation of natural forms. I combine contemporary aesthetics and ancient techniques, using reflective and absorbent qualities of my materials to shape my results. I abstract natural forms onto wooden shapes and use them in the clamp resist process. In some cases I screenprint, fold, or piece small sections together to create pattern. All of the stitching is done by hand, concealing the action in an invisible presence. My methods require me to allow the natural reaction of elements to play a part in the end result. The gate to chance remains open, so that a myriad of possibilities assist me in controlling the image from start to finish.

ELLE TERRY LEONARD
Architectural Ceramics, Mosaics & Wall Reliefs
Pages 20, 67

My ceramic work is created as an integral part of an architectural structure. My specialties are relief murals and handmade tile. Beautiful and durable, pieces are suitable for both interior and exterior application. My studio, Architectural Ceramics, provides a complete range of services, from design to fabrication to installation. Working primarily with the trade, I produce site-specific commissions for corporate and residential clients.

COMMISSIONS: Esalen Institute, Big Sur, CA; Brookside Middle School, Sarasota, FL; Tampa International Airport, Tampa, FL; Johns Hopkins Hospital, Baltimore, MD; Worldgate Marriott Hotel, Reston, VA; Worldgate Athletic Club, Reston, VA; Kaiser Permanente, Silver Springs, MD; Arvida Lobby, Longboat Key, FL; Chamber of Commerce, Sarasota, FL; City of Venice, Venice, FL

GUILD SOURCEBOOKS: *THE GUILD 1, 2, 3, 4, 5; Architect's 6, 8, 9, 10, 11, 12, 13, 14, 15; Designer's 13, 14, 15; Architectural & Interior Art 16*

LINDA LEVITON
Art for the Wall: Metal
Pages cover, 52, 276-277

Creating wall sculpture that evokes the color and texture of nature is central to my art. Both *Eve's Leaves* (page 276) and *Heart of Nature* (page 52 showcased in Career-Building Projects) are made from hammered leaves woven into a frame. The *Patterns of Nature/Wave* series (page 277) is composed of curved modular squares, creating flexibility for large installations and interior spaces. I offer this series in 22 patterns of copper, silver, and brass. With a variety of different patina colors the combinations are endless.

COMMISSIONS: Shades of Green Walt Disney World, Orlando, FL; Symantec Corp., New York, NY; Ross Heart Hospital, Columbus, OH; Kaiser Permanente, Pasadena, CA; Northwestern Mutual, Milwaukee, WI; Nestle/Ralston, St. Louis, MO; State of Ohio, Columbus, OH; Med Central Hospital, Mansfield, OH; Akron/Summit County Public Library, Akron, OH; St. Vincent's Hospital, Indianapolis, IN; Northwest Airlines, Detroit, MI

PUBLICATIONS: *Color on Metal,* 2001, Guild Publishing

EXHIBITIONS: SOFA, 2003; Craft America, 2004; American Craft Council 2004, 2005

BRENT LILLY
Paintings & Prints
Page 246

My lifelong artistic direction evolved through the 1960s and 1970s and beyond. I use "modular" acrylic paints on canvas in rich, scientifically formulated colors that flow from tubes onto my palette knives, then directly onto the canvas. Layering cool colors over warm, I create an optical three-dimensional effect, where complementary colors are in close proximity. These nonobjective, nonpolitical abstract color fields command attention in contemporary applications and mesmerize viewers with high-impact color, motion, and kinetic energy. Perhaps one can see in these paintings a brief link to pre-Cambrian ponds, where life began on our planet, or to the silent burst of a supernova giving birth to galaxies and new life elsewhere. I am available to create commissioned works of art that thrust our thoughts and senses through the threshold of the 21st century in a fresh way.

LINING ARTS INC.
Art for the Wall: Metal
Page 278

Lining Arts Inc. has a twenty-year history as a creative consultancy that delivers artistic solutions for design projects of every size. Our expertise ranges from wall finishes and trompe l'oeil to murals and sculpture. We work with architects, interior designers, art consultants, corporations, developers, and individuals to design visually compelling solutions for any space. Panel systems and a unique canvas technique can be used to ship our inspiring products right to your door. View our web site for our client list, corporate profile and portfolio at www.liningarts.com.

GUILD SOURCEBOOKS: *Architectural & Interior Art 19*

JOYCE P. LOPEZ
Fine Art Photography
Pages 265, 322

Photographed around the world, my images are often created from multiple images or double exposures, creating a more complex final image. The photos can be printed in all sizes on archival paper, fabric, vinyl, steel, aluminum, etc. I also do fiber sculpture; see *GUILD Sourcebook 18.*

RECENT PROJECTS: State of Illinois at Southern Illinois University; other corporate and private commissions

COLLECTIONS: State of Illinois; State of Washington; City of Chicago; Nokia Collection, TX; Sony Corp.; Health South; private collections

EXHIBITIONS: Austrian Hasselblad circuit exhibition, 2004, Austria, Germany, China, & Qatar; "New York, New York" second international exhibition of photography, 2003, APANY, New York, NY

AWARDS: Art in Architecture, 2004-2005, 2000, State of Illinois; Governor's Award, 2002, State of Illinois; Washington State Public Art, 1995

GUILD SOURCEBOOKS: *THE GUILD 1, 2, 3, 4, 5; Designer's 6, 7, 8, 9, 10, 11, 12, 13, 14, 15; Architectural & Interior Art 16, 17, 18, 19*

ARTIST STATEMENTS

LUKE DAVID SCULPTURE
Non-Representational Sculpture
Page 147

I create meaningful sculptures and fountains with strong visual imagery. My original abstract artwork also encourages individual interpretation. It is my desire to create works that are successful in appearance as well as concept. I design primarily with bronze and stainless steel. Water and lighting elements complete the installation, adding depth to the design and enhancing the installation site. I always take the audience into account, as well as the origin and context of the site. I do every aspect of the fabrication completely hands-on in my own custom fabrication studio. I have years of experience building and installing large-scale public works in a professional environment. My works have been installed in private gardens, incorporated into homes, highlighted in galleries, and displayed in public spaces and sculpture gardens.

CAMMIE LUNDEEN
Representational Sculpture
Page 186

From the studio window in my barn I can see many of my subjects. My life has always revolved around the care and illustration of animals. Horses have been the greatest influence on my work and continue to spur my imagination. My equine sculpture has been the subject of feature articles in such publications as *Appaloosa Journal, Paint Horse Journal, Equine Images, Southwest Art, and Art of the West.* My public placements include the American Royal Center, Kansas City, MO, City of Avon, CO, and in Helsinki, Finland, and New Market, England. The American Academy of Equine Art and the Society of American Artists have granted me awards. I am a member of the Society of Animal Artists, and American Women Artists, and an associate member of the American Academy of Equine Art.

GEORGE LUNDEEN
Representational Sculpture
Page 187

The challenge of taking an idea from a sketch into clay and then to bronze is the exciting part of being a sculptor. To create sculpture with a sense of life, grace, and simple understanding is my goal. My major installations include a sixteen foot aviator at Denver International Airport, a portrait of astronaut Jack Swigert in National Statuary Hall, the Capitol Building, Washington D.C., *Ben Franklin* for the University of Pennsylvania, *Robert Frost* for Dartmouth College, *Lewis and Clark* for the University of Nebraska, and several sculptures at St. Louis University, plus hundreds of life-size and larger pieces placed throughout the world. My work has received many awards and I am a member of the National Sculpture Society, a full academician of the National Academy of Design, and hold an honorary doctorate from the University of Nebraska. Besides that, I'm an ordinary guy.

350

ELIZABETH MacDONALD
Architectural Ceramics, Mosaics & Wall Reliefs
Pages 21-22, 68

I produce tile paintings that suggest the patina of age. These compositions are suitable for indoor or outdoor settings and take the form of freestanding columns, wall panels, or architectural installations. Public art commissions include Wilbur Cross High School, New Haven, CT, and the Department of Environmental Protection, Hartford, CT.

RECENT PROJECTS: Dartmouth-Hitchcock Medical Center, Lebanon, NH; Northern Lights Inn, Fairbanks, AK

COMMISSIONS: Conrad International Hotel, Hong Kong; St. Luke's Hospital, Denver, CO; Chapel at Mayo Clinic, Scottsdale, AZ

AWARDS: State of Connecticut Governor's Award for Visual Art

GUILD SOURCEBOOKS: *THE GUILD 1, 2, 3, 4, 5; Architect's 6, 7, 8, 9, 10, 11, 12, 13, 14, 15; Designer's 6, 8, 9, 10, 11, 12, 13, 14, 15; Architectural & Interior Art 16, 17, 18; Artful Home 1, 2*

MAXWELL MacKENZIE
Fine Art Photography
Page 266

These large format panoramas are taken from my two award-winning books, which explore the western landscape and the beautiful, simple buildings the pioneers left behind. *Abandonings* consists of 28 color images of derelict farmsteads, barns and empty schoolhouses amidst the golden fields and green hills of my native Midwest. *American Ruins, Ghosts on the Landscape* contains 30 black and white photographs of humble structures I found in Idaho, Montana, Minnesota, Wisconsin, and the Dakotas. This series has been exhibited all over the U.S. and is included in over 400 public and private collections, including Citibank, Exxon, Fannie Mae, J.P. Morgan, The Washington Post, and the American Embassies of Peru, Columbia, and Moscow. Images are available in four sizes ranging from 28" to 96", or larger by special arrangement.

ELIZABETH MacQUEEN
Public Art
Pages 94, 104

My passion as an artist is to translate the language of the body into a three-dimensional reality that symbolizes the real essence of movement, expression, and human dignity.

I am currently finishing a commission in San Jose, Costa Rica. The National Gallery of Costa Rica has offered an exhibition of my work in the fall of 2005. This is the sixth country in which I have created work.

RECENT PROJECTS: *The Past Present and Future*, 34'H bronze sculpture, Women's Basketball Hall of Fame, Knoxville, TN

GUILD SOURCEBOOKS: *Architect's 10, 12, 14; Designer's 14, 15; Architecture & Interior Art 18*

ARTIST STATEMENTS

IG MATA
Art for the Wall: Mixed & Other Media
Page 294

Photography is my passion. The challenge of combining its beauty with the delicate nature of glass to create unique works of art is a great motivation. My inspiration is the search for beauty and simplicity. I have perfected a technique of transferring photographic images onto glass, based on the historic use of hand-applied emulsions. I work with a wide variety of objects in three-dimensional form. The transparent nature of glass permits one to look beyond the image to the shadows projected on the surrounding space, adding a magical atmosphere and intensifying the dream-like quality of my pinhole photographs.

Recent commissions include works for private residences in the United States and Brazil and for corporate clients like Saks Fifth Avenue's Corporate Gift Collection and HBO's "The Sopranos," among others.

COLLECTIONS: Funarte Gallery (National Foundation for the Arts), Rio de Janeiro, Brazil

MARY JO MAUTE
Paintings & Prints
Page 247

My semi-abstract paintings and pastels are inspired by the natural forms of plants, animals, humans, and microscopic flora and fauna. With my spontaneous and improvisational process, shapes, meanings, and relationships emerge from deep within and shift as I work. My aim is to create a sensuous, luminous, primal place where order and chaos are delicately balanced.

COLLECTIONS: Private and public collections, include the Miriam Sample Collection, MT; Yellowstone Art Museum, MT; Missoula Museum of the Arts, MT; Deaconess Medical Center

EXHIBITIONS: Exhibiting regularly since 1987 when I earned an M.F.A. from the University of Colorado at Boulder. Recent exhibits include a national pastel competition juried by Wolf Kahn at Imagery Art Gallery, Glen Ellen, CA, a show at Mindport Exhibits in Bellingham, WA, and *Montana Connections: Modernism Then and Now* exhibition at Yellowstone Art Museum. I am also represented by the Toucan Gallery, Billings, MT.

AWARDS: Honorable Mention, 2005, *Pastel Journal*; Montana Artist Fellowship, 1987, Montana Arts Council

MAW STUDIO
Non-Representational Sculpture
Page 148

I have always concerned myself with sculptural compositions that reflect non-representational aesthetics, allowing for open interpretation. The lyrical forms that hint at three-dimensional calligraphic characters suggest a spirit-like essence within the arrangement of forms. I see the sculptures as positive and energetic studies designed to encompass some facet of tension, rhythm, visual harmony, and/or physical or visual movement. I prefer the immediacy and structural properties of steel. The material allows me to create shapes and forms that maintain their position without compromise, withstanding the elements of weather and/or other external variables. Finished surfaces vary from natural rust to painted or powder-coated colors, allowing me a freedom to express emotional nuances within the nature of each piece. I welcome private commissions and continue to compete for public commissions.

351

MAX-CAST
Public Art
Page 105

Our company, Max-Cast, is a unique combination of sculpture studio and full-service art foundry, staffed by a highly professional team of talented artists. Our artistic ability and technical expertise allow us to carry out nearly any sculptural project. Whether you are an artist looking for a first-class foundry to cast your art in bronze, iron or aluminum, or an architect seeking unique design elements, we will work closely with you to bring your concept to fruition. As artists, we can create your heart's desire. As technicians, we can perfect your sculpture in bronze. From historical restoration to portraiture, we will share your vision and make it a reality.

ROSLYN MAZZILLI
Public Art
Page 107

For over twenty-five years I have exhibited extensively and installed over twenty-five public and private commissioned sculptures throughout the country. I have successfully worked with architects, designers, structural engineers, communities, and public art committees.

Often my sculptures have become landmarks for the communities in which they are placed, contributing to civic awareness and a positive sense of place, that bring a quality of liveliness and life-affirming energy to the site.

I work in scales from monumental public art to smaller more intimate scales for gardens, interiors, and wall sculptures. My work is fabricated of structural aluminum, stainless steel, or bronze. The surfaces are coated with durable industrial coatings that are highly resistant to the elements.

RECENT PROJECTS: Jackson National Life Insurance Inc., Lansing, MI; Southwestern Oregon Community College, Coos Bay; City of Mercer Island, WA; Terra Vista Town Center, Rancho Cuca Monga, CA

GUILD SOURCEBOOKS: *Architect's 8, 12*

SUSAN McGEHEE
Art for the Wall: Metal
Pages 18, 279

Instead of fiber, I weave with wire and metals. I continue to employ the traditional tools, techniques, and patterns from when I worked in fiber. Weaving metals allows me to form a piece into a dimensional shape that will retain its form and undulating vitality. Primarily, I weave with anodized aluminum wire because even though a piece looks like copper, the anodized aluminum wire has the advantage of being lightweight, and retains its vibrant color and shine. The pieces are easy to install and maintain. I enjoy the fact that people will assume a piece is fiber and then are astonished to discover it is woven metal.

COMMISSIONS: Nokia, Burlington, MA; Wells Fargo, Minneapolis, MN; American Family Insurance, Madison, WI and Phoenix, AZ; Lawson Commons lobby, St. Paul, MN; St. Joseph's Medical Center, Milwaukee, WI; Fantasy Springs Convention Center, Indio, CA

ARTIST STATEMENTS

MAUREEN McGUIRE
Liturgical Art
Page 202

My career in glass has been continuous since 1964. With a B.A. in Design from Alfred University, an M.A. in sculpture and glass from Florence, Italy, and a four-year studio apprenticeship, I became one of the nation's first independent stained glass designers. I am therefore fully versed in all aspects of stained glass, it's relationship to architectural space, and the technical challenges of large-scale work. Though most of my work has been in churches, I especially enjoy working in a lyrical abstract way. I work on a commission basis, partnering with notable studios in the U.S. and Germany for the highest quality of execution and installation.

RECENT PROJECTS: Large chapel windows at the Episcopal High School, Jacksonville, FL

AWARDS: Several honor awards from the InterFaith Forum on Religious Art & Architecture; five Bene Awards from *Ministry and Liturgy* magazine

PUBLICATIONS: *The Art of Glass; Stained Glass Sourcebook; Stained Glass Quarterly; Glass Art* magazine; *Stained Glass* magazine

LEONE McNEIL
Liturgical Art
Page 203

Keeping the relationship of architecture, interior design, and stained glass in balance, with each enhancing the other, has been my goal. I have been designing stained glass windows for forty years, ever since earning my M.F.A. from Otis Art Institute in Los Angeles. Much residential work has been accomplished, but the larger works affecting a bigger environment have been the challenge of choice. The range of styles and methods include fusing, sandblasting, and painting in addition to leaded stained glass.

COMMISSIONS: Mendocino Presbyterian Church, Mendocino, CA; First Presbyterian Church, Fort Bragg, CA; St. David's Episcopal Church, Ashburn, VA; Hoag Memorial Hospital, Newport Beach, CA; numerous private residences

GUILD SOURCEBOOKS: *Architect's 8, 9, 10, 11*

DARCY MEEKER
Art for the Wall: Metal
Page 280

I torch copper for the enchanting patina, like butterfly wings, shimmering in shapes that unify and enliven a space. Seen up close, my detailed hand-tooling weaves its fascination, too, and sometimes a little paint highlights the design. My goal is harmonious space and a lively experience for the people in it. I also work and design in stone, clay, fabric, neon, and fiber optics.

COMMISSIONS: *Party Time*, 2005, private residence, Tyler, TX; *Shifting Sun with Birds*, 2005, private residence, Seattle, WA; *Peace, Love, and Serenity*, 2004, private residence, Yucaipa, CA; *Mountain Spirit*, 2003, private residence, Fincastle, VA; *Elephant Vine*, 2000, General Electric Company, Schenectady, NY

EXHIBITIONS: Galleries, universities, community colleges, and art centers in AZ, CO, FL, MD, NY, NC, OR, PA, SC, VA, WA, and DC

PUBLICATIONS: *Southwest Art*, 2003; *Dwell*, 2004; *Sculptural Pursuit*, 2003, 2004

352

RON MELLOTT
Fine Art Photography
Page 267

Photography is the expression of my vision, understanding, and interaction with the natural world. Formally trained as a biologist, my vision is more the "intimate" landscape, distilling each scene through composition, lighting, and choice of lens to what my senses dictate is the essence of the image. I try to answer the question, "why did I stop here?" In that sense, photography is a process of subtraction, as the camera's view is only a subset of all that our eyes and senses perceive. I photograph with large (4 x 5) and medium (680) format cameras on film. Prints are done traditionally with enlargers and, increasingly, with the Fuji Lightjet technology. Images are offered traditionally matted and framed in a variety of sizes. Mural-sized images are prepared as glassless mounts on Gatorfoam with a UV surface lamination in a variety of sizes.

GEORGE THOMAS MENDEL
Fine Art Photography
Page 268

As a location/freelance and fine art photographer, I have been working with this medium for more than twenty years. In this time I have produced a variety of portfolios which include architecture, waterscapes, and humanitarian projects. I work primarily in black and white as an art form, and my limited-edition prints are produced by way of traditional fiber-based gelatin silver (cold or warm tone per request). My creative use of light and composition is matched by my master craftsmanship in the darkroom, producing the highest level of quality and archival stability. Project portfolios are available to view on my website gallery, and commissioned project and documentation services are available by request.

PUBLICATIONS: *Beautiful Things*, 2000; *Death By Renaissance*, 2004

GUILD SOURCEBOOKS: *Designer's 15; Architectural & Interior Art 16, 17*

PETER W. MICHEL
Representational Sculpture
Page 188

My abstract figurative sculpture celebrates self, relationship, and community, as well as the spirit of playfulness. The brightly colored, whimsical work is scaled from intimate wall and tabletop pieces to monumental outdoor public art. Currently, the work is created using CAD software and computer-controlled water jet or laser-cutting methods to cut wood, aluminum, or steel. The work is most often painted with the rainbow colors. The constructive quality of my work reflects my training as an architect.

COLLECTIONS: Oakton Sculpture Park, Des Plaines, IL; Wandell Sculpture Garden, Urbana, IL

EXHIBITIONS: Sculpture Internationale, 2002, Atlanta; Pier Walk, 2000, 1999, Chicago; Chesterwood Museum, 1994, Stockbridge, MA

PUBLICATIONS: *Educational Psychology*, 8th Edition, 2002

GUILD SOURCEBOOKS: *Architectural & Interior Art 16*

ARTIST STATEMENTS

DIANNA THORNHILL MILLER
Murals & Trompe L'Oeil
Pages 224, 229

A Californian of Scottish and Cherokee descent, I was transplanted to the Midwest where it is necessary to emulate the missing sun through art. Coming from an academic background in color, design, and sculpture, I have utilized a variety of materials and techniques to create art that is both original and responsive—appropriate to its location in scale, concept, and purpose. The Leather Mosaic™ Mural is an Omni Art innovation that provides rich color and texture in a touchable, quality material. In formal geometric designs or thematic narratives, these works enhance more than 400 private, business, and cultural environments in the United States, Europe, and Asia.

RECENT PROJECTS: Kaiser Permanente, Los Angeles, CA; Columbus Public Library, OH; private residence, Pawleys Island, NC; First and Second Church, Boston, MA

COMMISSIONS: IBM; Lincoln Life; V.A.; Blue Cross; Magnavox; G.E.; Baxter Labs; I.T.T; Essex; Honeywell; Merrilott Centre for the Arts; Yale University; NIPSCO; Verizon; Sears Tower, Chicago

GUILD SOURCEBOOKS: *Architect's 8, 9; Designer's 10*

CLARK FLEMING MITCHEL
Representational Sculpture
Page 189

My training in figurative sculpture started in 1974 under the sculptors Robert Thomas and Boris Gruenwald. I worked during 1979 and 1980 in a marble sculpture shop in Pietrasanta, Italy. While living in Vermont during the early 1980s, I carved sculpture in Vermont marble. I worked as an architectural carver for the Cathedral Works Organization in Chichester, England from 1986 to 1988. This gave me formal training in molding and floral carving, masonry drafting, and letter incising. I have continued sculpting while working for several architectural stone firms in the San Francisco Bay Area as a manager, draftsman, and carver. I started Alma Stone Company in 1998. We carve stone architectural features (fireplaces and entries) and sculpture and incise letters in stone. We invite commissions for contemporary stone sculptures and fountains and traditional carved stone fireplaces and letter carving.

PAM MORRIS
Furniture & Lighting
Pages 208, 216

As owner of EXCITING LIGHTING, I work with clients who encompass top restaurants, hotels, and private collectors, including Wolfgang Puck, Sugar Ray Leonard, Terry McMillan, Kelsey Grammar, Georgio Armani, and the Hong Kong Regent Hotel. In my work, I create highly original and evocative illuminated pieces. I use light, together with blown, slumped, or cast glass and forged or cast metal, to create illuminated art pieces that reflect a special sense of place. I love the custom design process, and have also found it interesting and rewarding to have lectured and been published internationally.

GUILD SOURCEBOOKS: *Architect's 12, 13, 15; Designer's 14; Architectural & Interior Art 17, 18, 19; Artful Home 1*

353

MOTAWI TILEWORKS
Architectural Ceramics, Mosaics & Wall Reliefs
Page 69

Motawi Tileworks art tile studio was founded by Nawal Motawi in 1992. Over the last decade, we have created hundreds of installations for homes, businesses and public institutions. Aesthetically, our emphasis is on historically inspired design, particularly the early twentieth-century English and American decorative arts. We prefer projects that utilize our large collection of relief designs, our expertise with matte glazes or our cuenca polychrome technique. We specialize in custom-designed, beautifully glazed residential fireplace installations and murals.

RECENT PROJECTS: Mural, Grand Californian Hotel, 2000, Anaheim, CA

PUBLICATIONS: Arts and Crafts Style and Spirit: Craftspeople of the Revival, 1999; Old House Interiors, November 2003; Interior Design, October 2003

GUILD SOURCEBOOKS: *Architectural & Interior Art 19*

JAMES C. MYFORD
Non-Representational Sculpture
Pages 120, 149

My sculptures are found in corporate, museum, university, public, and private collections throughout the U.S. My works are also in collections in Japan, Sweden, Venezuela, Australia, and Brazil. My cast and fabricated aluminum sculptures, though often outwardly abstract, are closely linked to nature and reality. The energy and vitality expressed in my compositions reflect a subtle inner strength and spirit that expand and interact gracefully with space. My sculpture ranges in size from smaller indoor works to major outdoor site-specific commissions. Indoor works start at $1,000; outdoor works range from $8,000 to $80,000. A large selection of unique works for indoors and out can be viewed at the sculptor's residence and gallery by appointment.

RECENT PROJECTS: Soffer Organization, Pittsburgh, PA; Slippery Rock Redevelopment, Slippery Rock, PA

EXHIBITIONS: Larsen Gallery, Scottsdale, AZ; Joyce Petter Gallery, Douglas, MI; Lurie Fine Art Galleries, Boca Raton, FL; Forecast, Miami, FL; The Bonfoey Co., Cleveland, OH

GUILD SOURCEBOOKS: *Architect's 9, 10, 11, 12, 13, 14; Architectural & Interior Art 16, 17, 19*

W. R. NAGER—SCULPTOR, INC.
Non-Representational Sculpture
Page 150

After thirty years of sculpting I have come to realize that my work is a culmination of life experiences, attention to detail, desire, and God-given talent. I have studied under several master blacksmiths in the United States and Europe. I live to create, to dream, and to bring thoughts to life through iron, stainless steel, copper, and brass. My creations can be seen throughout the world in both the private and public sectors. Professionals from all walks of life appreciate the time and old-world craftsmanship required to forge metal into works of art. My most recent works can be found at Hedonism II resort in Negril, Jamaica, many private residences in Coral Gables, Florida, restaurants in Coconut Grove, Florida, and multimillion-dollar executive estates throughout the United States.

ARTIST STATEMENTS

NATIONAL SCULPTORS' GUILD
Public Art
Pages 108-109

Since 1992, the National Sculptors' Guild has consulted private and public collectors in the placement of fine art for the interior and exterior, specializing in limited edition and site-specific sculpture in bronze, steel, and stone. The National Sculptors' Guild is an association of its design team and nationally recognized sculptors chosen for their outstanding artistic abilities and varied styles, with the primary objective of conceiving and seeking out monumental placements for its members' artwork. Headed by Executive Director John W. Kinkade, the NSG has installed monumental-scale work by Guild members in public and private collections throughout the world.

Guild members include: Gary Alsum, Kevin Box, Kathleen Caricof, Chapel, Tim Cherry, Dee Clements, Jane DeDecker, Carol Gold, Bruce Gueswel, Denny Haskew, Tuck Langland, Mark Leichliter, Leo E. Osborne, Sandy Scott, and C.T. Whitehouse.

GUILD SOURCEBOOKS: *Architect's 9, 10, 11, 12, 14, 15; Architectural & Interior Art 16, 17*

BASHA RUTH NELSON
Art for the Wall: Metal
Pages 272, 281

Whether sculpture, construction, or installation, the hallmark of my artwork is creating unity between form and the volume in which the piece lives. My most recent constructions in aluminum, copper, and stainless steel flow with grace, dignity, and strength, engaging the viewer through surface and scale. For me the vertical, as a recurring theme, is elegant, pure, and one of the simplest yet strongest forms in nature. I've exhibited widely in the U.S. and abroad, and have created commissions in collaboration with architects and collectors.

COMMISSIONS: Corporate office, Hempstead, NY; Yoga Retreat Center, Rockville, MD; private residence, Miami, FL

COLLECTIONS: United States Embassy, Nassau, Bahamas; Robins Collection of Contemporary Art, Miami, FL

AWARDS: Lorenzo IL Magnifico Award for Sculpture, Biennale in Florence, Italy; Welfred McGibbon Award, Norton Gallery & Museum of the Palm Beaches, West Palm Beach, FL

PUBLICATIONS: *New Art International; Gallery Guide*

BRUCE A. NIEMI
Non-Representational Sculpture
Pages 106, 151

I create one-of-a-kind stainless steel and bronze abstract sculptures. "Aesthetically powerful," "graceful," and "energized with balance" are the terms that best describe both my small interior pieces and my large-scale public pieces. I work well with architects, designers, and developers and am able to meet budgets and timetables. The twenty-acre Niemi Sculpture Gallery & Garden continues to provide a great atmosphere in which to view interior and exterior sculpture by over thirty national artists.

COMMISSIONS: Las Olas Grand, 2004, Ft. Lauderdale, FL; Merrill Lynch, 2004, Chicago, IL; North American Group, 2003, Chicago, IL

COLLECTIONS: Frankfort Public Library, IL

EXHIBITIONS: Western Michigan University, 2004-2006, Kalamazoo, MI; *Heavy Metal/Graceful Forms*, 2004, University of Wisconsin-Madison, *Sculpture 2004*, Uihlein Peters Gallery, Milwaukee, WI

AWARDS: Solo show, 2004, Wisconsin Painters & Sculptors

GUILD SOURCEBOOKS: *Architect's 10, 11, 14, 15; Architectural & Interior Art 16, 17, 18, 19*

354

DANIEL OBERTI
Public Art
Pages 110, 194

Art is a gift that presupposes the dignity of its recipient. My works embrace concepts about time, space, light, and shadow. They reveal humanity's relationship to symbols, archetypes, and forms that uplift our spirits and instill a sense of contemplative solace. I am part of a lineage that defines the artistic self by forming works that inform and inspire inquiry within. I work to unveil the elusive and seek an audience and affinity with others who recognize the value of this pursuit.

COMMISSIONS: *Spheres and Circumagi*, 2004, Biogebidec Campus, San Diego, CA; *Venus* (the world's largest scale model of our solar system), 2004, Royal Technical Institute, Stockholm, Sweden; *Three Spheres*, 2002, Vineyard Creek Hotel, Santa Rosa, CA; *Time Peace*, 2000, South Carolina Governor's School for the Arts and Humanities, Greenville; *Sphaera Palermo*, 2000, Osservatorio di Palermo, Palermo, Italy

SHELLEY PARRIOTT
Public Art
Page 111

Color Field Sculpture redefines public and private spaces. My unique site-specific installations are polychromes of transparent steel mesh layered to create prismatic patterns of color and light.

Reviews:

"The beauty of these works is their ability to assert themselves without obscuring the marvelous views of land and riverscapes visible through the sheer mesh." *Kingston Daily Freeman*, NY

"Parriott's work is ethereal. Colorful wire mesh multiples interact with their surroundings as sunlight dances through the sculpture and beckons the viewer to take part." *Saugerties Times*, NY

EXHIBITIONS: Pfizer, Inc., NYC; Weill Cornell, New York, NY; Washington Design Center, DC; Max Planck Institute, Berlin, Germany; Galerie im Turm, Cologne, Germany

AWARDS: U.S. Embassy, Berlin, Germany; Lorenzo il Magnifico Sculpture Medallion, Biennale Internazionale, Florence, Italy; Best in Show, *Art of the Northeast*, Silvermine Guild, New Canaan, CT, (juried by Leo Castelli Gallery); New York Foundation for the Arts

NANCY "STEVIE" BROWN PEACOCK
Paintings & Prints
Page 248

Inspired by a childhood filled with New York City dance, theatre, music and art, I sketch musicians at work for my music-in-action paintings. Using these sketches as reference, I employ sacred geometry to make visible the energetic spiritual essence. I also paint onstage with bands and have been invited to paint glassblowers at work in the Hot Shop of Dale Chihuly's Museum of Glass (Tacoma, WA). My paintings can be seen on album covers of Keith Jarrett Trio, Acoustic Alchemy, National Public Radio CDs; and posters for Seattle Art Museum's *Art of Jazz* series, Seattle Youth Symphony, Odessa Brown Clinic, and others. I have been interviewed on radio and TV in California, Oregon, Washington, and Black Entertainment Television's *Jazz Scene* in Washington, D.C.

EXHIBITIONS: Attic Gallery, Portland, OR; Freed Gallery, Lincoln City, OR; The Jazz and Blues Co., Carmel, CA; The Jazz Bakery, Los Angeles, CA; Art Concepts Gallery, Tacoma, WA; Walnut Street Gallery, Fort Collins, CO

RECENT PROJECTS: NPR-KPLU "Sweet & Soulful," "School of Jazz" CD covers, 2003, 2005; Painting live at Big 'Sur JazzFest, West Seattle Jazz Festival, Portland Jazz Festival

ARTIST STATEMENTS

PEARL RIVER GLASS STUDIO
Liturgical Art
Page 205

Pearl River Glass Studio is committed to pursuing the craft of stained glass as an art form. We work in a broad range of styles and employ a wide variety of methods. Central to our mission is the principle of applying creative solutions to complex problems where thoroughness and quality count.

RECENT PROJECTS: Lobby window, St. Dominic's Hospital, Jackson, MS; church windows, Christ United Methodist Church, Jackson, MS

EXHIBITIONS: *Made in USA: Contemporary Crafts*, 2003, Peoria Art Guild

AWARDS: Governor's Award for Excellence in the Arts, 2002, Mississippi

PUBLICATIONS: *The Stained Glass Association of America Sourcebook* 2004, 2003, 2002, 2001, 2000, 1999, 1998; *Stained Glass Quaterly*, winter 2002

GUILD SOURCEBOOKS: *Designer's 15; Architectural & Interior Art 16, 17, 18, 19*

G. BYRON PECK/CITY ARTS
Murals & Trompe L'Oeil
Pages 20, 230

Full-service studios for the production of public art, murals, and mosaics for large-scale artwork or intimate private murals. Our studios have twenty-five years of experience working with architects, designers, and organizations to create solutions for any environment.

RECENT PROJECTS: 1,500' mosaic on the Potomac River waterfront, Washington, DC; 100' mural for the City of Los Angeles, Cultural Affairs Department; two murals for the newly built visitors center at historic Mount Vernon, Alexandria, VA; 60' mural for main subway station, Washington, DC

COLLECTIONS: The Kennedy Center for the Performing Arts, Washington, DC; Chamber of Commerce, Washington, DC; U.S. Embassy, Santiago, Chile; U.S. Embassy, Georgetown, Guyana; U.S. Nuclear Regulatory Commission, Rockville, MD; Marriott Corporation, Bethesda, MD

GUILD SOURCEBOOKS: *Architect's 6, 7, 8, 9, 10, 11, 12, 13, 14, 15; Architectural & Interior Art 16, 17, 18, 19*

ROBERT PERLESS
Public Art
Page 112

My sculptures make us aware of the unseen energies that surround us in our daily lives.

Sun Dagger helps us discover time in the sunlight. This sculpture, which was commissioned in 2004 by the Utah Public Art Program of the Utah Arts Council, functions as a unique celestial observatory, and amplifies the union and synergy of man and nature. It links viewers into the celestial mechanics of the rotation of the earth around the sun and works both as a noon transit and horizontal sundial, and as a seasonal calendar, celebrating the winter and summer solstices and the vernal and autumnal equinoxes.

My site-specific works are constructed of stainless steel, bronze, aluminum, and polymer prisms. I have created works for dozens of corporate installations including Xerox, Bristol-Myers Squibb, and the Coates Building at 555 Madison Avenue In New York City, as well as for public agencies such as the City of Corpus Christi and the Connecticut Commission on the Arts. My work is included in numerous museum collections.

GUILD SOURCEBOOKS: *Architect's 13, 15*

355

PETERS GLASS STUDIOS
Architectural Glass
Page 45

Established almost 100 years ago, our artistic glass studio is one of Germany's most prominent workshops, offering excellence in everything from classical glass painting to contemporary glass fabrication. Our studio is dedicated to service, quality, and innovation, and it has built its reputation by working with architects, artists, and designers to develop creative solutions for the most challenging of proposals. We maintain extensive facilities for all kinds of glass fabrication work, including traditional leaded and painted glass, sandblasting, etching, screenprinting with paint or enamels, lamination, air brushing, adhesives, and safety glass. The studio and its staff have introduced many new techniques related to contemporary glass design and large-scale float glass painting for architectural settings. Located in the heart of Europe, our company works for clients and artists throughout the world.

DAVID LAWRENCE PHELPS
Public Art
Page 113

My imagery originates from the family farm in the California Delta. Growing up surrounded by water and threatened by drought, I was unknowingly developing my lifelong aesthetic foundation. My figurative bronzes appear to emerge from the ground. They are serenely contemplative and imbued with a dry, subtle sense of humor.

COMMISSIONS: Oklahoma Medical Research Foundation, 2004, Oklahoma City, OK; Sharp Chapel, 2004, University of Tulsa; New Block Park, 2003, Tulsa, OK; Bricktown, 2000, Oklahoma City, OK; McCarren International Airport, 1999, Las Vegas, NV

COLLECTIONS: Burt Reynolds; Connie Seleka; John Tesh; Barbie Benton; St. Louis University; State of Oklahoma Permanent Art collection; DMB Corporation, Scottsdale, AZ; John Michael Kohler Arts Center, Sheboygan, WI; The Wornick Collection, St. Helena, CA; Oklahoma City Art Museum; Beretta Foundation, San Antonio, TX; Sandor Family Collection, Chicago, IL; Bloom Investment Council, Inc., Toronto, ON; Kiesewetter Import, Liebigstra, Germany

MICHAEL F. PILLA
Architectural Glass
Pages 46, 92

Glass, line, and form are the tools in the medium of light. This medium both serves and nourishes architecture, and through its presence brings life to a structure and its environment. It evokes a sense of awakening, transformation, and healing. Successful architecture has a life unto itself. Art glass becomes an integral part of that life, whether through a luminous wall or a radiant skylight. My art glass invites the light to dance and play. Light entices a space to share its secrets and reveal the spirit that is sometimes hidden in the architecture, and consequently touches the essence of our being. This nourishing quality awakens us to a healing of our mind and soul.

GUILD SOURCEBOOKS: *THE GUILD 4; Architect's 6, 7, 8, 9, 10, 12, 13, 15; Architectural & Interior Art 16*

ARTIST STATEMENTS

TERRY DAVITT POWELL
Art for the Wall: Mixed & Other Media
Page 295

My affinity for birds and animals has led me to an exploration of adaptability and coexistence. Though equilibriums are constantly upset, I find a strange beauty in the surprising new balances between the human and animal spheres that arise as humans continue to put their stamp on the physical world. Examining the conflicting forces of the natural and technological worlds through the use of representational shapes, color, movement, and patterning, I introduce my own sense of balance. I build with ink and paint on unsized paper to develop foundation imagery for change and adaptation. The paper is affixed to primed, wooden panels and sealed before I continue adding and removing colors in layers. Upon completion, the entire surface is sealed and varnished.

GUILD SOURCEBOOKS: *Architectural & Interior Art 19*

BEV PRECIOUS
Public Art
Pages 114-115

Dichroic glass is kinetic, exciting, and unequalled for creating intense color. When combined with stainless steel, aluminum, bronze, and limestone, dichroic glass enlivens a sculpture with transmitted and reflected color.

RECENT PROJECTS: Minnetrista Cultural Center, Inc., Muncie, IN; University of Indianapolis, IN; University of Wisconsin, Madison; Miami University, Middletown, OH; Charlotte County Courthouse, Punta Gorda, FL; Lansing Community College, MI

COMMISSIONS: Merrill Lynch, Pennington, NJ and Denver, CO; Nestle Research & Development, New Milford, CT and Marysville, OH

AWARDS: Design award, 1998, AIA Georgia

GUILD SOURCEBOOKS: *Architect's 8, 9, 10, 11, 12, 13, 14, 15; Architectural & Interior Art 17, 18*

JANE RANKIN
Representational Sculpture
Page 190

I create limited-edition bronze sculpture and specialize in life-size and tabletop figures, mostly of children and child-related things.

COMMISSIONS: Cerritos Plaza, 2003, City of Cerritos, CA; Harvest Community, 2002, Ft. Collins, CO; Town Hall, 1999, Cary, NC; Morse Park, 1998, Lakewood, CO

COLLECTIONS: City of Cerritos, CA; Newton, IA; Pueblo Public Library, Pueblo, CO; Dogwood Festival Center, Jackson, MS; Waukegan Public Library, IL; Colorado Springs Fine Art Center, CO; Buell Children's Museum, Pueblo, CO; Lincoln Children's Museum, NE; Creative Artists Agency, Beverly Hills, CA

EXHIBITIONS: Pueblo Street Gallery, 2001-2004, Pueblo, CO; American Numismatic Association, 2000-2002, Colorado Springs, CO

GUILD SOURCEBOOKS: *Architect's 14, 15; Architectural & Interior Art 16, 17, 18, 19*

356

SCOTT RAYNOR
Paintings & Prints
Page 249

I am a visual artist who is very curious and infinitely interested in the world around me. My sense of wonder motivates me to create paintings, drawings, and photographs in my studio in the rustic mountains of North Carolina. I focus primarily on paintings of interiors and still life in oil and watercolor as well as portraits. I earned my M.F.A. from UNC-Greensboro and studied painting via a fellowship in London. Currently I am a professor of art at High Point University, where I teach a wide range of art and art history courses. I've exhibited both nationally and abroad in one- and two-man shows and my work is represented in corporate and private collections. To learn more about my work or to inquire about commission opportunities, please visit my website at www.scottraynorstudio.com.

HENRY RICHARDSON
Public Art
Page 116

I use glass to explore geometric shapes that are created with careful attention to surface and color, chipping glass in the manner in which other artists chisel stone. Unlike stone sculptors, however, I work the material in a reductive and additive manner simultaneously, layering the glass while chipping it away to create texture. This smooth/rough texture refracts light, adding tactile and visual interest. In spite of their large scale, *Chiseled Orb* and *Mortal Coil* retain a light feeling, their heaviness visually reduced by the translucency of the glass. At times each work has a crystalline or icy quality, imparting a sense of both timelessness and impermanence. I see these contradictions as the basis for meaning in my work.

EXHIBITIONS: DeCordova Museum and Sculpture Park, Lincoln, MA, 2004

CLAUDE RIEDEL
Liturgical Art
Page 206

"It belongs in this place." Such sentiments should greet the unveiling of a Ner Tamid, as witnesses experience the richness of a profound coordination between the certainty of matter and the spirit of illumination. The light of God radiates from the Ner Tamid and blesses all it touches. My Ner Tamids marry timeless, ancient traditions with modern sensibilities. I seek to render the essence of my client's vision with sensitivity and fine craftsmanship appropriate to the specific architectural setting. A recent client wrote, "Your work emanates an aura of spirituality."

RECENT PROJECTS: Ner Tamid for Congregation Anshai Torah, Dallas, TX; Ner Tamid for Bet Shalom Synagogue, Minnetonka, MN; Ner Tamid for Shir Tikva Synagogue, Minneapolis, MN

PUBLICATIONS: *Architecture Minnesota*, cover and feature article about Bet Shalom Synagogue sanctuary

GUILD SOURCEBOOKS: *Architect's 15; Architectural & Interior Art 17*

ARTIST STATEMENTS

KEVIN ROBB
Non-Representational Sculpture
Pages 153, 328

I have made my mark on the national and international art scene with my unique, free-flowing sculptural expressions in bronze and stainless steel. These contemporary pieces work equally well in intimate environments or large-scale public areas, and can be found in private collections throughout North America and Europe.

RECENT PROJECTS: The Borgata Hotel, Casino, and Spa, Atlantic City, NJ; Frederik Meijer Gardens and Sculpture Park, Grand Rapids, MI; Desert Springs, JW Marriott Resort and Spa, Palm Desert, CA; ABA Realty, Englewood Cliffs, NJ. My exciting new collection, the *Kevin Robb Celebration Series*, provides dynamic, spirited snapsnots of moments impossibly suspended in time. My natural curiosity and integral understanding of how positive and negative spaces, shadow and light work together manifests itself in these pieces, bringing life, energy, and beauty to the spaces they occupy.

EXHIBITIONS: Rocky Mountain College of the Arts, 2003, Lakewood, CO; Westbank Community Library, 2003, Austin, TX; Loveland Sculpture in the Park, Loveland, CO, 2003

GUILD SOURCEBOOKS: *Architect's 12, 13, 14, 15; Architectural & Interior Art 16, 17, 18, 19; Artful Home 1, 2*

BERNARD J. ROBERTS
Non-Representational Sculpture
Pages 154-155

My hand-carved wood sculptures are used as models for bronze sculptures. The wood models provide for unique shapes and patterns, sharp edges, extensions, and textural areas and brings my personal carving style into the bronzes. Outdoor settings reveal additional qualities through reflected sunshine, moisture from rain or dew, and especially coverings of frost or snow. Each sculpture has a unique, individual form with a level of expression that is mature and courageous. My themes are procreation and the dynamics of life.

The ripples are manufactured from select species of wood and finished with a durable surface. Contours and variations of shapes enhance the natural beauty of the wood. The variety of shapes and different species of wood (light to dark) provide for considerable custom designing. To allow for personal arrangement, the ripples are set on individual pedestals. Without pedestals they can be placed in horizontal, vertical, stationary or mobile positions. Sizes range from twelve inches wide to eight (plus) feet tall.

GUILD SOURCEBOOKS: *Designer's 11, 12, 14; Architect's 15*

PRISCILLA ROBINSON
Art for the Wall: Mixed & Other Media
Pages 296-297

My art pieces are about color and texture. They are created from handmade paper, metal, glass, fiberglass, and polycarbonates. My unique technique works well for specific requirements of size and color and produces artwork that is durable and suitable for installation in public places. I welcome opportunities to design custom pieces.

COMMISSIONS: Stafford Performing Arts Center, lobby, Houston, TX; La Gorce Country Club, lobby, Miami Beach, FL; Equiserve, Canton, MA; Komazawa House, Setagaya, Tokyo, Japan

COLLECTIONS: Abbey at Spineto, Tuscany, Italy; Royal Library, The Hague; Museum of Charmey, Switzerland

EXHIBITIONS: Holland Paper Biennale

GUILD SOURCEBOOKS: *Designer 14; Architectural & Interior Art 16, 17; Artful Home 3*

TIMOTHY ROSE
Atrium Sculpture
Page 91

I combine drawing in space with the engineering of Calder. First I will do a composition in pencil, followed by a rendering in three-dimensional space. I have been building mobiles for more than thirty-five years, and am still amazed each time they go up in the air. Kandinsky, Malevich, and El Lissitzky inspire some of my work. While working with architects, individuals and corporations have selected my ideas and commissioned my work. Recent commissions include universities, public atrium spaces, and corporate lobbies, in addition to private homes.

RECENT PROJECTS: Chevron Texaco, San Ramon, CA; Gettysburg College, PA; Amgen Corporation, Thousand Oaks, CA

COMMISSIONS: Palmyra Cove Nature Center, 2003, Palmyra, NJ; office lobby, 2002, Oak Ridge, TN; University of Tennessee Black Cultural Center lobby, 2002, Knoxville

ROSETTA
Representational Sculpture
Pages 168, 191

My subjects are animals, but it is their life force in all of its visual splendor, rather than their realistic physical form, that inspires my stylized interpretations. My work ranges from miniature to monumental and has been exhibited nationally and internationally in museums and galleries, and in juried and invitational exhibitions.

RECENT PROJECTS: The Village at Walnut Creek, Westminster, CO; Saginaw Art Museum, Saginaw, MI; Camel Caravan, Dubai, UAE; Brookgreen Gardens, Pawleys Island, SC

COMMISSIONS: City of Steamboat Springs, CO; Florida Institute of Technology, Melbourne, FL; City of Dowagiac, MI; City of Lakewood, CO; Lincoln Park Zoo, Chicago, IL; Hewlett-Packard, Loveland, CO; Champaign-Urbana Mass Transit District, IL; Radio station KOXE, Brownwood, TX

AWARDS: Silver medal, 2003, National Sculpture Society; Award of Excellence, 2001, Society of Animal Artists; Gold medal and purchase awards, 2001 and 2000, Bosque Conservatory Art Council

TALLI ROSNER-KOZUCH
Fine Art Photography
Page 269

I am working with professional 4" x 5" and 8" x 10" cameras at night by candlelight, photographing with black and white, sepia, color, and Polaroid films. From them I create platinum prints, etchings, lithographs, and murals of all sizes. My images vary in style from architectural portraiture and documentary to landscapes and still life. I'm using my own signature techniques, achieving a unique blend of sepia and blue rough edge.

RECENT PROJECTS: Hotels and corporate offices all over the world

COMMISSIONS: Law offices, corporations and hotels

COLLECTIONS: Polaroid; Pfizer Corporation; Twin Lab Corporation; numerous corporations and private collections

EXHIBITIONS: U.S., Europe, and Israel

GUILD SOURCEBOOKS: *Architect's 13, 14; Designer's 13, 14, 15; Architectural & Interior Art 16, 17, 18, 19*

ARTIST STATEMENTS

JAMES THOMAS RUSSELL
Non-Representational Sculpture
Pages 17, 152, 156

The concept of my sculpture is based on the juxtaposition of contrasting contours. Opposites attract opposites. I use highly polished stainless steel because it is alive with reflective energy. Through this medium I transform my inner emotion into permanent form. I have edition sculptures that range from $5,000 to $50,000. Monumental sculptures start at $60,000.

COMMISSIONS: Coast Aluminum and Architectural, 2003, Santa Fe Springs, CA; Astra Zeneca Pharmaceuticals, 2002, Wilmington, DE; Chico Municipal Airport, 2001, Chico, CA

COLLECTIONS: Bellagio Hotel, Las Vegas, NV; Motorola Corporation, Beijing, China; Riverside Art Museum, Riverside, CA; A.T. Kearney Inc., Chicago, IL

EXHIBITIONS: *Impact*, 2004, Tadu Contemporary Art, Santa Fe, NM; *Miniatures*, 2004, Albuquerque Museum of Art, Albuquerque, NM

PUBLICATIONS: *Santa Fe Reporter*, October 2004; *Leaders* Magazine, September 2004; *Landscape Architect*, July 2000; *Focus Santa Fe*, March 2000

GUILD SOURCEBOOKS: *Architect's* 7, 8, 12, 14; *Architectural & Interior Art* 16, 17, 18, 19; *Artful Home* 2, 3

JEFFREY J. RUTLEDGE, M.F.A.
Non-Representational Sculpture
Page 157

For over 25 years I have been creating dynamic sculptures for corporations, government, and private art collectors. You might have seen my sculptures exhibited at the Chicago Navy Pier shows. I prefer to work in stainless steel for interior wall sculptures and large freestanding outdoor sculptures. This material is perfect for all weather and climates; it requires no maintenance and looks great in all lighting conditions. I will deliver and supervise the installation of my sculpture commissions. My sculptures range in price from $20,000 to $100,000. A color brochure and resumé are available.

RECENT PROJECTS: Jewish Education Center, Centerville, OH; Good Samaritan Health Clinic, Dayton, OH

COMMISSIONS: Children's Medical Center, Dayton, OH; Carillon Historical Park, Dayton, OH; Culture Works, Dayton, OH; Estate of Helene Curtis, Chicago, IL; NCR Corp., Dayton, OH; Crown Corp., New Breman, OH; TECO Corp., Union, OH

COLLECTIONS: Springfield Art Museum, Springfield, OH; Hobart Corp., Troy, OH; Dayton Teachers Credit Union, Dayton, OH; numerous private collectors

GAIL RUTTER-VanSLYKE
Art for the Wall: Fiber
Page 315

My fiber art covers a wide spectrum of techniques, concepts, and applications. It is sited in residences, corporate offices, and public buildings, in all sizes and price ranges. Installation can be wall-mounted or free-hanging. Design for my work integrates a crucial balance of internal concepts and external influences, especially stratagraphic imagery of geologic formations, a recurring theme. I use structures and materials that emphasize line: linear interlacing of hand-weaving with seed fiber yarns for crisp clarity. Weaving is the basis for most of my work; fabric is the essence of it all. When I found weaving, I found infinity. I know that my art-making is a God-given wellspring of ideas, unceasing in my thinking. The heartbeat of my life and work is the evolving, continuous production of original art.

PUBLICATIONS: *American Craft*, April/May 2002

SABLE STUDIOS
Atrium Sculpture
Page 93

I have collaborated successfully with art consultants, architects, and designers for over 35 years. My kinetic, acrylic mobiles integrate color, light, and movement to create a multidimensional experience. My custom-designed sculptures harmonize with private, corporate, and public spaces.

RECENT PROJECTS: Union City Senior Center, CA; Lucent Technologies, CO; Boys Town National Research Hospital, Omaha, NE

COMMISSIONS: Metro Plaza Building, San Jose, CA; Syntex Corporation, Hayward, CA; Berklee Performance Center, Boston, MA; Quantum Corporation, San Jose, CA; 3 Comm Corporation, Sunnydale, CA; Cadence Corporation, San Jose, CA

GUILD SOURCEBOOKS: *Architect's* 11, 12, 13, 14, 15; *Architectural & Interior Art* 16, 17, 18

RAMONA SAKIESTEWA
Art for the Wall: Fiber
Page 316

Grounded in my Native American heritage, I bring a contemporary sensibility to my tapestries, monotypes, and design work. With vibrant markings and geometric elements that dance across saturated fields of color, my one-of-a-kind wool tapestries are a bridge between modernist concepts and Native American weaving techniques. My work transcends conventional weaving motifs and connects disparate layers of past, present, and future with technical mastery and fluidity of design. My most recent work captures the dynamism of the galaxy, both cosmic and urban.

RECENT PROJECTS: Design consultant for ten years for the National Museum of the American Indian, Smithsonian Institution, Washington, DC; Chickasaw Cultural Center, Sulphur, OK; American West Heritage Center, Wellsville, UT

COMMISSIONS: Tempe Center for the Performing Arts, 2002-present, AZ

COLLECTIONS: The Heard Museum, Phoenix, AZ; The Newark Museum, NJ; Museum of New Mexico, Santa Fe

FAITH SCHEXNAYDER
Architectural Elements
Page 79

I am an artist, designer, and sculptor with an emphasis on architectural foam carving. Each piece is unique in design, artistic, cut by hand, and site-specific. While keeping the design for the client in mind, I allow each piece to evolve naturally into the artwork that it should become.

RECENT PROJECTS: Town Lake Trail Buggy, Town Lake Trail Buggy Foundation, Austin, TX, sponsored by Grand Communications and Austin Bone and Joint Clinic; Marquée, Boys and Girls Club, Austin, TX

COMMISSIONS: Lance Armstrong Tour de France victory float, 2000; stage for President George W. Bush's acceptance speech, 2000

COLLECTIONS: Halbert Antiques, 503 Coffee Bar, Pieces of the Past Antiques, Austin Museum of Art, Zilker Elementary School, and 709 W. Gibson Street, Austin, TX

EXHIBITIONS: Periodic public displays at City of Austin Trail of Lights, TX; 1998-present GSD&M's "Frosty & the Armadillos" Christmas display, Austin, TX

ARTIST STATEMENTS

DON SCHMIDT
Architectural Elements
Page 80

We at Custom Metals, Inc. produce architectural works that incorporate a variety of disciplines and media. Our endeavors include design, fabrication, installation, and restoration in new, and historic metals.

RECENT PROJECTS: State Capitol restoration, Madison, WI; Ganz Hall, Roosevelt University, Chicago, IL

AWARDS: Mitch Heitler Award, 2004, National Ornamental and Miscellaneous Metals Association (NOMMA); recipient of three gold medal Ernest Wiemann Awards, 2004, 2003, NOMMA

PUBLICATIONS: *Fabricator* 2004, 2003, 2002; *Fine Homebuilding*, 2004

JOAN SCHULZE
Art for the Wall: Fiber
Pages 317, 322

My mixed-media quilts reflect contemporary urban themes balanced by my ongoing love of nature, my expressive use of color, and finding beauty in the details. I work in various formats: collage (most notably the *Haiku* and *Tanka* series), scrolls, quilts, and pigment prints based on self-created materials using monoprint, photocopy, and transfer processes on silk, cotton, and paper. I work with collectors, designers, curators, and architects on commissions. I exhibit internationally.

RECENT PROJECTS: Foley Hoag, LLP, Washington, DC; Kaiser Permanente, San Jose, CA

COLLECTIONS: Renwick Gallery, Smithsonian American Art Museum, Washington, DC; Museum of Arts and Design, New York; Oakland Museum of California; Museo de Collage, Morelos, Mexico; Museé ArtColle, Sergines, France; Adobe Systems International; VISA International; Oblan Spivak, et. al., Alexandria, VA; Queen of Apostles Church, San Jose, CA; A.G. Edwards & Sons, St. Louis, MO; State Farm, Chicago, IL

PREVIOUS SOURCEBOOKS: *THE GUILD 3,* *4, 5; Designer's 8, 9, 10, 12, 13; Architectural & Interior Art 17*

MARSH SCOTT
Art for the Wall: Metal
Page 282

Working in pierced metals allows me to combine the narrative, symbolic, or abstract in a sculptural context. My work is often a collaborative expression reflecting geographic and cultural diversity to provide a site-specific installation. The positive and negative piercing defines the design while creating dynamic shadows. The hand-brushed surface reflects the colors of the surrounding environment.

COMMISSIONS: Various public art commissions in California; Kaiser Permanente, 2003-2004, Palmdale, Pasadena, and Downey, CA; Hyatt Regency Hotel and Spa, 2003, Huntington Beach, CA; Canal Plus U.S., CA; Discovery Museum, CA; Orange County Airport, Santa Ana, CA; Torrance Memorial Medical Center, CA

EXHIBITIONS: Los Angeles County Museum of Art; *Design for Living*, Millard Sheets Gallery, a Smithsonian affiliate, Pomona, CA; *Affaire in the Gardens*, Beverly Hills, CA; La Jolla Arts Festival, CA; Sawdust Art Festival and Festival of Arts, Laguna Beach, CA

GUILD SOURCEBOOKS: *Architectural & Interior Art 17, 18, 19*

MAUREEN A. SEAMONDS
Public Art
Page 117

My work incorporates the visual aspects of the landscape with the gestural expression of the human form. I encourage active participation in the sculptural experience and hope viewers will incorporate memory and imagination to create a personal "window on the world." I work in my historic Seneca Street Studio in downtown Webster, IA, to create these original sculptures. Suitable for indoor or outdoor spaces, the sculptures range in height from 36" to 8' with a price range between $500 and $10,000. Especially beautiful in garden spaces, the work can be used as a water feature and plumbing components can be included.

JOHN SEARLES
Art for the Wall: Metal
Page 283

My metal wall creations are an expression of my fascination with copper and aluminum. I am primarily interested in shape, design, and color. Copper has an amazing range of colors that can be developed with flame and fire, along with numerous chemically-induced colors. Aluminum is captivating when wire-brushed. I specialize in custom designs for designers and architects. My wall pieces are installed in numerous corporate and residential spaces throughout the country. Prices range from $750 to $15,000, depending on the size and complexity of the work. Many more samples of my work can be seen at www.SearlesArt.com.

RECENT PROJECTS: Mandarin Oriental Hotel, Washington, DC; Holiday Inn Capitol, Washington, DC; Hooper Lundy & Brookman, Los Angeles, CA

GERALD SICILIANO
Public Art
Pages 8, 118-119

For more than thirty years, Gerald Siciliano has been creating sculpture and three-dimensional objects for architects, collectors, corporations, designers, galleries, and municipalities worldwide. Offered in bronze, marble, granite, and stainless steel, these elegant and enduring works are produced to the highest standards, on time and within budget. From the intimate to the monumental, they will enhance any collection or setting. Your inquiries are welcomed via telephone, fax, e-mail, or the Internet.

COMMISSIONS: American Airlines, JFK-NYC; American Axle & Manufacturing de Mexico, Silao; Bristol-Myers Squibb, NJ; The Brooklyn Museum, NY; Canon Corporation, NJ; Changwon Provincial Government, Korea; Dong Baek Art Center Gallery, Korea; John Templeton Foundation, Mozart Companies, CA; Pusan Olympic Park, Korea; Sparks Exhibits & Environments, PA; Tangiers Waterfront Park, Morocco

ARTIST STATEMENTS

LEE SILTON
Art for the Wall: Mixed & Other Media
Pages 298-299

The social and physical challenges of my art have functioned as a launching point for me. I have chosen to work with materials such as wood, glass and bronze. Those media allow me to explore the structural features of making art, creating and exploring the endless interplay of volume, dimension, and negative space, as well as helping me fulfill my goals—architectural as well as spiritual. I like the physical demands of working with hard materials: preparing, cutting, and shaping objects that combine into a completed story. My work reflects the juxtaposed sounds of music and my compositions are visual reflections of the listening process.

RECENT PROJECTS: Grand Hyatt Hotel, Tokyo, Japan; Hotel Monaco, Washington, DC

COMMISSIONS: Numerous collections in the United States and abroad; Herb Nadel Architect, Los Angeles, CA

COLLECTIONS: Numerous private and public collections in the United States and abroad

EXHIBITIONS: Karen Lynne Gallery, Boca Raton, FL and Beverly Hills, CA; Gallery "C," Hermosa Beach, CA; Los Angeles County Museum, Los Angeles, CA

PUBLICATIONS: *IDFX* Magazine, England; *American Style* Magazine, U.S.A.; *Dubious* Magazine

SUSAN SINGLETON
Art for the Wall: Fiber
Page 318

Experimental varnishing and staining of paper surfaces led to the inspiration for my first ZIGGURAT artworks in the spring of 1990. Japanese washi paper is stitched together, forming a grid that is reflected in the metallic leafing and stenciling patterns. This work is my personal voice, a study of simplicity and light. It references ancient walls and objects from ancestral cultures. Minimal and primitive, yet formal and reserved, this work is handmade with irregular edges, hand-stitching, and textural papers. A remembrance of sailmaking, teepees, quiltmaking . . . temples.

RECENT PROJECTS: Johns Manville Plaza, Denver, CO; Novo Nordisk, Tokyo, Japan; Michael Kreiss, San Diego, CA; Curtis Mallet-Prevost, Colt and Mosle LLP, New York, NY; Nixon Peabody LLP, Boston, MA; Runzheimer International, Waterford, WI; La Costa Resort and Spa, San Diego, CA; Falling Rock, Nemacolin Woodlands Resort and Spa, Farmington, PA; The Rim Golf Club, Payson, AZ; Roppongi restaurant, Palm Springs, CA

JEFF G. SMITH
Architectural Glass
Pages 16, 47, 326

Unlike an easel painter, I must rediscover my "canvas" at the beginning of every commission. After learning about the needs and expectations of a facility's users, I carefully study the architectural concept and materials comprising the building itself. Melded with my design sensibilities, this analysis leads to an innovative contribution to the overall architectural environment, and a more fulfilling experience for those who work, worship, or visit there. My work explores the ever-changing and fully three-dimensional experiences stained glass can produce throughout its architectural context.

RECENT PROJECTS: San Antonio International Airport Terminals, TX; Oncology Center, St. Vincent Hospital, Indianapolis, IN; St. Bridget Catholic Church, Seattle, WA; St. Matthew Catholic Church, Windham, NH; Quentin N. Burdick Federal Courthouse, Fargo, ND; American Airlines' Admirals Club, Dallas/Fort Worth International Airport, TX; University of Alaska, Fairbanks; Washington Hebrew Congregation, Washington, DC; Salt Lake City Community College Library, UT; Wilcox Memorial Hospital, Lihue, HI

GUILD SOURCEBOOKS: *Architect's* 7, 8, 9, 10, 11, 12, 13, 14, 15; Architectural & Interior Art 16, 17, 18, 19

BARBARA SORENSEN
Non-Representational Sculpture
Page 158

I am a sculptor whose interest in geological formations and highly textured surfaces is reflected in my larger-than-life-size Goddesses. These abstract forms, originally created in clay and now cast in bronze, are available for intimate spaces and large-scale exterior environments. My work is exhibited and collected by museums and galleries throughout the U.S. and is included in many notable permanent collections of the public and private sector. Studios are located in Winter Park, Florida and Aspen, Colorado.

RECENT COMMISSIONS: University of Central Florida, Orlando; Town of Snowmass Village, CO

COLLECTIONS: University of Central Florida, Orlando; Everson Museum of Art, Syracuse, NY; City of Orlando, FL; Sun Trust Bank, Jacksonville, FL; Neiman Marcus, Orlando, FL

EXHIBITIONS: City of Orlando Public Gardens, Orlando, FL; Stetsen University, Deland, FL; Duval Smart Gallery, Aspen, CO; Florida State Capital, Tallahassee, FL; Gulf Coast Museum of Art, Largo, FL

CYNTHIA SPARRENBERGER
Representational Sculpture
Page 192

My work is figurative, with a loose, impressionistic quality. Because of my dance background, I am passionate about gesture, line, and movement, for it is these very elements that bring a sculpture to life.

RECENT PROJECTS: Life-size sculpture for Mynelle Gardens, Jackson, MS

COMMISSIONS: Private portrait, 2003; canine portrait, 2002, Sedalia, CO; private portrait, 2000, Parker, CO

COLLECTIONS: Mynelle Gardens, Jackson, MS; The Washington Ballet, Washington, DC

EXHIBITIONS: C.L. Wolfe Member Exhibition, 2005, New York, NY; Catharine Lorillard Wolfe Exhibition, 2004, New York, NY; Loveland Sculpture Invitational, 2003, 2002, CO; Renaissance Sale, 2001, Houston, TX; American Art Classic, 2001, Houston, TX; Sculpture in the Park, 2000, Loveland, CO

PUBLICATIONS: *Artists of Distinction*, 2003; *The Hilton Head Monthly*, 2001, SC; *The Clarion Ledger*, 2001, Jackson, MS

KRISPEN SPENCER
Paintings & Prints
Page 250

My paintings evolve from thoughts about nature's ethereal qualities—the inception of a storm, the genesis of a star, the budding of a flower, the turning of a leaf. To contemplate our lives as part of nature's creativity is to know that there are always possibilities for surprises and new beginnings. At crucial intervals during my painting process, layers of transparent pigments are poured onto the canvas. Images may appear, disappear, and reappear. The spontaneity and unpredictability of the process help to make the final work intriguing. As one gallery owner commented, "Every time you look, you see something new." My work has been commissioned for a university and for private residences and has won numerous awards in juried competitions. I recently held solo exhibitions at 1550 Gallery in Kerrville, Texas, and Old Katy Glassworks in Denison, Texas. Please visit www.KrispenArt.com.

ARTIST STATEMENTS

SPOLAR STUDIO
Murals & Trompe L'Oeil
Page 231

Creating interiors that dazzle the eye and speak to the soul: This is what Spolar is all about. We bring a myriad of techniques to the task, including traditional and innovative design, fine art mural canvases, sculpted murals, handpainted wallpaper, trompe l'oeil, faux and decorative finishes, Mac-driven computer-generated imagery, large-format museum-quality printing, a reference library, and three-dimensional/fabricating facilities. But more importantly, we bring imagination and great passion. That, together with our commitment to completing projects on time and on budget, has allowed us to thrive in the Milwaukee and Chicago areas since 1988. Thanks to twenty-five foot high ceilings and a modular design, our fully equipped 10,000 square feet studio can be configured to meet the specific needs of any client, anytime, anywhere.

STEPHANIE STANLEY
Paintings & Prints
Page 251

I seek to represent a spiritual experience, so I invoke the power of color and texture in all my work. A true "color field" painter (like Rothko and Noland), I am concerned with exploring the effect of pure color on canvas. Being the daughter of artists, I was compelled to express myself at an early age. Inspired by my dreams, meditations, and experiences, my collection is filled with variant textures and vibrant colors. I think that while abstract impressionism is non-representational with regard to form, my work nevertheless represents very real and specific ideas. My work is created with oil or acrylic on canvas in varying dimensions, and all edges of the canvas are painted. A sample of my work can be viewed at www.sangitaart.com.

MARK STASZ
Non-Representational Sculpture
Pages 124, 159

I am recognized for my trademark use of fabricated metal and hand-carved stone. My sculpture and fountains are contemporary and timeless, minimalist and rugged. I enjoy suspending massive blocks of stone in graceful arcs of bronze or steel, using asymmetrical compositions, and incorporating different textures. I use rich, weathered-looking patinas to enhance the natural state of the materials. During my 15 years as a professional sculptor, I have created more than 120 site-specific commissions for private, corporate, and public collections. Natural and artificial landscapes, religious symbols, history, and modern architecture all serve as sources of inspiration.

COLLECTIONS: Boise Art Museum, ID; Chaminade University of Hawaii, Honolulu; Los Angeles County Airport, CA; University of Montana, Bozeman; City of Boise Arts Commission, ID; Shafer Vineyards, Napa, CA; Tuthill Corporation, Chicago, IL; Upper Iowa University, Fayette, IA

361

ARTHUR STERN
Architectural Glass
Pages 3, 16, 48-49

I create site-specific architectural glass installations, primarily in leaded glass, as well as other art glass techniques. Specializing in the collaboration with design professionals and clients, my studio currently has installations in 36 states, as well as Japan and Hong Kong. Commissions range from residential work to large public art projects and churches. I have been widely published and have won numerous awards, including several American Institute of Architects design awards, as well as honors from the Interfaith Forum on Religion, Art & Architecture, The Construction Specifications Institute and *Ministry & Liturgy* magazine's BENE Awards. Each project receives the same thorough attention to detail and fine craftsmanship. I also work in other media, including wood and glass bas-relief sculpture, mixed-media works on canvas and works on paper.

JANE STERRETT
Paintings & Prints
Pages 224, 252

I am an experienced artist whose work combines photographic imagery with painterly effects to produce a unique and vibrant personal style that is strong in color and tactile values. My work is versatile and adaptable to a variety of subject matters. My mixed-media collages have been commissioned by corporate and editorial clients internationally.

COMMISSIONS: Johnson & Johnson, 2004, New Brunswick, NJ; St. Joseph Hospital, 2004, St. Louis, MO; MBNA/Bank One, 2002, Wilmington, DE; Immunex, 2002, Seattle, WA; Childrens Hospital at Montefiore, 2001, New York City; Trigon Healthcare, 2000, Richmond, VA; Hymmen Group, 1998, Bielefeld, Germany; Opus One Restaurant, 1998, Naples, FL

GUILD SOURCEBOOKS: *Designer's 14, 15; Architectural & Interior Art 16, 17*

DAVID STROMEYER
Non-Representational Sculpture
Page 160

For 35 years I have explored a variety of spatial questions through sculpture, photography, film, furniture design, and architecture. About half of the resulting 350 sculptures are large, outdoor pieces. Typically I work in painted steel, though I have also used stainless steel, concrete, wood, and resins. I fabricate all of my work at my studios in Texas and Vermont. Many works, from tabletop and wall reliefs to large outdoor pieces, are available for immediate purchase. I welcome commissions for public and residential sites as well.

COMMISSIONS: States of Massachusetts and Connecticut; Montgomery and Charlotte Counties; Omni Hotels; Cornell University

COLLECTIONS: National Building Museum; National Museum of American Art; DeCordova and Delaware Museums; Swarthmore College; SUNY Plattsburg; Dixie Industrial Supplies Corporation; Hobart Industries; Hornick Industries

PUBLICATIONS: *New York Times; Newsweek; Art News; New York Magazine*

GUILD SOURCEBOOKS: *THE GUILD 5; Architect's 6, 7*

ARTIST STATEMENTS

MARTIN STURMAN
Art for the Wall: Metal
Pages 284–285

I create original contemporary sculptures and furniture in carbon steel or stainless steel. My work is suitable for indoor or outdoor placement. Stainless steel surfaces are burnished to achieve a beautiful shimmering effect. Carbon steel sculptures are painted with acrylic and coated with polyurethane to preserve color vitality. I encourage site-specific and collaborative efforts.

COMMISSIONS: Hyatt Westlake Plaza Hotel, Westlake Village, CA; Tesoro Galleries, Beverly Hills, CA; Manhattan Beach Car Wash, Manhattan Beach, CA; McGraw-Hill Publishing Company, Columbus, OH

COLLECTIONS: McDonald's Corporate Art Collection, Oakbrook, IL

GUILD SOURCEBOOKS: *Architect's 12, 14; Designer's 7, 8, 9, 10, 11, 12, 13, 14, 15; Architectural & Interior Art 16, 17, 18, 19; Artful Home 2*

RICHARD SWANSON
Non-Representational Sculpture
Page 161

My sculptural explorations, though eclectic, are united by their emphasis on movement and balance. Some defy gravity with a precarious balancing act. Others sway, rock, or simply imply motion. With all of them I strive to balance a sense of design with a sense of humor. I work with architects and engineers in siting large sculptures, with choreographers in making interactive sculptures, and with private collectors in scaling work to fit their indoor or outdoor settings. Medium-size garden/atrium sculptures range from $7,000 to $10,000.

RECENT PROJECTS: Engineering & Physical Sciences atrium, Montana State University

COLLECTIONS: Los Angeles County Museum of Art; Eiteljorg Museum, Indianapolis; Mansfield Center for Pacific Affairs, Washington, DC

COMMISSIONS: Holter Museum of Art, 2005, Helena, Montana

AWARDS: Individual Artist Fellowships from Art Matters Foundation, New York; New Forms: Regional Initiative (seven Western states); Montana Arts Council

PUBLICATIONS: *Sculpture* magazine, November 19

RICHARD TAYLOR
Non-Representational Sculpture
Page 163

My sculptures are found indoors and outdoors, some freestanding and some wall-mounted. My designs often derive their inspiration from music and poetry. I enjoy the collaborative process with clients by expressing their themes and ideas sculpturally in metal and color. The outdoor pieces are created using aluminum and industrial paints and are extremely durable in all weather conditions. My work ranges from expressive public and corporate commissions to bright and lively pieces for children.

COMMISSIONS: Central Library, Milwaukee, WI; City of Mt. Vernon, IL; Marnell Corrao, Shreveport, LA; Fifield, Chicago, IL; U.S. Robotics, Chicago, IL; St. Lukes Hospital, Milwaukee, WI; Flad Architects, Madison, WI

COLLECTIONS: Visa; QuadGraphics; Rockwell International; General Electric Medical Systems; Southwestern Illinois College

EXHIBITIONS: Chicago Navy Pier Exhibition; OK Harris Works of Art, New York City; Robert Kidd Gallery, Birmingham, MI; Mary Bell Gallery, Chicago; Sylvia Schmidt Gallery, New Orleans

362

JULIE BETTS TESTWUIDE
Fine Art Photography
Page 270

I am mostly recognized for my evocative images that are a mixture of photography and painting. I work to create works of art that are delicately detailed and saturated with the light and mood reminiscent of an impressionist painting. Whether the scene has been captured on a scenic coastline, a rural landscape, or winding through a European village, I try to create images that are timeless and focus on simple beauty.

My artwork has been widely published and exhibited in galleries throughout the world. It is showcased in many private and public collections including numerous Ritz Carltons, The Polo Club in Boca Raton, Savannah Golf Club, and many other hotels throughout the country. Visit my website at www.juliearts.com.

GUILD SOURCEBOOKS: *Designer's 14, 15; Architectural & Interior Art 16*

TERRY THOMMES
Public Art
Page 121

I work in cast and fabricated metals as well as stone and cast concrete. My studio creates durable sculptures with structural integrity to suit a wide range of public art projects. I also work on commission and collaborate with architects and landscape designers to create work for private and corporate collections. My sculpture can be up to twenty-five feet in height and often incorporates a kinetic element that allows the piece to either rock or pivot on itself. Prices range from $5,000 to $150,000.

RECENT PROJECTS: *Line Current,* 200' floating installation, *Sculpture Key West,* 2005, FL; Clemens Bruns Schaub Architect, Vero Beach, FL; 38 custom bronze lamps, private residence, Lyford Key, Bahamas; Art collaboration with Collective Design, Stuart, FL

COMMISSIONS: 3i Innovations, 2005, Palm Beach Gardens, FL; Borlund Center, 2005, Palm Beach Gardens, FL; Port Salerno Fire Station, 2002, FL

COLLECTIONS: Terrance McNally, New York, NY; David Maxfield, Washington, DC; Tim Allen, Sherman Oaks, CA; Whitney Houston, Englewood Cliffs, NJ

GUILD SOURCEBOOKS: *Architects 11, 14, 15; Artful Home 3*

CASSIE TONDRO
Paintings & Prints
Page 253

I use color, texture, and gesture to create unique paintings that convey a sense of energy and excitement. The inspiration for my work comes from nature, emotions, and dreams. My woven paintings are created by working on two pieces of unstretched canvas at once and cutting them into strips after they have been painted. I then weave the strips together to form a harmonious whole. These paintings brighten and enliven any space and are meditative as well as lively.

COMMISSIONS: Englewood Hospital and Medical Center, 2004, Englewood, NJ; Nina Visnovska and Lubomir Visnovsky, 2004, Slovakia

COLLECTIONS: Toish Ellerson, Los Angeles, CA; Richard Feldhake, Phoenix, AZ; Jacqui and Jon Irwin, Thousand Oaks, CA; Helen Leipold-Johnson, Racine, WI

EXHIBITIONS: Art in Embassies Program, 2005, United States Embassy, Yaounde, Cameroon; *Dia de los Muertos,* 2004, Texas Tech University, Lubbock, TX; *Potpourri,* 2004, Gallery on High, Pottstown, PA; solo exhibition, 2003, Topanga Canyon Gallery, Topanga, CA

AWARDS: Third Place-Acrylics, 2002, Malibu Art Association juried exhibition

ARTIST STATEMENTS

LUIS TORRUELLA
Public Art
Page 122

I design in a contemporary abstract context. My Caribbean heritage is reflected in my work's color, rhythm, and movement. I collaborate with architects, designers, and developers on public and private commissions.

COLLECTIONS: Museo de Arte de Puerto Rico, San Juan; Mead Art Museum, Amherst, MA; Centro de Bellas Artes Luis A. Ferre, San Juan, PR; Skokie Northshore Sculpture Park, IL

EXHIBITIONS: Palma de Mallorca, 2001, Spain; Galeria Botello, 2002, 1997, 1994, 1992, San Juan, PR; State Institute of Theatrical Art, 1992, Moscow; World Exposition 1992, Seville, Spain; numerous private collections

GUILD SOURCEBOOKS: *Architect's 14, 15; Architectural & Interior Art 16, 17, 18, 19; Artful Home 1*

WAYNE TRAPP
Non-Representational Sculpture
Pages 164-165

I believe that a successful sculptural form must pass the test of time both aesthetically and physically, and should complement and interact with its environment, inviting viewers' reflections and responses. Because I emphasize lasting materials—stainless steel, granite, marble, bronze, and weathering steel—my sculptures age gracefully. I have shared my work in projects including museums, city parks, university campuses, hospitals, churches, corporations, and individuals for over thirty-five years. I especially enjoy the collaborative process, and work with architects, designers, builders, and individual clients to create site-specific work that integrates their unique needs and intentions, whether spatial, budgetary, environmental, or personal. I welcome both small- and large-scale projects and have an established record of working with clients to meet strict budgets and timelines. Commissions range between $5,000 and $150,000; references of satisfied clients available upon request.

ELLEN TYKESON
Representational Sculpture
Page 193

Sculpture is storytelling in form, weaving together compelling design, meaningful content, and interplay of shape and surface. The goal is always to create a work that connects in a lasting way with those who see it. Beauty is a many faceted quality in art. I believe it can provide an avenue to begin this communication.

RECENT PROJECTS: *Journey*, PeaceHealth Community Hospital, Cottage Grove, OR; *Slugfest*, The Oregon Garden, Silverton, OR; *William Shakespeare*, private collection; *Gertrude Bass Warner Memorial*, Jordan Schnitzer Museum of Art, University of Oregon, Eugene, OR

EXHIBITIONS: Springfield Museum, 2004, Springfield, OR; Diva Gallery, 2004, Eugene, OR; Silvercreek Gallery, 2002, Silverton, OR; National Sculpture Society Annual Show, 2001, Brookgreen Gardens and National Sculpture Society Headquarters, New York, NY

JAMES TYLER
Public Art
Page 123

My *Brick Series* sculptures are constructed from hundreds of individually shaped, meticulously crafted ceramic bricks. There is often an interactive element, where internal sound and/or light components are utilized to create an ever-changing dialogue between artwork and viewer. These installations range in scope from the smaller *Brickhead* series starting at about five feet in height with relatively simple electronics, to the huge *Colossus Project* artworks, an exciting new series of immense ceramic brick sculptures with state of the art computerized operating systems. Site-specific in design and content, these are truly the next generation of interactivity in public art.

COMMISSIONS: Davis Square subway station, MBTA Arts on the Line project, Somerville, MA; Lechmere Canal Park, Cambridge, MA; Maine Maritime Aquarium, Boothbay, ME; Davlan Park, Indianapolis, IN

TYLER STUDIOS, LTD.
Architectural Elements
Page 81

My background in jewelry has strongly influenced my current larger work. I strive for a well-developed rapport between form, color, and texture, with painstaking care given to the preparation and creation of diverse surfaces. Combining ancient and modern techniques of forging and welding and integrating both reclaimed and raw materials, my pieces emerge with distinction. They are included in private collections, installed in commercial and public spaces, and have involved collaborations with designers and architects. Recently, I have been experimenting with the forging of large plates and working with reclaimed urban/industrial iconography.

PUBLICATIONS: *Fireplace Accessories*, Dona Meilach, 2002

KAREN URBANEK
Art for the Wall: Fiber
Page 319

I build painterly images and sculptural forms—both abstract and representational—in luminous layers of complex color and texture. My extensive color palette comes from natural sources and environmentally responsible working methodologies. Constructed primarily of compacted tussah silk fiber with a penetrating coating that adds crispness and strength, surfaces range from smooth and translucent to dense high relief. Works may be double-sided and hang freely or might be composed of separate layers and elements. They are light in weight, easy to ship, mount, maintain, and clean; framing is optional. Commissions accepted. Visuals and pricing available upon request.

COLLECTIONS: Lockheed Martin Corp.; Aspect Communications; Kaiser Hospital; McGraw-Hill Publishing Co.; Grace Cathedral

GUILD SOURCEBOOKS: *Designer's 13, 14, 15; Architectural & Interior Art 16, 17, 18, 19*

ARTIST STATEMENTS

JANET VAN ARSDALE
Fine Art Photography
Page 271

In my travels around the world, I have aspired to capture the essence of the subject, whether it is a European landscape or the detail of a flower. I achieve this by experimenting with different techniques, including x-ray, hand coloring, Polaroid transfers, black and white, sepia, and translating digital renderings into oil paintings and watercolors. I have started to create collage images, including a series of images of Los Angeles County for the Marriott LZX. I have worked for the past 35 years with designers to create custom artwork specific to the needs of my clients. Sizes range from 5" x 5" to 40" x 60". Samples and résumé are available on our website at www.janetvanarsdale.com.

ALICE VAN LEUNEN
Art for the Wall: Fiber
Pages 5, 320-321

My artworks explore pattern, texture, and reflection. My approach is light-hearted. Many of the artworks make musical or literary allusions and feature calligraphic marks and symbols. Works range in size from small, intimate pieces to major architectural installations. Commissions are welcome.

COMMISSIONS: Mulia Bank Complex, Djakarta, Indonesia; National High Magnetic Field Laboratory, Tallahassee, FL (with Walter Gordinier); Fairview Auditorium, OK; Kaiser Permanente, San Diego, CA; Kodiak Auditorium, Kodiak Island, AK; Playboy Towers, Chicago, IL

COLLECTIONS: Atlantic County Office Building, Atlantic City, NJ; General Motors, New York, NY; Seattle City Light, WA; Calvin Klein Cosmetics, Wayne, NJ

AWARDS: Oregon Individual Artist Fellowship, 1993

GUILD SOURCEBOOKS: *THE GUILD 1, 4, 5; Architect's 6, 7, 12, 13; Designer's 6, 9, 10, 11; Architectural & Interior Art 16, 17; Artful Home 1, 2*

SUSAN VENABLE
Art for the Wall: Mixed & Other Media
Pages 386, 296, 300

My work is an exploration of structure, surface, and the relationship between the two. The constructions are bas-reliefs of stacked steel grids woven with copper wire and juxtaposed with encaustic paintings. I want to maximize the physicality of the materials, seeking an energy field through structure and surface. My exploration, on a perceptual and tactile level, is to create a transcendent reality, not to recall a specific place or object. Archaeology, rituals, repetition, ruins, magic, and the art of indigenous societies are all strong influences on my creative process. My work can be seen in public spaces, homes, and museums. The commissions/installations have involved collaboration with collectors, architects, and designers throughout the world. The materials are durable, low maintenance, and suitable for installation in public areas.

KERRY VESPER
Furniture & Lighting
Page 217

I conceive and build furniture as sculpture. Using imported plywood and exotic and domestic hardwoods, I stack and glue layers together to approximate the form I intend to create. As a sculptor shapes a form, I refine each piece with carving, grinding, and sanding tools. To preserve the natural color and grain of the wood, I apply many coats of clear tung oil/urethane finish. The exposed layers of Baltic birch plywood create parallel lines that define the form of each piece. This design element, combined with solid wood, is distinctive in most of my work. I especially enjoy working directly with clients to create pieces that are based on their ideas and tastes.

GUILD SOURCEBOOKS: *Artful Home 2*

SERANDA VESPERMANN
Architectural Glass
Page 50

Simply put, I love glass. I fell in love with it at age five, fascinated by how a beveled piece of clear glass broke up the sun's rays into a rainbow of light. The colors, the textures, even the smooth outlines of lead speak volumes to me. These are the messages I seek to reveal to others. The project shown on my page is a six-foot round window at the Cable Center in Denver, Colorado. It depicts the burst of energy, programming, and information at the core of the cable industry that expands past the rectangle of a TV screen into the world beyond. Mouthblown European glass is employed with hand-chipped dalles de verre.

RECENT PROJECTS: 96" x 68" triptych for the entrance of a private residence.

GUILD SOURCEBOOKS: *Architect's 14; Architecture & Interior Art 18*

VITRAMAX GROUP
Art for the Wall: Mixed & Other Media
Page 301

With the marriage of new materials, mastery of evolving techniques, the re-interpretation of conventional glass elements, and the fresh eyes of nontraditional glass artists on its creative team, VitraMax Group finds itself prepared for the demands of an increasingly sophisticated customer base. Our capabilities range from the creation of functional art, such as glass sinks, lighting, furniture, shower doors, and countertops, to large-scale public art and commercial projects. We specialize in site-specific commissions and installations.

RECENT PROJECTS: The Congressional Medal of Honor Memorial, Indianapolis, IN; Indiana State Museum, Indianapolis, IN; Louisville Water Company, KY; Louisville Medical Center, KY; J.W. Marriott Hotel, New Orleans, LA

ARTIST STATEMENTS

KENNETH F. vonROENN, JR.
Architectural Glass
Pages 19, 51

We focus on expanding the roles of glass in architecture. With a broad range of new techniques, we are able to meet the functional and aesthetic requirements of diverse architectural applications. These techniques have been developed and refined from new and emerging technologies, creating dynamic opportunities for glass to enhance architecture. We provide a complete range of services for a broad range of work, from design to fabrication to installation. Our work is noted sympathetic integration with architecture and for its innovative application of new technologies.

RECENT PROJECTS: George Bush Airport, Houston, TX; Jewish Hospital Medical Center East, Louisville, KY; Siteman Cancer Center, St. Louis, MO; Loma Linda University, San Bernadino, CA

COMMISSIONS: Ronald Reagan Washington National Airport, DC; Bank of America, Charlotte, NC; Wachovia Bank, Charlotte, NC; M. D. Anderson Cancer Center, Houston, TX; Mountain View City Hall, CA; Christ Church Episcopal Cathedral, Cincinnati, OH

GUILD SOURCEBOOKS: *The Guild 4, 5; Architect's 6, 7, 8, 9, 10, 11, 13, 14, 15; Designers' 6; Architectural & Interior Art 16, 17, 18*

WKRP, INC.
Art for the Wall: Mixed & Other Media
Page 302

WKRPinc. is a design team of three artists from MaNose Studios, Inc. in Aspen, Colorado and is an acronym for its members: Kurosh ValaNejad, Robert Brinker, and Pamela Joseph. We recently developed an exciting series of paintings, wallpaper, and fabric designs. The patterns are based on original artworks using images from Mexican soft-core pornographic comic books which are digitally manipulated and mirrored horizontally and vertically to create repeatable tiles. The wallpaper and fabrics reference historic patterns from the Victorian era. Viewed from a distance, the abstract configurations resemble intricate tendrils or an exotic Persian carpet. Close inspection reveals the entwined body parts. The designs vary from bold and colorful to subdued pastels. The wallpaper can be digitally printed or silk-screened and is custom-made to the client's specifications.

LOIS WALKER
Paintings & Prints
Pages 254-255

My work is always an exploration of the visual seeking to communicate the inexplicable. I work in many media, creating two- and three-dimensional pieces ranging in price from $400 to $6,000 with oils, acrylics, found objects, cloth, hardware, antiques, and words. I try to allow each material its own unique voice. My art is never passive.

EXHIBITIONS: *Revelations*, 2002, Port Washington Library, NY; *Adam and Eve*, 2002, South Huntington Library, NY; *Inner Exiles: Shadow Poets, Paintings and Poetry*, 2000, Sylvia White Gallery, Santa Monica, CA

AWARDS: Award of excellence, 2004, Firehouse Gallery Nassau Community College, Garden City, NY; third award, 1998, Palm Springs Desert Museum, CA; award of excellence, 1995, Tri-County Art League of Long Island, NY; award of excellence, 1994, Heckscher Museum of Art, Huntington, NY

PUBLICATIONS: *Northport Journal*, March 2002; *Xanadu 21/22*, 2000; *Xanadu 20*, 1998; *Artspeak*, November 1997

GUILD SOURCEBOOKS: *Architectural & Interior Art 19*

365

WANNER SCULPTURE STUDIO
Representational Sculpture
Page 195

We have created figurative sculpture for over 200 architectural settings throughout the United States. Our sculpture spans secular and religious themes, and ranges from small to over life size in scale. We have worked successfully with architects, art consultants, designers, and contractors for over thirty-five years on projects for hospitals, cathedrals, churches, government buildings, corporations, and more. Our in-house foundry has enabled us to maintain a strong competitive advantage. Please visit our website at www.wannersculpturestudio.com for more information about our work and us.

GUILD SOURCEBOOKS: *Architect's 9, 10; Architectural & Interior Art 17*

LIBBY WARE
Architectural Ceramics, Mosaics & Wall Reliefs
Page 71

My artistic tools are illusion, perception, and the physical and psychological impact of a limited palette. The wall hangings I am showing in this volume employ the circle as the central motif. The impression of virtual or physical circles is created by the intersections of black glaze and white porcelain. The basic structure of each wall piece is a simple cube. Each cube is high fired, has a 5-5/8" face, weighs 2.5 pounds, and is hung separately on a French cleat which holds it invisibly flush with the wall. The durability of porcelain makes the wall relief suitable for outdoor settings as well as a rich contemporary addition to residential, corporate, and public settings. Because of the cube construction, any number of cubes can be placed in any combination suitable to the size of the wall. Completed pieces are available and commissions are welcome.

BARBARA WEBSTER
Art for the Wall: Fiber
Page 323

My quilts begin with my digital photographs of nature. They are printed on 100% cotton and are colorfast. I especially welcome commissions where I can photograph scenery meaningful to my client.

COMMISSIONS: Holy Cross Hospital, Silver Spring, MD; Mountain Air Country Club, Burnsville, NC; Biltmore Swim Club, Asheville, NC

EXHIBITIONS: Gallery Eleven Eleven Sculpture Space, 2004, Washington DC; Art Quilts at the Sedgwick, 2004, Philadelphia, PA; NC Crafts Gallery, 2004, Carrboro, NC; US Embassy, 2004, Guatemala; New Morning Gallery, 2003, Asheville, NC; Blue Spiral Gallery, 2003, Asheville, NC; Grovewood Gallery, 2003, Asheville, NC; Handworks Gallery of American Craft, 2003, Acton, MA; Mint Museum of Craft and Design, 2002

AWARDS: Quilt 2004, Festival of Quilts, Birmingham, England; First Place, Group, 2003, American Quilters Society Show, Paducah, KY; First Place, 2003, Cleveland Metroparks Quilt Show; First Place, 2000, Burnsville Quilt Show

PUBLICATIONS: *American Quilter; FiberArts Magazine; Bobbin; LDB Interior Textiles; Quilts Japan; Quilter's Newsletter Magazine*

ARTIST STATEMENTS

EDWIN C. WHITE
Non-Representational Sculpture
Page 167

My fascination with origami, coupled with my background in both graphic and product design, often challenges me to treat metals as one would paper. I normally choose sheet stock for material, and rely on multiple and often parallel cuts, perforations, and a lot of 'tugging' to coax a shape from its two-dimensional source. As a result, the forms have an innate simplicity that is difficult to duplicate in my other, more involved welded or mixed media assemblies. When I began 'expanding' works that incorporated this abundance of cuts, moiré patterns naturally evolved that I now attempt to incorporate in my designs.

RECENT PROJECTS: Hilton Hotel, Kuala Lumpur, Malaysia; Cyberport Meridian Hotel, Hong Kong; sculpture proposal, Four Seasons Hotel, Hong Kong

COLLECTIONS: Department of Cultural Resources, Raleigh, NC; North Carolina Aquarium, Manteo, NC

EXHIBITIONS: International Sculpture Center, Hamilton, NJ; Botanical Gardens, Chapel Hill, NC

ERNEST WILMETH
Art for the Wall: Mixed & Other Media
Page 303

The artwork I do consists of two separate styles. Some of the works are collage and some are mixed media with metal leaf. Both styles are done with acrylic paint on canvas and 300-lb watercolor paper. The collages are more spontaneous, whereas the mixed media works containing leaf are much more controlled. In the mixed media work my aim is a minimalist approach. Prices for the collages are lower, as they require less time.

COMMISSIONS: Brownstein Hyatt & Farber; UNM Health Science Center

EXHIBITIONS: Fusion Form Function, 2004, Union Street Gallery, Chicago, IL; Arts International 2004, International Museum of Art, El Paso, TX; From the Ground Up, 2004, Museum of Fine Arts, Las Cruces, NM

AWARDS: Best of Show, Arts International 2004; Award of Achievement, 2004, From the Ground Up; Juror's Award, 2000, Impressions: Works on Paper

BRUCE WOLFE
Representational Sculpture
Pages 19, 196-197

Most of the subjects of my portraits are imposing, dynamic personalities. I hope to portray that energy and presence, putting my ego aside to make a likeness that reflects the spirit of the subject—rather than just a mask and body. My recent projects include a monumental bronze of Barbara Jordan at the Austin-Bergstrom International Airport in Texas. I was chosen to complete this portrait after a comprehensive artist selection process. I installed two large bronze figures at the Old Mission in Santa Barbara, CA, and unveiled two additional figures of Christ and Mary Magdalene there on Easter Sunday 2003. I have also created a bronze bust of Chong-Moon Lee, a major donor to the New Asian Art Museum in San Francisco, CA.

366

STEPHEN YATES
Paintings & Prints
Page 257

My paintings are nature-based abstractions that suggest water, plants, and landscapes. They range in size from 12" x 12" to 5' x 10' and are part of private and public collections. I accept commissions for a broad range of sizes and imagery. A portfolio of past and recent work is available on my website or can be sent as a CD upon request.

RECENT PROJECTS: Good Samaritan Foundation, Puyallup, WA; University of Washington-Cascadia Community College co-library, Bothell, WA; work selected for 13 universities, colleges, and schools throughout Washington

COLLECTIONS: Bremerton Government Center; Microsoft Corporation; City of Seattle; City of Portland, OR; Eastern Washington University, Cheney, WA; Evergreen State College, Olympia, WA

EXHIBITIONS: Ten Paintings, CENTRUM Arts Foundation, McCurdy Pavilion, Port Townsend, WA; Recent Paintings, Blue Heron Arts Center, Vashon, WA; Stephen Yates Paintings, Port Angeles Fine Arts Center, Port Angeles, WA; Pleasure Craft, Washington Biennial, Tacoma Art Museum, Tacoma, WA

JUANITA YODER
Liturgical Art
Page 207

Suspended paintings on silk for liturgical, public, and private spaces comprise my commissioned work. I create work of spiritual and artistic integrity that melds personal expression with liturgical and architectural considerations. Suspension sets up a kinetic relationship between the viewer and the art, while color and movement express an essence for the environment. My commissions have included seasonal liturgical pieces and permanent installations of paintings, altar cloths, and the Stations of the Cross. My work is also available in kinetic processional kites (used at national Catholic and Presbyterian conventions and cathedrals) and stained glass.

RECENT PROJECTS: Church of St. Thomas More, Glendale, AZ; National Presbyterian Worship Convention, Montreat, North Carolina

COMMISSIONS: Lawrenceville School Chapel, 2004, Lawrenceville, NJ; Good Shepherd Catholic Community, 2003, Colleyville, TX; Our Lady of Mercy Church, 2002-2003, Potomac, MD; Princeton University Chapel, 2001, 1999, 1997, Princeton, NJ

GUILD SOURCEBOOKS: Architect's 15; Architectural & Interior Art 16, formerly listed as Juanita Y. Kauffman.

LARRY ZGODA
Architectural Glass
Pages 52-53

Having come into stained glass and the architectural crafts in the 1970s, I have many works that have paralleled the renaissance in ornamental architecture. Original design, meticulous craftsmanship, and innovation in material and architectural application have been my hallmarks. Often the works refer to the past or period architecture, but they are always unique and original. Today I work in various media in the assembly and ornamentation of an environment. These include glass, metal, wood, and mosaic. I'm especially interested in how a work of ornament beneficially changes the nature of an environment.

GUILD SOURCEBOOKS: THE GUILD 1, 2, 3, 4, 5; Architect's 6, 7, 8, 9, 10, 11, 12, 13, 14, 15; Architectural & Interior Art 17, 18, 19; Artful Home 1, 2

Location Index

LOCATION INDEX

369

LOCATION INDEX

370

Index of Artists & Companies

INDEX OF ARTISTS & COMPANIES

INDEX OF ARTISTS & COMPANIES

INDEX OF ARTISTS & COMPANIES

374